Principles of Organic Chemistry

Also by Peter R. S. Murray
Structural and Comparative Inorganic Chemistry
(with P. R. Dawson)
Pan Study Aids: Advanced Chemistry
(*published in conjunction with Pan Books*)

Principles of Organic Chemistry

A Modern and Comprehensive Text for Schools and Colleges

Peter R.S. Murray, B.Sc., Ph.D., C.Chem., M.R.S.C.

Second Edition

HEINEMANN EDUCATIONAL

**Heinemann Educational a division of
Heinemann Educational Books Ltd.,
Halley Court, Jordan Hill, Oxford OX2 8EJ**

OXFORD LONDON EDINBURGH MADRID
ATHENS BOLOGNA PARIS MELBOURNE
SYDNEY AUCKLAND SINGAPORE TOKYO
IBADAN NAIROBI HARARE GABORONE
PORTSMOUTH NH (USA)

ISBN 0 435 65643 0

Printed in Hong Kong by Dah Hua Printing Press Co., Ltd.

Preface

Preface to the First Edition

It has been my objective to provide a textbook suitable for both teachers and students which comprehensively covers the modern approach to Advanced and Scholarship organic chemistry. The work has been extended considerably to make it suitable for other courses of similar academic level and should provide a useful introductory reading for first year undergraduates.

The book has been developed in two sections, the first of which deals with the fundamental theoretical principles essential for introducing mechanistic organic chemistry. There is also included in this section a sizeable chapter on methods of isolating and identifying compounds, including the principles and mechanics of modern spectroscopic and chromatographic techniques. In Part II, which provides the much greater part of the text by volume, these principles are applied to each of the different homologous series of compounds. In addition, there are chapters on Polymers, Carbohydrates, and Amino Acids, Proteins and Polypeptides. The arrangement of material in two sections in this way allows some flexibility for the teacher to choose his preferred sequence, integrating the ideas introduced in Part I with the more specific reactions in Part II.

I wish to convey my gratitude to Mr P. R. Dawson, Mr J. H. Deakin, Dr K. Mullen and Mr J. J. Wharton for their invaluable criticisms and suggestions during the early stages of preparation, and I should also like to express my appreciation to Heinemann Educational Books, especially to Mr H. MacGibbon and his advisers, for their advice and assitance during the development of the text.

1972   P.R.S.M.

Preface to the Second Edition

In this second edition nomenclature has been modified in order to bring it into line with the recommendations made by the Association for Science Education in their publication, *Chemical Nomenclature, Symbols and Terminology*. In cases where the compound is widely known by an alternative, but often less systematic, name, both the A S.E. recommended name and the alternative name are used in conjunction. In this way it is hoped that unnecessary confusion will be avoided for those students and teachers who are more familiar with the more traditional nomenclature. In other respects, this edition is not appreciably different from the first, although reprinting has provided an opportunity to include some additional information and make a few amendments.

1977   P.R.S.M.

Contents

Page

PREFACE v

Part I

1. Introduction 1

2. The Nature of the Atom 5

3. Bonding and Molecular
   Structure 14

4. Naming Organic Compounds 24

5. Isomerism and Optical
   Activity 26

6. Structure and Physical
   Properties 35

7. Reactants and Reactions 40

8. The Mechanism, Energetics
   and Kinetics of a Reaction 49

9. Identification of Organic
   Compounds 54

Part II

10. Alkanes (Paraffins) 87

11. Alkenes (Olefins) 98

12. Alkynes (Acetylenes) 114

Page

13. Aromaticity and Benzene 122

14. Methylbenzene (Toluene) 142

15. Halohydrocarbons 148

16. Alcohols 166

17. Phenols 181

18. Ethers 195

19. Amines and their Derivatives 201

20. Aldehydes and Ketones 220

21. Carboxylic Acids 246

22. Derivatives of Mono-
    carboxylic Acids:
    Acyl Chlorides, Anhydrides,
    Esters and Amides 259

23. Sulphonic Acids 273

24. Amino Acids, Proteins and 278
    Polypeptides

25. Carbohydrates 283

26. Polymers 297

ANSWERS TO QUESTIONS 318

INDEX 323

Part I

1 Introduction

Chemistry is a study of the elements and of how they react together to form compounds. ORGANIC CHEMISTRY relates solely to the chemistry of the compounds of carbon, which in the majority of cases also contain hydrogen. At first, it is difficult to realize the vast extent of this field of study until one appreciates that the number of compounds containing carbon and hydrogen is many times greater than the sum total of all the compounds of all the other elements and is increasing every year.

The term 'organic chemistry' is rather misleading in as much as it is a relic of days when chemical compounds were categorized into only two classes, organic and inorganic, depending largely upon their source of origin. Organic compounds were derived from living organisms such as vegetables and animal matter, whereas inorganic compounds were obtained from mineral sources.

Organic substances were known to man in prehistoric times and although nothing was known about them, other than their function and source of origin, they were utilized in a variety of ways. Sugar in fruit was used for sweetening purposes and for making simple wines. Oils and fats from vegetables and animal matter were employed for making soap, and vegetable pigments, such as indigo and alizarin, were used for dyeing fabrics.

It was not until the sixteenth and seventeenth centuries that any really significant progress in isolating new organic substances was made. During this period, compounds such as methanol, propanone (acetone) and ethanoic (acetic) acid were extracted from pyroligneous acid, which was obtained from the dry distillation of wood. Towards the end of the eighteenth century, with the wide application of solvent extraction to plant and animal matter, numerous new compounds were added to the list of those already known. It was during this era that a Swedish chemist, Scheele, succeeded in extracting 2-hydroxypropane-1,2,3-tricarboxylic (citric) acid from lemons, and later others isolated 2,3-dihydroxybutanedioic (tartaric) acid from grapes, 2-hydroxybutanedioic (malic) acid from apples, 2-hydroxypropanoic (lactic) acid from sour milk, uric acid from urine, 3,4,5-trihydroxybenzenecarboxylic (gallic) acid from nut galls and ethanedioic (oxalic) acid from wood sorrels. Between 1772 and 1777, Lavoisier conducted a series of experiments on combustion, and it was during these experiments that he identified the presence of carbon and hydrogen in organic compounds, since they yielded carbon dioxide and water respectively as the products of combustion. Furthermore, he was able to determine the amount of carbon dioxide evolved by dissolving it in a solution of potassium hydroxide.

Gradually the presence of other elements such as oxygen, nitrogen and sulphur, was found to be common to large groups of organic substances, and for the first time something was known about their chemical nature.

During the early nineteenth century, as more and more elements were being discovered, it became apparent that those elements associated with compounds derived from living organisms were limited to only a few and also that they tended to be readily combustible.

In 1828 the German chemist, Wohler, became the first person deliberately to synthesize an organic substance in the laboratory. After a chance observation that an aqueous solution of ammonium cyanate (NH_4CNO) evaporated, producing carbamide (urea), NH_2CONH_2, he then repeated the experiment several times to confirm his conclusion.

Nowadays preparative techniques and principles have become so lucid that organic compounds can be prepared with almost as much ease as most inorganic.

The Unique Nature of Carbon

The ability of an atom to attract the electrons in a chemical bond towards itself when combined with different atoms in a compound is termed the ELECTRONEGATIVITY of the atom. Small atoms tend to have higher electronegativity values than large ones, especially those with nearly filled shells of electrons. On traversing the periodic table, the electronegativity values of the elements increase on moving from Group I across to Group VII. The values within a group tend to increase on ascending it.

This means that carbon, being the first element in Group IV, has an electronegativity value which is not sufficiently different from those of most other elements with which it combines to enable it to form wholly ionic (electrovalent) compounds. In chemical combination it therefore forms bonds which, although possessing various degrees of polarity, are essentially covalent in character.

Group I	Group II	Group III	Group IV	Group V	Group VI	Group VII
Li	Be	B	C	N	O	F
1.0	1.5	2.0	2.5	3.0	3.5	4.0
Na	Mg	Al	Si	P	S	Cl
0.9	1.2	1.5	1.8	2.1	2.5	3.0
K	Ca					Br
0.8	1.0					2.8
						I
						2.5

Hydrogen has an electronegativity value of 2.1.

The above table illustrates Pauling's electronegativity values for some of the most commonly encountered elements. Those elements with which carbon combines by forming covalent bonds are enclosed in the box and are principally in Groups V, VI and VII. This means that in bonds in which an electronegativity difference does occur between carbon and elements bonded to it, carbon tends to be the less electronegative atom, except when bonded to hydrogen or phosphorus.

The carbon atom possesses the unique ability to form multiple bonds between itself and other carbon atoms, $>C=C<$ and $-C\equiv C-$, and also with the atoms of certain other elements such as oxygen, $>C=O$, sulphur, $>C=S$, and nitrogen, $-C\equiv N$.

It is also one of the few elements for which CATENATION (the ability to form chains of identical atoms) is an essential feature of its chemistry. These chains may exist as short or long open systems, where several modes of branching are possible (as will be seen later), or alternatively as closed ring systems. Each different arrangement corresponds to a different compound with its own distinctive properties. In order to be able to catenate, an element must have a valency of at least two and be able to form fairly strong covalent bonds with itself. Carbon has a valency of four, permitting the existence of multiple bonds in chains of carbon atoms in certain compounds.

Characteristic Properties of Organic Compounds

Organic compounds are generally gases, volatile liquids or low melting-point solids, they tend to be insoluble in water unless they contain polar groups, such as —OH, —COOH, —SO_3H etc., but are usually soluble in organic, non-polar solvents, such as tetrachloromethane (carbon tetrachloride), ethoxyethane (diethyl ether), benzene etc. On burning in excess oxygen they yield carbon dioxide and water (except when the compound contains no hydrogen, which is comparatively rare), and the complete combustion of hydrocarbons (i.e. compounds containing only carbon and hydrogen) yields these as the only products.

Organic reactions are generally slow in comparison with many inorganic reactions and often require energy, usually in the form of heat. The reactions seldom proceed to completion, and consequently careful purification is necessary in order to isolate the desired product in a high state or purity. This contrasts quite markedly with many inorganic reactions which often proceed to completion instantaneously, especially those that take place in polar media.

The phenomenon known as isomerism is commonplace in organic chemistry. Isomerism is the ability of certain compounds, possessing the same molecular formula, to exist in different forms on account of their having different structural arrangements of atoms. For example, the formula C_2H_6O applies to two entirely different compounds, ethanol and methoxymethane, which possess distinctly different properties.

$$
\begin{array}{cc}
\begin{array}{c}
\text{H}\;\;\text{H} \\
|\;\;\;| \\
\text{H}-\text{C}-\text{C}-\text{OH} \\
|\;\;\;| \\
\text{H}\;\;\text{H}
\end{array}
&
\begin{array}{c}
\text{H}\;\;\;\;\;\text{H} \\
|\;\;\;\;\;\;| \\
\text{H}-\text{C}-\text{O}-\text{C}-\text{H} \\
|\;\;\;\;\;\;| \\
\text{H}\;\;\;\;\;\text{H}
\end{array}
\end{array}
$$

Ethanol   Methoxymethane (dimethyl ether)

In this field of study, we can concentrate on a relatively small group of commonly encountered elements: carbon, hydrogen, oxygen, nitrogen, sulphur, phosphorus, and the halogens.

In order to understand and appreciate just how the molecules of compounds are formed from their constituent elements, it is essential to have at least a qualitative knowledge of the structure of the atoms of these elements, and then to consider the type of bonding involved in joining these atoms together.

QUESTIONS

1. In which one of the following pre-dominantly covalent molecules is the departure from equal sharing of the bonding electrons greatest?

   A H_2
   B CH_4
   C CH_3CH_3
   D NH_3
   E H_2O

2. In what way is the chemistry of carbon a reflection of its position in the periodic table?

2 The Nature of the Atom

The Fundamental Particles

All atoms consist of a central nucleus of extremely high density surrounded by one or more orbital electrons. The number of protons determines the atomic number of an element and also gives the element its identity. As the chemist is concerned primarily with electrons and electronic theory, it is generally convenient for him to consider the nucleus in a simplified form, comprising protons and neutrons.

With the exception of the normal hydrogen atom, whose nucleus consists of a single proton, the nucleus invariably contains neutrons which, together with the protons, make up most of the mass of the atom, i.e. the mass number. The number of neutrons present is generally similar to the number of protons, although in the larger atoms the number of neutrons exceeds the number of protons. This can, in certain cases, cause instability of the nucleus, resulting in radioactive emission.

The protons and neutrons are particles of approximately the same mass, but whereas each proton carries a unit positive charge, the neutron is electrically neutral. The number of protons in the nucleus is always equal to the number of orbital electrons, each of which possesses a unit negative charge, so that an overall neutral atom results.

The mass of an electron is only approximately 1/1840 of the mass of either a proton or a neutron. Since these electrons occupy a vast volume of space relative to the volume of the nucleus, the electron density is negligible compared with the density of the nucleus, thus allowing their mass to be justifiably ignored when considering atomic mass.

Particle	Relative mass	Relative charge
Proton	1	+1
Neutron	1	0
Electron	1/1840	−1

All known elements are built up from these three fundamental particles. The simplest atom is hydrogen, the next simplest is helium.

The structures of all other elements can be built up by a series of successive additions of one proton and consequently one electron to the basic hydrogen structure, until the heaviest atom,* lawrencium, is arrived at. This is made up of 103 protons and 103 electrons. The increase in the number of neutrons does not follow such a regular pattern.

The Rutherford–Bohr theory of atomic structure portrays electrons in certain well-defined orbits or shells about a central nucleus with a limited number of electrons in each shell, the actual number being determined by energy considerations. Each shell of electrons represents a particular energy level, and the

*Elements of higher atomic number than lawrencium have been made synthetically and detected, but their half-life is so minute that they are of little practical significance and are seldom included in periodic table charts.

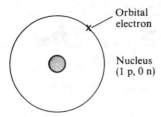

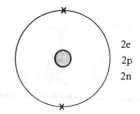

Fig. 2.1 Hydrogen atom: atomic number 1

Fig. 2.2 Helium atom: atomic number 2

number of electrons in any one shell is limited accordingly. The innermost shell is defined by the PRINCIPAL QUANTUM NUMBER, $n = 1$, (sometimes referred to as the 'K-Shell'), and contains a maximum of two electrons. The second shell is defined by the principal quantum number, $n = 2$, ('L-Shell') and contains a maximum of eight electrons. The third shell, $n = 3$, ('M-Shell') has a maximum of eighteen electrons, and so on, with the maximum number of electrons in further shells becoming progressively greater.

Shell	K	L	M	N
Principal quantum number, n	1	2	3	4
Maximum number of electrons	2	8	18	32

Nucleus   2e   8e   18e   32e   **Fig. 2.3**

$n = 1$ $n = 2$ $n = 3$ $n = 4$
(K) (L) (M) (N)

The negatively-charged orbital electrons are attracted towards the positively-charged nuclear protons, those electrons nearest to the nucleus being firmly held by strong attractive forces whereas those further away are less firmly held by weaker attractive forces. The more firmly held electrons have a low potential energy while those less firmly held have a higher potential energy. Therefore, on moving further away from the nucleus, each shell represents electrons of progressively higher energy.

Quantum Theory

The quantum theory states that orbital electrons can only exist in certain definite energy levels and cannot have all possible energy values. Thus, whenever an electron is transferred from one energy level to another, a definite integral amount of energy, a QUANTUM, corresponding to a particular frequency of radiation, is absorbed or emitted. The essence of this is that the energy of a body can only change in definite whole-number multiples of this unit of energy known as a quantum, and that this energy is only emitted or absorbed when an electron undergoes a transition from one energy level to another.

$$\text{Energy change} = n \times \text{Quantum},$$

where n is a whole number.

The energy emitted by an electron in undergoing a transition between two energy states, E_1 and E_2, is given by the Einstein–Planck equation:

$$E_1 - E_2 = h\nu$$

where h represents Planck's constant and ν the frequency of the radiation.

Modern Concepts of the Atom

The theories of Rutherford and Bohr and the interpretation of atomic spectra by Sommerfeld were satisfactory as far as they went, but they provided no means of accounting for the binding forces between atoms or for the shapes of molecules. The inadequacies of these theories are a result of considering the electron as a discrete particle. Modern science requires the atom to be interpreted more as a mathematical concept, rather than to be visualized pictorially as it was by Bohr.

De Broglie (1924) postulated the *dual nature of electrons*. He suggested that just as light waves can behave as particles, so electrons might be capable of behaving as waves of radiation. Further, Heisenberg (1927), in his UNCERTAINTY PRINCIPLE, stated that *it is impossible to know both the energy and position of any particle such as an electron at the same time.*

Utilizing these concepts, Schrödinger devised a WAVE EQUATION which provided the basis for a mathematical image of the atom. The significance of the wave equation is that *the solution of it provides a means of measuring the probability of finding an electron in a particular volume of space.* However, as the number of electrons in an atom increases beyond three or four, the mathematical complexity of the problem requires the introduction of simplifying approximations. These approximations are of no real significance here, but the solutions of the calculations, treated qualitatively, provide a considerable insight into the study of molecular formulae, the nature and strength of chemical bonds, and also the shapes of molecules.

Atomic Orbitals

Since the classical concept of electrons orbiting the nucleus in certain well-defined circular orbits is no longer valid, it is necessary to introduce an entirely different principle for locating electrons. Instead, *the volume of space where there is a high probability of finding u particular electron* is considered. This volume of space is called an ORBITAL, the actual shape of which has been deduced from wave-mechanical calculations. Moreover, each of these atomic orbitals can accommodate no more than two electrons.

Electron Spins

In the same way as the earth rotates about its own axis as it orbits the sun, an electron can be thought to spin on its own axis as it orbits the nucleus. In any one orbital, the spins of the two electrons must be in opposite directions, i.e. the spins are said to be OPPOSED or PAIRED.

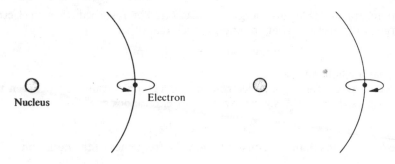

Fig. 2.4 Opposed or paired spins

Spectral Studies

As already stated, each shell represents a particular energy level and is described by a principal quantum number, n. The study of the frequency of atomic spectral lines has enabled the energy levels available to electrons in atoms to be depicted, and has also shown that the main levels, defined by a principal quantum number, are further divided into sub-levels of slightly different energy. These levels are defined by a secondary quantum number called the AZIMUTHAL QUANTUM NUMBER, l, having values $0, 1, 2, \ldots, n-1$.

s, p, d and f Orbitals

When $l = 0$, the orbital is spherical about the nucleus and is called an s ORBITAL. When $l = 1$, the orbital is dumb-bell shaped and is called a p ORBITAL. When $l = 2$, the orbital is double dumb-bell shaped and is called a d ORBITAL, and when $l = 3$, the orbital is even more complicated and is called an f ORBITAL.

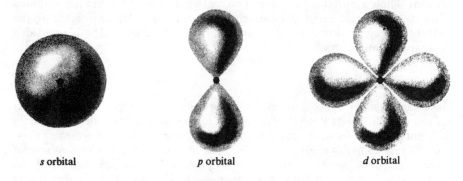

s orbital   *p* orbital   *d* orbital

Fig. 2.5

For orbitals defined by the same principal quantum number, the s orbital is the one of lowest energy. This is followed by the p, d and f orbitals respectively, which are of progressively higher energy.

There are two further sub-levels in addition to the one defined by the azimuthal quantum number. These are given by the magnetic quantum number, m_l, and the spin quantum number, m_s. The magnetic quantum number is deter.nined by observing the way in which an applied magnetic field splits the spectral lines, and the spin quantum number simply denotes the opposed spins of the electrons in any one orbital. This means that no two electrons in any one atom can be defined by the same four quantum numbers. This principle is known as the PAULI EXCLUSION PRINCIPLE.

In organic chemistry we are concerned primarily with electrons in *s* and *p* orbitals since the atoms of most of the elements with which we are concerned, i.e. carbon, hydrogen, oxygen, sulphur, nitrogen, fluorine, chlorine, do not possess electrons in *d* and *f* orbitals. Where we do encounter atoms that do contain electrons in these orbitals, e.g. bromine and iodine, they are not valence electrons, i.e. they do not affect the valency or oxidation state of the atom, and therefore do not directly affect the type of reactions and the properties that these elements exhibit.

The letters *s*, *p*, *d* and *f* are derived from the spectroscopic terms; sharp, principal, diffuse and fundamental, which are used to define certain spectral lines in atomic spectra.

Orientation of Atomic Orbitals in Space

Since *s* orbitals are spherical about the nucleus, the chance of finding one of the orbital electrons is the same in all directions.

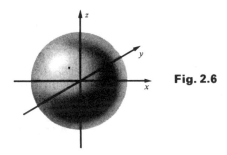

Fig. 2.6

There are three exactly similar *p* orbitals in any one energy level, and as each one can contain a maximum of only two electrons, there are, at the most, six *p* electrons in any one level. These are divided between three dumb-bell shaped orbitals which are arranged mutually at right angles to each other, pointing along *x*, *y* and *z* axes. These orbitals are called p_x, p_y and p_z respectively.

Fig. 2.7

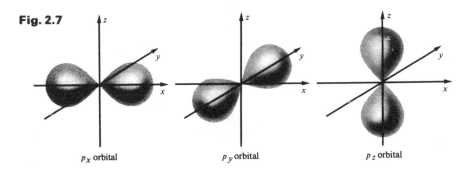

p_x orbital p_y orbital p_z orbital

Combining the *p* orbitals of any one energy level:

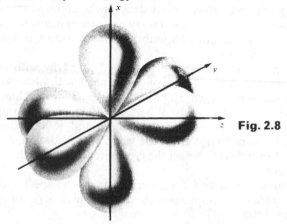

Fig. 2.8

All three *p* orbitals are of equvalent energy, and are of slightly higher energy than the *s* orbital governed by the same principal quantum number.

Between spherical *s* orbitals of different energy, there is a region in which the probability of finding an *s* electron becomes negligible and approaches zero. This volume of space is called a NODAL SURFACE.

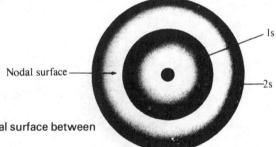

Fig. 2.9 The nodal surface between 1*s* and 2*s* orbitals

Similarly, there is a volume of space within the *p* orbitals where the likelihood of finding the electrons approaches zero. This region is called the NODAL PLANE, and lies at right angles to the *x*, *y* and *z* axes.

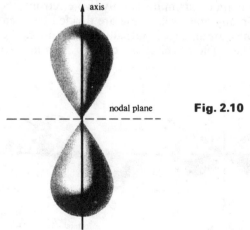

Fig. 2.10

The boundary surface of an atomic orbital is drawn so that the chance of finding a particular electron within this region is about 95 per cent.

Electronic Build-up and Hund's Rule

The first orbitals to be filled with electrons are those of lowest energy. Therefore, when considering electrons all governed by the same principal quantum number, the first two electrons fill the s orbital, the next three enter each of the p orbitals in turn (which, remember, are all of equivalent energy), and then the following three electrons form pairs of electrons in these same orbitals.

Pairing takes place only after each of the equivalent p orbitals has obtained one electron, since a certain amount of extra energy is required for pairing electrons within an orbital. This is in accordance with HUND'S RULE, which states that *in a given energy level (i.e. within the s level, or p level etc.) the number of unpaired electrons should be a maximum.*

A convenient way of representing the electronic structure of an atom is to use the letters s, p, d and f to describe the orbitals, prefixed by the principal quantum number denoting the energy level. A superscript to the letter is used to specify the number of electrons in each orbital.

For example, consider the electronic structure of the carbon atom (six electrons) and the oxygen atom (eight electrons) in their GROUND STATE (i.e. lowest energy state). In each case, the first two electrons enter the $1s$ orbital and the next two the $2s$ orbital. The remaining two carbon and four oxygen electrons enter the $2p$ orbitals.

$$\text{Carbon}: 1s^2\, 2s^2\, 2p^2$$

$$\text{Oxygen}: 1s^2\, 2s^2\, 2p^4$$

The p orbitals can be further divided into the p_x, p_y and p_z orbitals and represented as:

$$\text{Carbon atom, ground state}: 1s^2\, 2s^2\, 2p_x^1\, 2p_y^1$$

$$\text{Oxygen atom, ground state}: 1s^2\, 2s^2\, 2p_x^2\, 2p_y^1\, 2p_z^1$$

This may be shown diagrammatically, using arrows for electrons and boxes for energy levels.

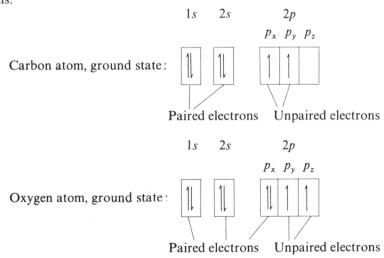

The process of feeding electrons into orbitals of successively higher energy in this way until the electronic structure of an element is complete is in accordance with the *Aufbau* principle. The purpose of having the arrows pointing in opposite directions is to indicate the opposed spins of the two electrons in any one orbital.

It is not until electrons start to fill the orbitals defined by the principal quantum number 3 (*M* shell), which contains a maximum of eighteen electrons, that the filling of the double dumb-bell shaped *d* orbitals is observed.

There are five *d* orbitals in any one energy level, and since each one can contain a maximum of 2 electrons, there are a maximum of ten *d* electrons in each level. For example,

Bromine atom, ground state: $1s^2\ 2s^2\ 2p^6\ 3s^2\ 3p^6\ 3d^{10}\ 4s^2\ 4p^5$

f electrons arise in the orbitals defined by the principal quantum number 4 (*L* shell) which has a maximum of thirty-two electrons.

Interpretation of the complex spectral patterns observed for different elements indicates that the energy levels of orbitals defined by a particular principal quantum number overlap with those defined by another. For example, the $4s$ orbitals are of lower energy than the $3d$ and are thus filled first. Similarly, the same applies to the $5s$ and $4d$ orbitals, and so on. The diagram below (Fig. 2.11) depicts the approximate energy levels of the different orbitals. The relative energy of each type of orbital is represented by a horizontal line, and the maximum number of electrons capable of occupying them is specified in the brackets.

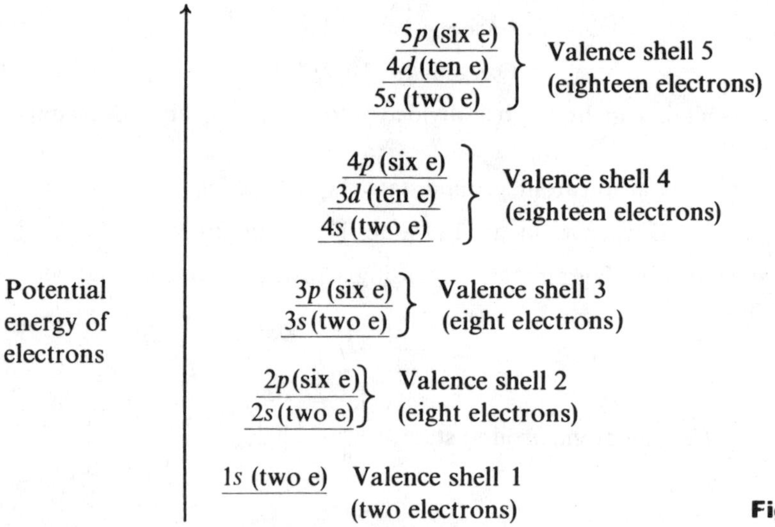

Potential energy of electrons

5p (six e)
4d (ten e)
5s (two e) } Valence shell 5 (eighteen electrons)

4p (six e)
3d (ten e)
4s (two e) } Valence shell 4 (eighteen electrons)

3p (six e)
3s (two e) } Valence shell 3 (eight electrons)

2p (six e)
2s (two e) } Valence shell 2 (eight electrons)

1s (two e) Valence shell 1 (two electrons)

Fig. 2.11

Levels of approximately the same energy content are described as VALENCE SHELLS which, unlike the principal quantum shells, need not necessarily be defined by the same principal quantum number. It is, however, important to appreciate that, despite the terminology, it is only those electrons in the higher energy valence shells which actually determine the valency or oxidation state of an element.

In general, electrons may be expected to occupy the orbitals in the ascending sequence depicted in the chart, although discrepancies arise for certain elements of high atomic number.

The following scheme (Fig. 2.12), in which the parallel diagonal lines join together orbitals of progressively higher energy, provides a useful guide as to the order in which orbitals of atoms in the ground state are filled by electrons.

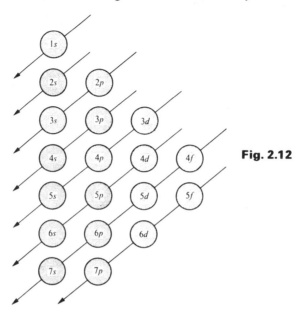

Fig. 2.12

QUESTIONS

1. Which one of the following electronic structures represents the ground state of a highly electronegative element?

   A $1s^2\, 2s^2\, 2p^1$
   B $1s^2\, 2s^2\, 2p^6\, 3s^1$
   C $1s^2\, 2s^2\, 2p^6\, 3s^2\, 3p^5$
   D $1s^2\, 2s^2\, 2p^6\, 3s^2\, 3p^6$
   E $1s^2\, 2s^2\, 2p^6\, 3s^2\, 3p^6\, 3d^{10}\, 4s^1$

2. The term atomic orbital refers to

   A a circular path
   B an elliptical path
   C an energy level
   D a volume of space
   E a valence shell

3. Which one of the following statements is *wholly* correct?

   A All electrons in each valence shell are defined by the same principal quantum number.
   B A $3d$ electron is of higher energy than a $4s$ electron.
   C p_x, p_y and p_z orbitals defined by the same principal quantum number differ only very slightly in energy.
   D There is a reasonable chance of finding an electron in a nodal region.
   E Electrons of highest energy are those nearest to the nucleus.

Bonding and Molecular Structure

Formation of Molecules

In order for atoms to combine to form molecules, the process has to be thermodynamically favourable. The energy involved in the initial stages of the process is sufficient in many cases to cause an unpairing of electrons, and to allow an atom to exhibit its most common covalency, which depends on the number of unpaired electrons.

Atoms which have more unpaired electrons through having acquired energy are said to be in an EXCITED STATE.

The Covalency of Carbon

At first sight, the carbon atom would seem to have a covalency of two, as it possesses only two unpaired electrons in its ground state.

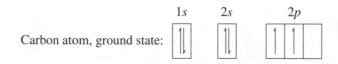

Carbon atom, ground state:

However, when it combines with another atom or molecule the carbon atom acquires sufficient energy to cause an unpairing of the $2s$ electrons.

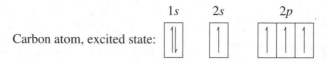

Carbon atom, excited state:

The atom now has four unpaired electrons and exhibits a covalency of four. According to this reasoning, there appears to be one unpaired $2s$ electron and three unpaired $2p$ electrons, of marginally higher energy, available for bonding. In fact, *carbon exerts its tetravalency by using four electrons of identical energy which are indistinguishable from each other.*

Hybridization

sp³ Hybridization of the Carbon Atom

Quantum mechanical calculations show that this is achieved by blending the $2s$ electron with the three $2p$ electrons to form four exactly similar orbitals. Since these orbitals are formed from the hybridization of an s and three p orbitals, they are referred to as sp^3 hybrid orbitals.

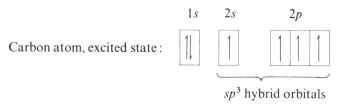

Carbon atom, excited state:

$1s$ $2s$ $2p$

sp^3 hybrid orbitals

These orbitals are of a shape different from that of the s or p orbitals from which they are formed, and they are directed towards the corners of a regular tetrahedron.

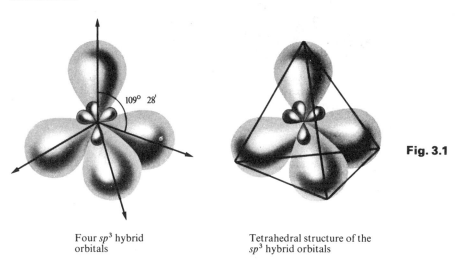

Fig. 3.1

Four sp^3 hybrid
orbitals

Tetrahedral structure of the
sp^3 hybrid orbitals

This represents the most stable configuration, since the orbitals are orientated in space in such a way that the electrons are as far apart as possible, ensuring that the repulsive forces between the electrons in the different orbitals are reduced to a minimum. The tetrahedral arrangement of orbitals means that they are inclined at angles of 109° 28' to each other.

sp^2 and sp Hybridization of the Carbon Atom

It is by no means essential for the carbon atom to have all four of its unpaired electrons hybridized, and many compounds are encountered in which the carbons have only three and sometimes only two of these electrons hybridized.

The hybridization of the $2s$ with two $2p$ orbitals results in the formation of *three sp^2 hybrid orbitals* of equivalent energy, thus leaving a single occupied $2p$ orbital unaffected.

$1s$ $2s$ $2p$

Carbon atom, excited state:

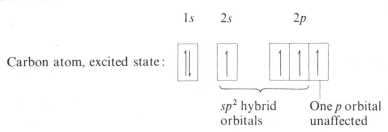

sp^2 hybrid
orbitals

One p orbital
unaffected

The three sp^2 hybrid orbitals are planar to each other and inclined at angles of $120°$.

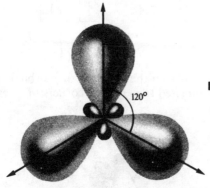

Fig. 3.2 Three sp^2 hybrid orbitals

Two sp hybrid orbitals are derived by the hybridization of the 2s with only one of the 2p orbitals, leaving two 2p orbitals unaffected.

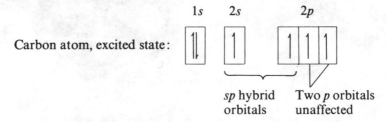

The sp orbitals are linearly opposed, so that the repulsive forces between the electrons are minimized.

Fig. 3.3 Two sp hybrid orbitals

The Formation of Covalent Bonds

When a covalent bond is formed, electrons are shared between two atoms, and these atoms must approach sufficiently closely for the orbital of one atom to overlap with the orbital of the other. Since each orbital can contain a maximum of two electrons, it follows that in the formation of a covalent bond an orbital of one atom containing one electron overlaps with a singly occupied orbital of the other. Thus both atoms have a share in two bonding electrons.

Molecular Orbitals

The overlapping of two atomic orbitals results in the formation of two MOLECULAR ORBITALS, one having a lower energy value than the energies of the constituent atomic orbitals and the other having a higher energy. The molecular orbital of lower energy is referred to as the BONDING ORBITAL, and the one of higher energy is called the ANTI-BONDING ORBITAL. The latter need not be considered in the discussion of stable covalent bond formation. These molecular orbitals are distributed over the constituent atoms, and the two electrons involved in forming the bond may be contained in either orbital. The greater the degree of overlapping between the atomic orbitals, the stronger the bond formed.

Sigma and Pi Bonds

For all single covalent bonds, orbitals overlap so as to form SIGMA (σ) bonds. Confining our interest for the moment to *s* and *p* orbitals, these bonds result from any of three possibilities:

(1) the overlapping of two *s* orbitals;

(2) the overlapping of two *p* orbitals linearly opposed to each other;

or

(3) the overlapping of an *s* and *p* orbital.

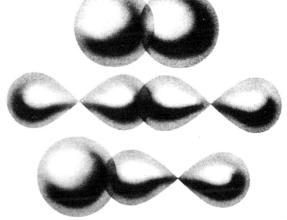

Fig. 3.4

The bonding electrons in sigma bonds are most likely to be located near an imaginary line joining the two nuclei of the atoms involved.

The lateral overlap of two parallel *p* orbitals of adjacent atoms results in the formation of an entirely different type of covalent bond which is called a PI (π) BOND.

Fig. 3.5

The degree of overlapping is less than in the formation of sigma bonds, and the bonding electrons are located away from the imaginary line joining the nuclei of the atoms. Consequently, they are weaker than the sigma bonds and, being more exposed, are more vulnerable to cleavage by an attacking reagent during a chemical reaction.

Carbon-Carbon Single Bonds

In the case of hybridized orbitals, sigma bonds result from the overlapping of either an *s* or a *p* orbital with the hybrid orbital. For example, in methane, CH_4, the carbon is sp^3 hybridized and each hybrid orbital overlaps with the *s* orbital of each of the four hydrogen atoms.

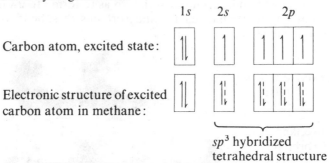

represents the electrons contributed by each of the four hydrogen atoms.

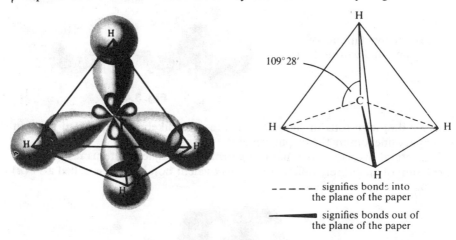

Fig. 3.6 The tetrahedral structure of methane

The methane molecule is completely symmetrical, with the hydrogen atoms located at the four corners of a regular tetrahedron.

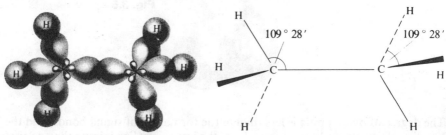

Fig. 3.7 The structure of ethane

In ethane, C_2H_6, the tetrahedral arrangement of atoms about each carbon is retained, but in this molecule the two carbons are attached to each other by means of a σ bond which results from the overlapping of two sp^3 orbitals.

Carbon-Carbon Double Bonds

In the formation of carbon–carbon double bonds, $>C{=}C<$, only three of the four valence electrons are hybridized to form sp^2 orbitals. This leaves the one remaining unpaired $2p$ electron unaffected by the hybridization.

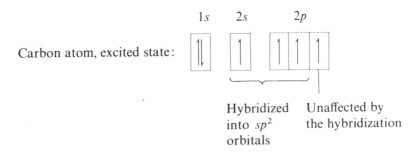

Carbon atom, excited state:

Hybridized into sp^2 orbitals   Unaffected by the hybridization

The sp^2 hybrid orbitals are planar and inclined at angles of $120°$ to each other, with the unhybridized p orbital set at right angles to this plane. The simplest and most easily considered unsaturated molecule which contains a carbon–carbon double bond is the alkene, *ethene (ethylene)*, C_2H_4.

All the carbon–hydrogen bonds are σ bonds formed by the overlap of the carbon sp^2 hybrid orbitals with the s orbitals of the hydrogen atoms. One of the carbon–carbon bonds is formed by the overlap of two sp^2 orbitals from each of the adjacent atoms, resulting in a σ bond, and the other obtained by the overlapping of the adjacent p orbitals, forming a π bond.

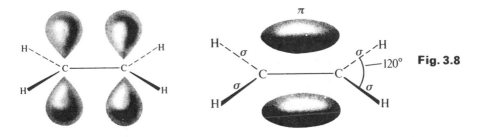

Fig. 3.8

The resulting molecular orbital containing the π electrons is spread over both carbon atoms and is located above and below the plane of the rest of the molecule. It must be remembered that although this π bond appears as two electron clouds, it still constitutes only one bond.

Carbon-Carbon Triple Bonds

In the formation of carbon–carbon triple bonds, $-C{\equiv}C-$, only two of the valence electrons are hybridized to form sp orbitals, leaving two p orbitals unaffected.

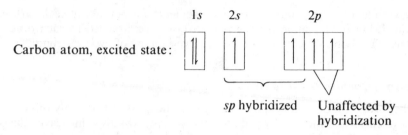

sp hybridized   Unaffected by hybridization

The simplest hydrocarbon containing a triple bond, *ethyne (acetylene)*, is a *linear molecule*. The carbon and hydrogen atoms are attached by σ bonds which are formed by the overlapping of the *sp* orbitals of the carbon with the *s* orbitals of the hydrogen atoms. One of the carbon–carbon bonds is a σ bond which results from the overlapping of the other *sp* orbitals of each carbon.

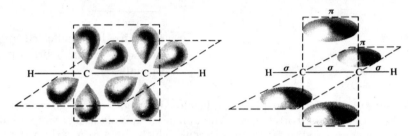

Fig. 3.9

The remaining two carbon–carbon bonds are both π bonds which are formed as a result of the overlapping of adjacent *p* orbitals. Since these two bonds lie at right angles to each other (the dotted lines clearly illustrate the planes in which these two bonds lie), the ethyne molecule is virtually encased by clouds of negatively charged electrons.

The Length and Strength of Carbon–Carbon Bonds

Physical methods are available by which it is possible to measure the lengths of chemical bonds, i.e. the distance between the nuclei of two bonded atoms. These lengths are usually quoted in nanometres ($1 \text{ nm} = 10^{-9} \text{ m}$).

The length of a carbon–carbon single bond in ethane (0.154 nm) is greater than that of the double bond in ethene (0.134 nm), which is in turn greater than the triple bond in ethyne (0.120 nm). Furthermore, the lengths of these different types of bond in other compounds do not deviate very much from these values.

Bond	Bond length/nm	Bond energies/kJ mol^{-1}
C—C in ethane	0.154	349
C=C in ethene	0.134	681
C≡C in ethyne	0.120	815

This means that adjacent carbon atoms become closer together as the number of bonds joining them becomes greater.

The relative strengths of carbon–carbon single and multiple bonds are shown by their respective bond energies, determined by thermodynamics. The carbon–carbon single bond energy in methane is 349 kJ mol^{-1}, whereas that of the double bond in ethene is 681 kJ mol^{-1} and that of the triple bond in ethyne is 815 kJ mol^{-1}.

These energy measurements indicate that a double bond is stronger than a single bond, but it is not twice as strong. A triple bond is stronger than both single and double bonds, but it is not three times as strong as a single nor 3/2 times as strong as a double.

This is quite plausible if one considers the type of bonding involved in each case, bearing in mind that a σ bond is stronger than a π bond because of the much greater degree of overlap of the atomic orbitals involved. Carbon–carbon single bonds are always σ bonds, whereas double bonds are made up of one σ and one π bond, and triple bonds contain one σ and two π bonds.

Rotation about Carbon–Carbon Bonds

The carbon atoms of saturated hydrocarbons are joined to each other by single σ bonds, thus allowing the hydrogen atoms or alkyl groups attached to two adjacent carbon atoms to rotate freely relative to each other. This FREE ROTATION about carbon–carbon single bonds can probably best be illustrated by making a simple model of ethane (CH_3—CH_3), and rotating the two methyl groups (CH_3) about the carbon–carbon bond. There are an infinite number of different ways in which the three hydrogen atoms on one carbon can arrange themselves with respect to the three hydrogen atoms on the other carbon simply by turning the methyl groups. Such *variations in the arrangements of atoms of a particular molecule, which do not involve the breaking of bonds, are called* CONFORMATIONS.

Atoms that are not bonded together attract each other over a certain distance. As these non-bonded atoms approach each other more closely, these attractive forces, referred to as VAN DER WAALS' FORCES, vanish and a strong repulsive force emerges, which causes a sharp rise in the energy content of the molecule, making it less stable. These attractive forces are the same intermolecular forces which are responsible for the deviation of real gases from ideal behaviour, and are named after the man who first took their effect into account in modifying the equation $pV = nRT$. Strictly speaking, it is not quite correct to refer to these NON-BONDED INTERACTIONS as taking place between the atoms in the molecules involved: more precisely, they are forces between the electron pairs in the hydrogen–carbon bonds.

In the *eclipsed conformation* the hydrogen atoms are in their most crowded state, producing a maximum degree of non-bonded interaction. It is this arrangement that represents the conformation of highest energy and, therefore, it is the least stable. In the *staggered conformation* the atoms are farthest apart, and it is this arrangement that coincides with the lowest energy value for the molecule. The eclipsed and staggered conformations represent the two extreme cases and between them an infinite number of possible structures exist. Since the molecule is most stable when its energy is at a minimum, it would be expected that the ethane molecule should exist primarily in the staggered form. However, the energy difference between the eclipsed and staggered conformation is comparatively small at room temperature, causing hardly any BARRIER TO THE ROTATION about the carbon–carbon single bond, and it is presumed that under these conditions all possible conformations exist.

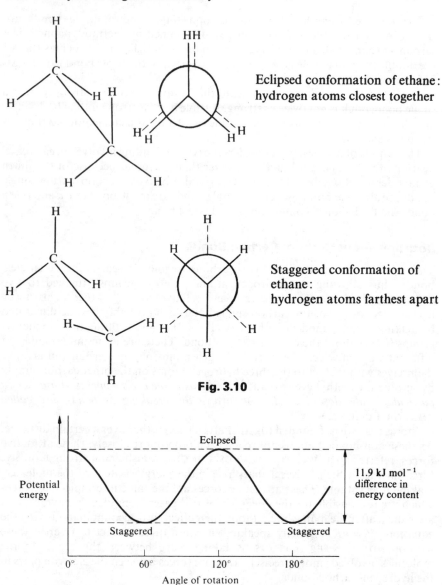

Eclipsed conformation of ethane: hydrogen atoms closest together

Staggered conformation of ethane: hydrogen atoms farthest apart

Fig. 3.10

Eclipsed

Staggered   Staggered

Potential energy

11.9 kJ mol⁻¹ difference in energy content

0°   60°   120°   180°

Angle of rotation

Fig. 3.11 Potential energy changes for ethane on rotation about its carbon–carbon single bond

The energy difference between eclipsed and staggered conformations becomes greater if larger and more electronegative atoms are substituted for the hydrogen. At very low temperatures, two conformational isomers of 1,1,2,2-tetra-bromoethane ($CHBr_2.CHBr_2$) have been detected. This is because of the greater steric hindrance and stronger repulsive forces between the bonded pairs of electrons of the larger and more electronegative bromine atoms.

A carbon–carbon double bond is a much more rigid system and there is considerable opposition to rotation. This may be exemplified by the simplest unsaturated molecule, ethene ($CH_2\!=\!CH_2$), which has two identical favoured structures. The energy barrier between these structures is 168 kJ mol^{-1}, compared with the very much smaller value of 11.9 kJ mol^{-1} for the difference between the staggered and eclipsed conformations of ethane.

Since free rotation is impaired by the double bond, molecules having a substituent atom or group on each of the carbons have two alternative structures; these are described as GEOMETRICAL ISOMERS. Examples of these are illustrated by the alkyl-substituted alkenes below.

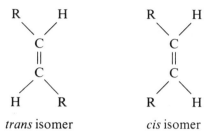

trans isomer   cis isomer

One isomer is known as the *cis* isomer and the other as the *trans*. The *cis* compound is the one which has identical or similar atoms or groups on the *same* side of the double bond, whereas the *trans* compound has them on *opposite* sides. Since the groups are farthest apart in the *trans* form, this is the form with lowest energy and therefore the more stable.

QUESTIONS

1. What do you understand by the terms 'molecular orbital', 'hybridization' and 'pi bond'? Illustrate your answer with reference to methane, ethene and ethyne, paying particular attention to the geometrical features of each molecule.

2. The following statements refer to different types of overlapping by molecular orbitals.

    In which case is a sigma bond *not* formed?

    A two s orbitals
    B two linearly opposed p orbitals

C two laterally opposed p orbitals
D an s orbital with an sp^2 orbital
E two sp^2 orbitals

3. The carbon atoms in propyne, $CH_3C{\equiv}CH_3$, are arranged at

    A 60° to each other
    B 90° to each other
    C 109° 28' to each other
    D 120° to each other
    E 180° to each other (i.e. linearly)

4 Naming Organic Compounds

Modern systems for naming aliphatic compounds are based upon the names of the alkanes, so it seems logical to deal with the naming of these compounds first.

With the exception of the first four members of the series, methane, ethane, propane and butane, the number of carbon atoms in the molecule is indicated by the Greek prefix for that particular number followed by the letters '-ane'.

		Names of alkanes			
Number of carbons	Name	Formula	Number of carbons	Name	Formula
1	Methane	CH_4	6	Hexane	C_6H_{14}
2	Ethane	C_2H_6	7	Heptane	C_7H_{16}
3	Propane	C_3H_8	8	Octane	C_8H_{18}
4	Butane	C_4H_{10}	9	*Nonane	C_9H_{20}
5	Pentane	C_5H_{12}	10	Decane	$C_{10}H_{22}$

Different conventions utilize these names in different ways. The most universal and systematic method is that devised by a commission appointed by the International Union of Pure and Applied Chemistry, which is referred to as the IUPAC System. It provides a convenient and relatively straightforward method for naming even the most complicated molecules, and has the advantage that the same basic principles are employed for each series of compounds.

Common (or semi-systematic) names are sometimes retained for the names of many of the more simple compounds of the various homologous series, but for more complicated molecules the more widely applicable IUPAC system is generally adopted.

Common (Semi-systematic) Names

Many of the simpler compounds are named from their function or their source, and despite attempts to persuade chemists to adopt the IUPAC system universally for all compounds, these common names are still widely used.

In some respects the common name does have certain advantages even for complex structures, for although the IUPAC name may generally define structure more clearly it can, in some instances, be much more clumsy to use, especially if it is having to be continually repeated. Conversely, of course, it can rightly be argued that in a great number of cases the common name gives no indication of structure whatsoever.

One might reasonably suppose that the chemist is more interested in how a compound reacts rather than how it is named, but nonetheless at the present time the problem of standardizing nomenclature for all types of compounds is still a long way from being fully resolved. The preferred names adopted in this book are in accordance with those recommended by The Association for Science

---

*Italic prefixes C_9H_{20} (*nonane*) and $C_{11}H_{24}$ (*undecane*) are preferred to the Greek *enna* (nine) and *hendeca* (eleven).

Education in their publication, *Chemical Nomenclature, Symbols and Terminology for Use in School Science.*

The IUPAC (Geneva) System of Nomenclature

The following provides an outline of the systematic principles adopted:

(1) The longest continuous chain of carbon atoms containing the functional group is selected and named according to the parent alkane.

(2) The carbon atoms of the chain are numbered in order to indicate the positions of any substituents in the chain. The end of the chain from which the numbering starts is chosen so as to use the lowest values, e.g.

$$\overset{1}{C}H_3 - \overset{2}{C}H - \overset{3}{C}H_2 - \overset{4}{C}H_2 - \overset{5}{C}H_3$$
$$|$$
$$Cl$$

2-Chloropentane

(3) The names of the substituents prefix the name of the parent alkane alphabetically and the positions of substitution precede the whole.

(4) The numbers assigned to the functional groups are chosen so as to be as small as possible. These are usually placed between the stem and the ending of the name. The functional group numbers are given precedence over those assigned to other substituents. For example, consider the naming of the following alcohols. Simple alcohols are named by dropping the '-e' from the end of the name of the parent alkane and adding the suffix '-ol'.

CH_3CH_2OH
Ethanol
(parent alkane, ethane)

$$\overset{3}{C}H_3 - \overset{2}{C}H - \overset{1}{C}H_2 - OH$$
$$|$$
$$CH_3$$
2-Methylpropan-1-ol
(parent alkane, propane)

The nomenclature of compounds possessing other functional groups is dealt with as they are introduced in subsequent chapters.

QUESTIONS

1. Give the IUPAC names for the following:

A $CH_3CH_2CHCH_3$
           |
           CH_3

B CH_3CHCH_2Cl
        |
        $CH_2CH_2CH_3$
          Cl

C CH_3CH_2CCHOH
           |
           CH_3

         Cl   OH
         | |
D $CH_3CH - CH - CHCH_3$
       |
       CH_2CH_3

2. The correct name for the structural formula

         CH_3 CH_3
         | |
$CH_3CCH_2CHCH_3$ is
         |
         CH_3

A   1,1,4,4-tetramethylbutane
B   2,2,4-trimethylpentane
C   2,4,4-trimethylpentane
D   2,2,4-trimethyloctane
E   2,4,4-trimethyloctane

5 Isomerism and Optical Activity

Isomerism is the phenomenon whereby certain compounds possessing the same molecular formula exist in different forms because they have different arrangements of atoms. This concept illustrates the fundamental importance of molecular structure in organic chemistry. There are two main types of isomerism—STRUCTURAL ISOMERISM, in which the atoms are *linked together in different ways*, and STEREOISOMERISM, in which the atoms have *different spatial arrangements*. These general classes can be sub-divided into different categories which describe more precisely the various isomers.

Structural Isomerism

CHAIN or BRANCHED-CHAIN ISOMERS are those which have different carbon chains or skeletons. For example, there are two butanes:

$$CH_3-CH_2-CH_2-CH_3 \qquad\qquad CH_3-CH-CH_3$$
$$\qquad\qquad\qquad\qquad\qquad\qquad\qquad\qquad |$$
$$\qquad\qquad\qquad\qquad\qquad\qquad\qquad\qquad CH_3$$

Butane   2-Methylpropane
                          (Isobutane)

There are four structural isomeric alcohols corresponding to the formula C_4H_9OH:

$$CH_3-CH_2-CH_2-CH_2-OH \qquad CH_3-CH_2-CH-CH_3$$
$$\qquad\qquad\qquad\qquad\qquad\qquad\qquad\qquad\qquad\qquad |$$
$$\qquad\qquad\qquad\qquad\qquad\qquad\qquad\qquad\qquad\qquad OH$$

Butan-1-ol   Butan-2-ol

$$\qquad\qquad\qquad\qquad\qquad\qquad\qquad\qquad CH_3$$
$$\qquad\qquad\qquad\qquad\qquad\qquad\qquad\qquad |$$
$$CH_3-CH-CH_2-OH \qquad CH_3-C-CH_3$$
$$\qquad\quad | \qquad\qquad\qquad\qquad\qquad\qquad\qquad |$$
$$\qquad\quad CH_3 \qquad\qquad\qquad\qquad\qquad\qquad OH$$

2-Methylpropan-1-ol   2-Methylpropan-2-ol
(Isobutyl alcohol)   (*tert*-Butyl alcohol)

Furthermore, butan-2-ol exists in two stereoisomeric forms (*see* page 29).

METAMERISM is a form of isomerism which can occur when two or more alkyl groups are attached to the same functional group, as in ethers or ketones. Metamers belong to the same homologous series. For example, there are three ethers corresponding to the molecular formula, $C_4H_{10}O$:

$$CH_3—CH_2—O—CH_2—CH_3 \qquad\qquad CH_3—O—CH_2—CH_2—CH_3$$

Ethoxyethane   1-Methoxypropane
(Diethyl ether)   (Methyl propyl ether)

$$CH_3—O—CH—CH_3$$
$$|$$
$$CH_3$$

2-Methoxypropane
(Methyl isopropyl ether)

Molecules which have a substituent in different positions on the same carbon skeleton are referred to as POSITIONAL ISOMERS.

$$CH_3—CH_2—CH_2—OH \qquad\qquad CH_3—CH—CH_3$$
$$|$$

Propan-1-ol   OH

Propan-2-ol

Isomerism between compounds in different homologous series is called FUNCTIONAL GROUP ISOMERISM. For example, ethanol and methoxymethane both have the same molecular formula, C_2H_6O:

$$CH_3—CH_2—OH \qquad\qquad CH_3 —O—CH_3$$

Ethanol   Methoxymethane
(Dimethyl ether)

Compounds whose structures differ in arrangement of atoms but which are in dynamic equilibrium with each other are described as TAUTOMERS. For example, a structure with an —OH group attached to a doubly bonded carbon is called an *enol*, and is in equilibrium with the structure which contains a $>C=O$ group (a *keto* structure).

$$—C=C—OH \rightleftharpoons —C—C=O$$

Enol structure   Keto structure

The equilibrium lies very much towards the right-hand side for simple structures. This phenomenon is considered and discussed further on pages 118 and 229.

Stereoisomerism

GEOMETRICAL ISOMERISM is probably the simplest type of stereoisomerism. It occurs in compounds in which free rotation is prevented by the presence of multiple bonds, a ring structure, or steric factors (*see* page 23). The structures of geometrical isomers differ only in configuration, i.e. spatial arrangement, giving rise to a *cis* isomer, which has identical or similar atoms or groups on the *same* side of the double bond, and a *trans* isomer, which has them on opposite sides.

H   COOH   H   COOH
  \ /   \ /
   C   C
   ‖   ‖
   C   C
  / \   / \
H   COOH   HOOC   H

cis-Butenedioic acid   *trans*-Butenedioic acid
(Maleic acid)   (Fumaric acid)

These isomers, which are both solids, possess quite different physical properties.

Physical property	cis-Butenedioic acid	trans-Butenedioic acid
Melting point/°C	139	287
Density/g cm^{-3}	1.59	1.64
Solubility in water at 25°C/g per 100 g water	78.8	0.7

The stereoisomers, *cis*- and *trans*-butenedioic acid can easily be distinguished by means of a number of their chemical properties. For example, heating *cis*-butenedioic acid to 160 °C gives a small proportion of the acid anhydride, although much better yields are obtained by carrying the reaction out under reduced pressure and at a temperature of 100 °C. The *trans* isomer, on the other hand, sublimes on heating to 200°C but otherwise remains chemically unchanged.

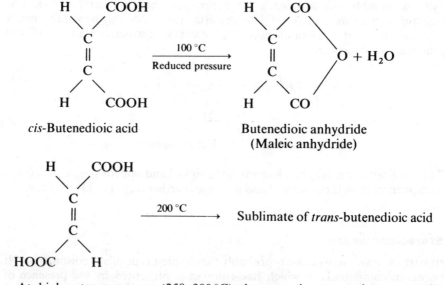

cis-Butenedioic acid   Butenedioic anhydride
                                 (Maleic anhydride)

H   COOH
  \ /
   C
   ‖
   C
  / \
HOOC   H

$\xrightarrow{200\ °C}$ Sublimate of *trans*-butenedioic acid

At higher temperatures (250–300 °C) the *trans* isomer undergoes partial rearrangement to the *cis* isomer and gives a small yield of butenedioic (maleic) anhydride.

Optical Isomerism

If four different atoms or groups are attached to the same carbon, there are two isomers which are *not superimposable on their mirror images*. These isomers are referred to as ENANTIOMERS or ENANTIOMORPHS of each other and the non-superimposable structures are said to be CHIRAL.*

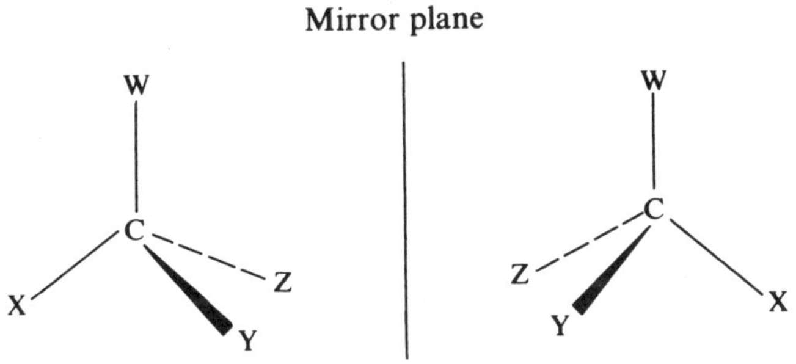

Mirror plane

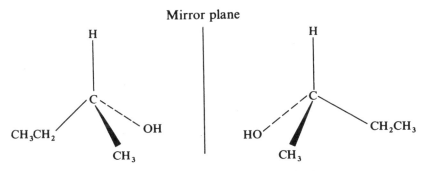

Fig. 5.1 Non-superimposable mirror images – enantiomers

The central carbon atom, to which four different atoms or groups are attached, is called a CHIRAL CENTRE.

One of the simplest compounds containing a chiral carbon is butan-2-ol, giving rise to a fifth isomer of butanol (*see* page 26).

Mirror plane

Fig. 5.2 Optical isomers of butan-2-ol

Similarly, 2-chlorobutane, $CH_3CH_2CHClCH_3$, and other compounds of analogous structure also exist as stereoisomers.

Enantiomers have identical physical constants (melting points, boiling points etc.) but may be distinguished from each other by their ability to rotate the plane of polarized light in opposite directions. It is because they exhibit this property that such isomers are said to be OPTICALLY ACTIVE. If the rotation of the plane is in a *clockwise* direction (i.e. to the right), the substance is said to be DEXTROROTATORY (indicated by *d* or a + sign) and if the rotation is in an *anti-clockwise* direction (i.e. to the left), the substance is LAEVOROTATORY

Chirality (meaning 'handedness') replaces the less accurate terms 'asymmetry' and 'dissymmetry', although the latter words will certainly be encountered in older literature. Adoption of the words 'chiral' and 'chirality' was proposed by Cahn, Ingold and Prelog (1964) based upon an original definition by Kelvin (1893)—'I call any geometrical figure, or any group of points, *chiral*, and say it has *chirality*, if its image in a plane mirror, ideally realized, cannot be brought to coincide with itself.' E.g. As the right hand is to the left hand.

(indicated by *l* or a − sign). The degree of rotation may be determined by means of a POLARIMETER.

Two of the most studied compounds containing a single chiral centre and which exhibit these properties are *2-hydroxypropanoic acid (lactic acid)* and *2-aminopropanoic acid (alanine)*.

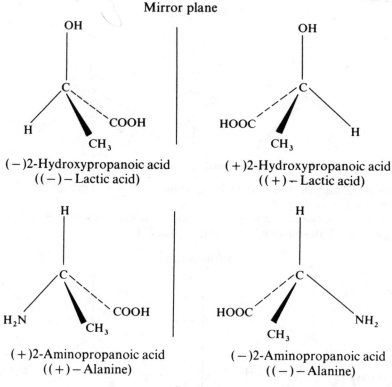

Mirror plane

(−)2-Hydroxypropanoic acid
((−)−Lactic acid)

(+)2-Hydroxypropanoic acid
((+)−Lactic acid)

(+)2-Aminopropanoic acid
((+)−Alanine)

(−)2-Aminopropanoic acid
((−)−Alanine)

Fig. 5.3

When enantiomers are mixed together in equal proportions, the rotating capacity of one isomer is exactly cancelled by that of the other. Such a mixture is called a RACEMATE or RACEMIC MIXTURE and is, as might be expected, OPTICALLY INACTIVE.

If one enantiomer undergoes a reaction, and in doing so forms a product which has the configuration of the other isomer, the molecule is said to have undergone INVERSION OF CONFIGURATION. A typical example of this is the Walden inversion reaction.

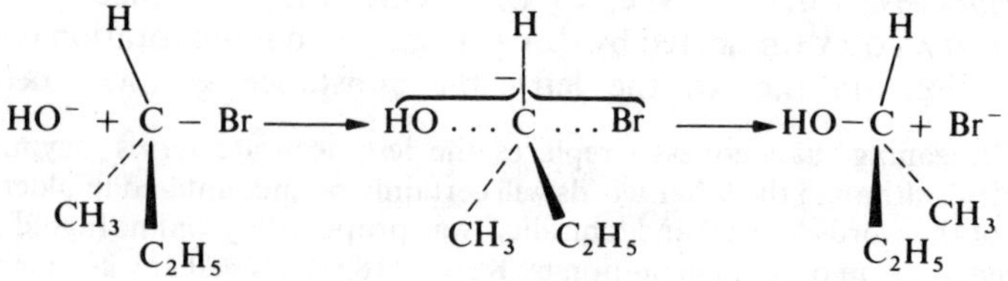

Fig. 5.4 Walden inversion reaction

This process is analogous to an umbrella being blown inside out.

2,3-Dihydroxybutanedioic (tartaric) acid affords a good example of compounds containing *two similar chiral centres*, the stereoisomerism of which is accounted for in terms of three possible configurations:

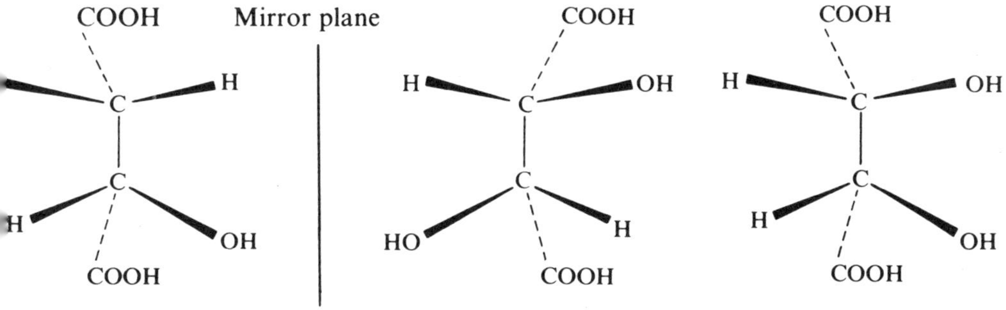

3-Dihydroxybutanedioic acid	(+)2,3-Dihydroxybutanedioic acid	Meso structure
−)–Tartaric acid)	((+)–Tartaric acid)	

Fig. 5.5

Each molecule may be regarded as being composed of two similar groups linked together by the two chiral carbons.

If the configuration of both of these groups is dextrorotatory, then they have the effect of reinforcing each other and the molecule as a whole will be dextrorotatory also. Conversely, if both groups are laevorotatory the molecule as a whole will be laevorotatory.

A third possible configuration, referred to as the *meso* form of the acid, exists in which one group is the (+)– form and the other is the (−)– form. In this case, the rotatory powers of each part of the molecule exactly compensate for each other and the molecule overall is optically inactive. This isomer is said to be INTERNALLY COMPENSATED, whereas the racemic mixture, containing equal proportions of the (+)– and (−)– isomers, is said to be EXTERNALLY COMPENSATED.

Resolution of Optical Isomers

The separation of racemic mixtures into their component (+)– and (−)– isomers is referred to as their RESOLUTION. One of the most convenient and practical ways of accomplishing this was developed by Louis Pasteur and involves reacting the racemate, (±)–A, with an optically active compound, (+)–B, to form (+)–A/(+)–B and (−)–A/(+)–B derivatives. These are known as DIASTEREOISOMERS; they are no longer enantiomers of each other, and can therefore be separated by techniques which utilize their difference in physical properties, the most common of these being solubility. For a racemic acid, an optically active amine provides a useful reagent, enabling the salts to be formed as the diastereoisomers.

After separation by, say, recrystallization, the components of the original racemate may be regenerated from the diastereoisomers. Racemic acids are generally most easily resolved from their salts by treating with a dilute mineral acid.

Pasteur originally used the principles of this technique to separate a racemic mixture of (+)– and (−)– ammonium sodium 2,3-dihydroxybutanedioate (tartrate).

Plane-polarized Light

Ordinary light may be regarded as vibrating at right angles to its direction of propagation (transverse wave motion) in an infinite number of planes. When it is passed through certain solids, light is found to vibrate in only one plane and is said to be PLANE POLARIZED. The diagrams below illustrate the vibrations of ordinary and plane-polarized light for a beam propagated perpendicularly to the plane of the paper.

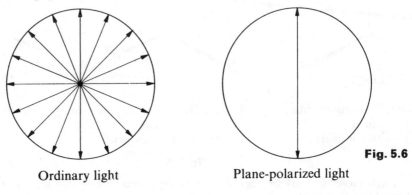

Fig. 5.6

Ordinary light   Plane-polarized light

The Polarimeter

Optical activity in a compound is both detected and measured by means of a POLARIMETER. The simplest type of instrument consists simply of a monochromatic light source (e.g. a sodium lamp), two Nicol or Polaroid lenses functioning as a *polarizer* and an *analyser*, and a tube containing a solution of the substance under examination.

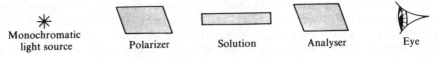

Monochromatic
light source   Polarizer   Solution   Analyser   Eye

Fig. 5.7 A simple polarimeter

With the tube empty, the maximum amount of light reaches the eye when the lenses are so arranged as to pass light vibrating in the same plane. The analyser is then turned through 90° to a position of extinction before placing the tube, filled with the solution, in position. Owing to the rotation of the plane of polarization, the observer will see a brighter field of view. The analyser is again rotated until the extinction position is restored. The difference in the readings of the analyser gives the angle of rotation of the beam. The concentration may be calculated from the equation given below.

Specific Rotation

The degree of rotation of the plane of polarized light depends on the number of molecules of the substance encountered by the light along its path. It is therefore necessary to introduce some standard whereby the rotating powers of different substances may be compared.

SPECIFIC ROTATION is defined as that rotation produced by a solution of length 10 centimetres and unit concentration (i.e. $1 \, \mathrm{g \, cm^{-3}}$) for the given wavelength of light at the given temperature.

Consider a system in which the analyser is rotated through $\alpha°$ at a temperature of t °C and using the sodium D-line as the source. The specific rotation $[\alpha]_D^t$ is given by:

$$[\alpha]_D^t = \frac{100\alpha}{1c}$$

where 1 is the length of tube in decimetres and c is the number of grams of substance per 100 cm³ of solution. The specific rotation varies with both the wavelength of the light and the temperature.

Conformations of Cyclohexane

Like all alkanes, cyclohexane, C_6H_{12} (*see* page 96), is a saturated hydrocarbon, all carbon atoms being sp^3 hybridized. A hexagonal planar arrangement of carbon atoms, which would necessitate carbon–carbon bond angles of 120°, as opposed to the favoured tetrahedral bond angles of 109° 28′, would be highly strained.

By rotation about the carbon–carbon single bond, cyclohexane can achieve two puckered conformations both of which are completely free from strain. These are the CHAIR conformation, in which interaction between non-bonded atoms is reduced to a minimum, and the BOAT conformation, which is more sterically crowded.

Fig. 5.8

Chair conformation of cyclohexane   Boat conformation of cyclohexane

A sample of the compound exists predominantly in the chair form, which is the more stable conformation by about 21–25 kJ mol⁻¹. This energy barrier is insufficient to prevent rapid interconversion between the two isomers and separation of them is therefore impossible, the boat isomer being merely a transition state between interconverting forms.

Consideration of the chair form shows that six hydrogen atoms are attached to the carbons by bonds arranged above and below the general plane of the molecule. These bonds are termed AXIAL (*a*) BONDS and are shown below as dotted lines. Those attached to the six hydrogens which are generally in the same plane as the carbon atoms are termed EQUATORIAL (*e*) BONDS and are indicated as unbroken lines.

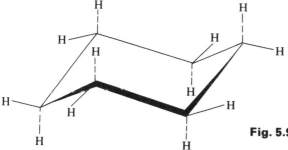

Fig. 5.9 Axial and equatorial bonds in the chair form

For *disubstituted derivatives* of cyclohexane, *cis–trans isomerism* can occur depending on whether the substituents are both on the same side of the general plane or on opposing sides.

QUESTIONS

1. Which one of the following structural formulae exists in both *cis* and *trans* forms?

   A CH_2=$CHCH_3$
   B $(CH_3)_2C$=$CHCH_3$
   C CH_3CH=NOH
   D C_6H_5CH=$C(CH_2Cl)_2$
   E C_6H_5CH=CHC_6H_5

2. The two esters, $CH_3COOCH_2CH_3$ and $CH_3CH_2COOCH_3$, may be classified as

   A metamers
   B positional isomers
   C functional group isomers
   D geometrical isomers
   E chain isomers

3. Which one of the compounds having the following structural formulae can be resolved into optical isomers?

   A $(CH_3)_2CHCH_2OH$
   B $(CH_3)_2CHOCH_3$
   C NH_2CH_2COOH
   D $NH_2CH(CH_3)COOH$
   E CH_3CH=$CHCH_2CH_3$

4. The angle through which plane-polarized light is rotated by a solution of an optically active isomer is independent of

   A the absolute temperature
   B the concentration of the solution
   C the length of the tube
   D the cross-sectional area of the tube
   E the wavelength of light

5. The isolation of an optically active isomer from a racemic mixture is referred to as

   A inversion
   B resolution
   C compensation
   D enantiomerism
   E conformational analysis

Structure and Physical Properties

6

The physical properties of a compound depend primarily upon the nature of the bonds holding the atoms in the molecules together and also upon the size and shape of the molecules themselves. Organic compounds are largely covalent although most of them show some degree of ionic character.

Polarization of a Covalent Bond

A covalent bond is formed by the sharing of two electrons, one being contributed by each of the constituent atoms. However, these electrons are not distributed exactly equally between the two atoms unless they happen to be identical or, alternatively, possess exactly equal ELECTRONEGATIVITY VALUES (*see* page 2). Generally, small atoms attract electrons more readily than do larger ones, and those which have nearly filled shells tend to have higher electronegativity values than those with only partly filled shells.

The electrons in a bond joining two atoms of different elements, A and B, are displaced towards the more electronegative atom, which acquires a relatively negative charge ($\delta-$) while the other atom becomes relatively positive ($\delta+$). The bond is said to be POLARIZED, although the term has a wider application and may also be used to describe molecules or groups.

$$A \overset{\delta+}{\rule{2cm}{0.4pt}} B \overset{\delta-}{} \qquad A \longrightarrow B \qquad A \;\blacksquare\; B \qquad \textbf{Fig. 6.1}$$

$$\text{I} \qquad\qquad\qquad \text{II} \qquad\qquad\qquad \text{III}$$

The relative charges are indicated quite clearly by I, whereas in II, the greater attractive force exerted by B is indicated by the arrow along the bond. In III, the more heavily shaded region represents that part of the volume in which the effective electron density is greatest. For convenience, it is usually preferable to use either I or II.

A molecule that has an asymmetrical distribution of electrons is said to possess a DIPOLE MOMENT, which is a measure of its tendency to line up along the direction of an electric field.

$$- \;\Big|\; A^{\delta+}\rule{1cm}{0.4pt}B^{\delta-} \;\Big|\; +$$

$$\text{Electric field}$$

The value of a dipole moment (p_e) is a product of the size of the charge (in coulombs, C) and the distance of separation in the molecule (d metres) and is measured in coulomb metres, C m.

For polyatomic molecules, the dipole moment is the vector sum of the individual bond moments. Methane has a zero dipole moment since the electron distribution within the molecule is completely symmetrical, but in asymmetrical haloalkane molecules there is a net dipole moment in favour of the more electronegative halogen. However, the tetrachloromethane (carbon tetrachloride) molecule has no dipole moment since, like methane, it is tetrahedrally symmetrical.

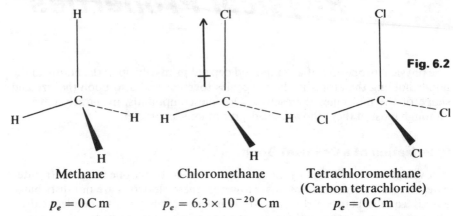

Fig. 6.2

Methane	Chloromethane	Tetrachloromethane (Carbon tetrachloride)
$p_e = 0\,C\,m$	$p_e = 6.3 \times 10^{-20}\,C\,m$	$p_e = 0\,C\,m$

The symbol $+\!\!\longrightarrow$ indicates the direction of the net dipole moment for the chloromethane molecule.

Melting Points

The ions or molecules present in crystalline solids are bound together into a regular, symmetrical structure. Melting involves breaking down this structure into the much more random arrangement that is characteristic of liquids.

In ionic solids, a positive ion is surrounded by a number of negative ions and *vice versa*. This means that each ion is associated with several oppositely charged ions and not specifically with any one in particular. For example, in a sodium chloride crystal the sodium is octahedrally surrounded by six chloride ions, and each chloride is similarly surrounded by six sodium ions. These *interionic* attractions between oppositely charged ions are strong, and therefore the melting points of ionic solids are high.

Organic solids, being composed of molecules which are predominantly covalent, are held together by van der Waals' molecular forces and by DIPOLE–DIPOLE interactions, both of which are comparatively weak. Consequently these solids have correspondingly lower melting points.

Van der Waals' forces are attractive forces between non-bonded atoms. They can exist between atoms within a molecule which are not attached to each other (as described for the conformations of ethane) or between the atoms of different molecules. The attractions are weak and function only over a short range. As these non-bonded atoms approach each other more closely, the attractive forces vanish and a repulsive force emerges.

The dipole–dipole interaction is an attractive force between the relatively positive end of one polar molecule and the relatively negative end of another.

$$A^{\delta+}\!\!-\!\!-\!\!B^{\delta-}$$

$$B^{\delta-}\!\!-\!\!-\!\!A^{\delta+}$$

The size and shape of the molecules of a solid are closely related to its melting point: compounds composed of large molecules tend to have higher melting points than those composed of small ones, and the more symmetrical the molecule the higher the melting point. For geometrical isomers, the greater symmetry attributable to the *trans* compound means that it will have a higher melting point than the *cis*.

A close examination of the physical constants of the carboxylic acids shows that an 'even' member of the series has a higher melting point than the 'odd' members immediately above and below it. X-ray analysis has shown that this alternation is dependent upon the packing of the crystals in the solid.

Boiling Points

Although the molecules in liquids are in random motion, certain cohesive forces exist between them. When the temperature of a liquid is increased, more individual molecules break away and exist by themselves in the gas phase: in other words, the vapour pressure of the liquid is increased. The liquid boils when its vapour pressure equals the external pressure.

In organic liquids, these cohesive forces again take the form of van der Waals' molecular forces and dipole–dipole interactions.

Organic liquids whose molecules contain —OH groups tend to have abnormally high boiling points. This is accounted for in terms of HYDROGEN BONDING: where hydrogen is bonded to oxygen it may serve as a bridge between two oxygen atoms of different molecules, forming a covalent bond with one and holding the other solely by electrostatic forces. This is, in effect, a very strong dipole–dipole interaction. Hydrogen bonding accounts for the unexpectedly high boiling points of water, alcohols, carboxylic acids etc. (Hydrogen bonding may also be observed in organic compounds in which hydrogen is bound to nitrogen.)

Because of the electronegativity difference between oxygen and hydrogen, the bonding electrons are attracted towards the oxygen atom, thus leaving the hydrogen nucleus partially exposed. This leaves the way open for an oxygen atom of another similar molecule to donate a lone pair of electrons.

The strength of a hydrogen bond, which is about 21 kJ mol^{-1}, is only 10–20 per cent that of most covalent bonds.

Hydrogen bonding is encountered in two different forms, INTERMOLECULAR and INTRAMOLECULAR. INTERMOLECULAR HYDROGEN BONDING occurs between separate molecules giving rise to *association* in the liquid and solid phases. It causes an elevation in the boiling point, surface tension and viscosity of the compound. Water forms a series of hydrogen bonds, which cause it to have an exceptionally high boiling point, since in order to convert the liquid into steam all these extra attractive forces have to be broken down.

$$---\overset{\delta+}{H}---\overset{2\delta-}{\underset{|}{\ddot{O}}}:---\overset{\delta+}{H}---\overset{2\delta-}{\underset{|}{\ddot{O}}}:--$$
$$\overset{}{\underset{H^{\delta+}}{}} \qquad \overset{}{\underset{H^{\delta+}}{}}$$

Alcohol molecules similarly associate in the liquid phase but exist as monomers in the vapour phase.

$$\overset{\delta+}{H}---\overset{\delta-}{\underset{|}{\ddot{O}}}:---\overset{\delta+}{H}---\overset{\delta-}{\underset{|}{\ddot{O}}}:$$
$$\overset{}{\underset{R}{}} \qquad \overset{}{\underset{R}{}}$$

The greater polarity of carboxylic acid molecules and the formation of two intermolecular hydrogen bonds gives rise to a boiling point higher than for the corresponding alcohols:

$$
\begin{array}{c}
\overset{\delta-}{\ddot{O}:} ---\overset{\delta+}{H}---\overset{\delta-}{\ddot{O}} \\
\end{array}
$$

R—C $\quad\quad\quad$ C—R

$$
\overset{\delta-}{O}---\overset{\delta+}{H}---\overset{\delta-}{:O}
$$

Ethanoic (acetic) acid, like most other carboxylic acids, forms a dimer in the liquid phase.

INTRAMOLECULAR HYDROGEN BONDING occurs between different atoms within the same molecule and gives rise to what is, in effect, a ring structure. This phenomenon is used to explain why 2-nitrophenol (m.p. 46 °C, b.p. 216 °C) has a greater volatility than either the 3- (m.p. 96 °C) or 4- (m.p. 112 °C) derivatives.

2-Nitrophenol

In this case, the intramolecular hydrogen bond is formed between one of the oxygen atoms of the nitro group and the hydrogen atom of the hydroxyl group.

Solubility

Solubility depends largely upon the intermolecular forces between the dissolved substance, irrespective of whether it is a solid or a liquid, and the solvent. The solubility of a non-electrolyte in water depends, to a certain extent, on whether the compound can form hydrogen bonds with water. For compounds containing —OH groups, the best solvents tend to be those which also contain —OH groups. This gives rise to an extremely useful adage: 'like dissolves like'.

Another factor contributing to the solubility of a substance is its size. The alkanes are all virtually insoluble in water, but the smallest member of the series, methane, is appreciably more soluble than any of the larger members. Furthermore, any possibility of hydrogen bonding in this instance is deemed unlikely.

Viscosity

The resistance of liquid to flow, caused by internal friction within the liquid, is dependent in part upon the van der Waals' forces and dipole–dipole interactions between the molecules. Since the van der Waals' forces depend upon the size and shape of the molecules and the dipole–dipole interactions depend upon the temperature, these factors also affect the viscosity of a liquid.

Some simple relationships between viscosity and structure:

(1) In a series of compounds which follow a regular structural pattern (i.e. a homologous series), viscosity increases with relative molecular mass.

(2) Straight-chain isomers are more viscous than branched-chain isomers.

(3) The viscosity of a *trans* isomer is greater than its corresponding *cis* isomer.

(4) Viscosity varies according to the degree of association within a liquid.

QUESTIONS

1. Which one of the molecules of the following compounds possesses a dipole moment?

   A CH_4
   B $CHCl_3$
   C CCl_4
   D CH_3CH_3
   E $CH{\equiv}CH$

2. Without referring to data tables, deduce which is the most volatile of the following compounds.

   A H_2O
   B CH_3OH
   C CH_3CH_2OH
   D CH_3OCH_3
   E $CH_3CH_2OCH_2CH_3$

3. The strength of a hydrogen bond is about

   A half that for a covalent bond
   B one-tenth that for a covalent bond
   C one-fiftieth that for a covalent bond
   D one-hundredth that for a covalent bond
   E one-thousandth that for a covalent bond

7

Reactants and Reactions

In a chemical reaction, the reactant molecule undergoing attack is referred to as the SUBSTRATE and the general term used to describe the attacking species is the REAGENT. The substrate and the reagent interact to yield the products of the reaction.

Homolytic and Heterolytic Fission

During the course of a chemical reaction chemical bonds have to be broken in order that new compounds may be formed. This breaking, or FISSION, of bonds can happen in any of three different ways, depending essentially upon the electronegativity values of the two atoms, A and B, joined by the bond.

$$
\text{A:B} \quad
\begin{array}{ll}
\xrightarrow{\;1\;} & \text{A}^{\cdot} + \text{B}^{\cdot} \quad \text{A and B having similar} \\
 & \qquad\qquad\;\; \text{electronegativity values} \\
\xrightarrow{\;2\;} & \text{A:}^{-} + \text{B}^{+} \quad \text{A more electronegative} \\
 & \qquad\qquad\;\; \text{than B} \\
\xrightarrow{\;3\;} & \text{A}^{+} + \text{B:}^{-} \quad \text{B more electronegative} \\
 & \qquad\qquad\;\; \text{than A}
\end{array}
$$

Where the difference in electronegativity between bonded atoms is small, as in 1, rupturing the bond between them results in the formation of very reactive FREE RADICALS with each atom acquiring one of the bonding electrons. This process is termed HOMOLYTIC FISSION.

Where one atom is distinctly more electronegative than the other, there is a tendency for both bonding electrons to remain with the more electronegative atom after rupture of the bond. This process is termed HETEROLYTIC FISSION. The more electronegative atom gains a single negative charge owing to the acquisition of an extra electron, and the less electronegative atom becomes positively charged.

The shift of a pair of electrons is indicated by a curly arrow,

e.g. $\quad$ $\geq$C—Cl $\longrightarrow$ $\geq$C$^+$ + Cl$^-$

and the movement of a single electron during homolytic fission is depicted by a barbed, or half, arrow

e.g. $\quad$ Cl—Cl

Heterolytic fission is the type most frequently encountered in organic chemistry, which means, perhaps rather surprisingly, that ionic species play a significant part in this predominantly covalent field.

Acids and Bases

The classical definitions for acids and bases, derived from the Arrhenius definitions, state that acids are substances that furnish oxonium (hydroxonium) ions (H_3^+O) and bases are substances that furnish hydroxide ions (^-OH) in solution.[*] Such definitions are quite adequate when dealing with reactions in aqueous media but are otherwise rather limited.

The *Brønsted-Lowry* definitions (1923) consider an ACID to be *a donor of protons* (a proton being effectively a hydrogen ion, H^+) and a BASE to be *an acceptor of protons*. Although rather similar to the classical definitions, this system incorporates certain molecules and ions that were not originally classified.

More generally applicable definitions were proposed by G. N. LEWIS (1923). These allow most substances to be classified as either an acid or a base to varying degrees, depending upon their function in a chemical reaction. He suggested that an acid–base reaction is simply one which involves the donation of a pair of electrons from the basic species to the acidic species. Consequently, acids and bases may be defined as follows.

A LEWIS ACID is *a species which accepts electron pairs* and a LEWIS BASE is *a species which donates electron pairs*.

Electrophiles and Nucleophiles

A Lewis acid is therefore an electron-deficient species, and in a chemical reaction it will seek an electron-rich site on a basic species. Lewis acids are commonly referred to as ELECTROPHILIC ('electron-loving') REAGENTS or simply ELECTROPHILES, and Lewis bases as NUCLEOPHILIC ('nucleus-loving') REAGENTS or NUCLEOPHILES.

Examples of electrophilic reagents are: H^+, Cl^+, Br^+, I^+, $^+NO_2$, RN^+_2, R_3C^+.

Examples of nucleophilic reagents are: H_2O, ROH, ^-OH, RO^-, Cl^-, Br^-, I^-, NH_3, RNH_2, CN^-.

This can be summarized in tabular form.

Acids	Bases
Donors of protons	Acceptors of protons
Acceptors of electron pairs	Donors of electron pairs
Electrophiles	Nucleophiles

This reasoning can be extended one stage further in order to include *oxidation and reduction reactions*. Reduction may be viewed as a process which involves the gain of electrons by a substance and oxidation as a process which involves the loss of electrons. Those substances which possess the characteristic property of giving up electrons are called REDUCING AGENTS and those which accept electrons are said to be OXIDIZING AGENTS. Electrophilic reagents are therefore oxidizing agents and nucleophilic reagents are reducing agents.

Strengths of Organic Acids and Bases

The dissociation of weak acids and bases in aqueous solution is a reversible process. For an aqueous solution of a weak monobasic acid, HA, the acidity constant, K_a, for the equilibrium,

$$HA + H_2O \rightleftharpoons H_3^+O + A^-$$

is given by,

$$K_a = \frac{a_{H_3^+O} \times a_{A^-}}{a_{HA}}$$

where $a_{H_3^+O}$, a_{A^-} and a_{HA} represent the relative activities (active masses) of the respective species. As the water is present in large excess, its relative activity may be considered to be effectively constant and its value approximately unity.

In practice it is more usual to adopt the molecular and ionic concentrations (represented by square brackets) of the different species present, since in many equilibrium processes of this type these values approach those of the activities.

$$K_a \approx \frac{[H_3O^+][A^-]}{[HA]}$$

This ideal state assumes that there is no interaction or interference between the different species present in solution and that their activity coefficients, f, approach unity, as is shown by the following relationship.

Activity = Molecular or Ionic Concentration × Activity Coefficient, f

Similarly, for an aqueous solution of a weak base, B, the basicity constant, K_b, for the equilibrium process,

$$B + H_2O \rightleftharpoons BH^+ + {}^-OH$$

is given by,

$$K_b \approx \frac{[BH^+][{}^-OH]}{[B]}$$

Generalizing these equations for K_a and K_b, and representing H_3O^+ as simply H^+, the dissociation constants can be written,

$$K_a \approx \frac{[H^+][Base]}{[Acid]} \quad \text{and} \quad K_b \approx \frac{[Acid][{}^-OH]}{[Base]}$$

$$K_a \times K_b = [H^+][{}^-OH] = 10^{-14} \text{ mol}^2 \text{ dm}^{-6} \text{ at } 25 \text{ °C}$$

the ionic product of water, K_w.

The constants K_a and K_b provide an extremely useful measure of acidity and basicity, although they are more conveniently represented in the logarithmic forms:

$$pK_a = -\log K_a \text{ and } pK_b = -\log K_b$$

hence, $pK_a + pK_b = 14.00$.

pK_a values may therefore be converted into pK_b values, and *vice versa*, by means of this relationship. The values are usually quoted for temperatures of 25 °C.

Mineral acids are so highly ionized in aqueous solution that their pK_a values are not measurable.

Effect of Solvent

The influence of the solvent upon the dissociation of acids and bases into ions can be considerable. Dissociation is promoted by the more polar solvents of high dielectric constants, such as water, which help to dissipate the electrostatic energy of the charged ions and hence stabilize them in solution.

Water further aids the ionization process by solvating the ions, and has the added advantage of being able to function as an acid or a base with equal facility, thus promoting the ionization of bases and acids alike.

The acidic and basic characteristics of the various types of compounds and their pK_a and pK_b values are considered separately in their respective forthcoming chapters.

Functional Groups and Homologous Series

Simple organic compounds are categorized according to their FUNCTIONAL GROUPS. These are *groups of atoms or bonds common to a series or family of compounds and which govern the principal chemical properties of the series.*

Each series follows a regular structural pattern in which each member differs from the next by a constant amount. Such a series is called a HOMOLOGOUS SERIES and the individual members of it are referred to as HOMOLOGUES.

This may be excmplified by consideration of the first, and probably the simplest, series of compounds encountered in organic chemistry, the ALKANES. The alkanes are a series of hydrocarbons, i.e. they contain only carbon and hydrogen, and their general structural formula is given by C_nH_{2n+2}, where n is an integer with a value of one or more.

Successive homologues differ in composition by the increment $-CH_2-$. The first member of the series, methane, has a formula CH_4 ($n = 1$); this is followed by ethane, C_2H_6 ($n = 2$), propane, C_3H_8 ($n = 3$), and so on.

The table below gives the general structural formulae of many of the aliphatic homologous series and also specifies their functional groups.

The general formula, C_nH_{2n+1}, common to most aliphatic series, and obtained by the abstraction of a hydrogen atom from the parent alkane, is referred to as an ALKYL GROUP or RADICAL. The letter 'R' is the conventional means of

Homologous series	General structural formula	Functional group
Alkanes	C_nH_{2n+2}	—
Alkenes	C_nH_{2n}, where n is 2 or greater	$>C=C<$
Alkynes	C_nH_{2n-2}, where n is 2 or greater	$-C\equiv C-$
Alcohols	$C_nH_{2n+1}OH$	$-OH$
Ethers	$C_nH_{2n+1}O$, where n is 2 or greater	$-O-$
Aldehydes	$C_nH_{2n+1}CHO$	$\overset{H}{\diagdown}C=O$
Ketones	$C_nH_{2n+2}CO$, where n is 2 or greater	$>C=O$
Carboxylic acids	$C_nH_{2n+1}COOH$	$-C\overset{O}{\underset{OH}{\diagup\diagdown}}$
Primary amines	$C_nH_{2n+1}NH_2$	$-NH_2$

representing the general formula of an alkyl group, and proves especially useful when referring to the properties and reactions of a homologous series, thus avoiding the necessity of having to consider specifically the individual members of the series. For example, the formulae, RH, ROH, RCHO etc. represent the alkanes, alcohols and aldehydes respectively.

Each alkyl group is named from the parent alkane by *dropping the ending '-ane'* and replacing it with '*-yl*'. The alkyl group derived from *methane* is the METHYL GROUP —CH_3, the one derived from *ethane* is the ETHYL GROUP —C_2H_5, the one derived from *propane* is the PROPYL GROUP, etc.

Saturated and Unsaturated Hydrocarbons

Since all carbon valencies of alkanes are saturated with hydrogen, alkanes contain only carbon–hydrogen and carbon–carbon single bonds. They are said to be SATURATED, and are described as saturated hydrocarbons.

Compounds possessing carbon–carbon multiple bonds are said to be UNSATURATED. Hydrocarbons possessing one set of carbon–carbon double bonds, $>C=C<$, form the homologous series called the ALKENES, and those possessing a set of carbon–carbon triple bonds, —$C\equiv C$—, are called the ALKYNES. In both these series, the carbon–carbon multiple bond represents the functional group.

The second and third bonds are π bonds, formed by the overlapping of p orbitals. The electrons in these bonds, described as π electrons, are much more exposed than the electrons in the σ bonds of the molecule, making them much more vulnerable to attack, particularly by electron-seeking reagents or electrophiles.

Types of Reaction

Organic reactions are categorized in four basic types: (1) substitution or displacement reactions; (2) elimination reactions; (3) addition reactions; and (4) rearrangement reactions. All four types of reaction may be initiated by electrophilic, nucleophilic or free radical attack upon the substrate.

Substitution or Displacement Reactions

These reactions involve the direct displacement of an atom or group by another atom or group.

$$\begin{array}{ccccc} H & H & & H & H \\ | & | & & | & | \\ H-C-C-Y + Z & \xrightarrow{\text{substitution}} & H-C-C-Z + Y \\ | & | & & | & | \\ H & H & & H & H \end{array}$$

The number of atoms or groups of the substrate displaced depends upon the nature of the reactants and also upon the conditions under which the reaction is carried out. When only one atom or group is displaced, the product yielded by the reaction is referred to as the MONOSUBSTITUTED derivative of the substrate. If two and three atoms or groups of the substrate are displaced, the products are referred to as the DISUBSTITUTED and TRISUBSTITUTED derivatives respectively.

Elimination Reactions

These reactions involve the removal of atoms or groups of atoms from two adjacent atoms to form a multiple bond.

The most commonly encountered elimination reactions are those which involve the removal of atoms or groups from adjacent carbon atoms to yield alkenes.

$$
\underset{\substack{|\ \ \ | \\ Y\ \ Z}}{\overset{\substack{H\ \ H \\ |\ \ \ |}}{H-C-C-H}} \xrightarrow[-YZ]{\text{elimination}} \underset{}{\overset{\substack{H\ \ H \\ |\ \ \ |}}{H-C=C-H}} + YZ
$$

Both in theory and in practice, substitution and elimination reactions can take place concurrently to yield a mixture of substitution and elimination products. The nature of the products formed is determined largely by the steric (*see* page 48) and electronic (*see* page 46) factors involved in the reaction, although the conditions under which the reaction is carried out can often be modified in order to produce the desired product in greater abundance.

Addition Reactions

These reactions are so called since the attacking reagent simply adds itself across an unsaturated bond of the substrate to yield a saturated product, or at least one in which the degree of unsaturation is reduced. Addition is essentially the reversal of elimination.

$$
\underset{\substack{H \qquad\qquad H}}{\overset{\substack{H \qquad\qquad H}}{C=C}} + YZ \xrightarrow{\text{addition}} \underset{\substack{|\ \ | \\ Y\ \ Z}}{\overset{\substack{H\ \ H \\ |\ \ |}}{H-C-C-H}}
$$

$$
H-C\equiv C-H + YZ \xrightarrow{\text{addition}} \underset{\substack{|\ \ | \\ Y\ \ Z}}{\overset{}{H-C=C-H}}
$$

In most of their reactions, unsaturated systems function as sources of electrons, i.e. as nucleophiles, and consequently are more vulnerable to attack by electron-deficient species, i.e. electrophiles.

Rearrangement Reactions

These involve the migration of an atom or group from one site to another within the same molecule.

The rearrangement may refer to the migration of a functional group from one position to another within the molecule:

$$
\underset{\substack{| \\ Cl}}{R-CH-CH=CH_2} \xrightarrow[\text{functional group}]{\text{migration of}} R-CH=CH-CH_2-Cl
$$

or it may simply relate to the rearrangement of the carbon skeleton of the molecule:

$$
\begin{array}{ccc}
\text{R} & & \text{R} \\
| & \text{rearrangement of} & | \\
\text{R}'\!-\!\text{C}\!-\!\text{CH}_2\!-\!\text{Cl} & \xrightarrow{\text{carbon skeleton}} & \text{R}'\!-\!\text{C}\!-\!\text{CH}_2\!-\!\text{R}'' \\
| & & | \\
\text{R}'' & & \text{Cl}
\end{array}
$$

Rearrangement may be followed by elimination or addition to form a more stable product.

Factors Influencing a Reaction

A reaction may be facilitated or inhibited by the distribution of electrons in the region of the site of reaction in the substrate and also by the nature and size of the atoms or groups surrounding the site. These factors are classified as ELECTRONIC and STERIC FACTORS.

Electronic Factors

A covalent bond is usually polarized to some extent, since the atoms almost invariably have different electronegativity values, i.e. different powers of attracting the electrons in the bond. Consequently, displacement of the electrons towards the more electronegative atom creates a certain degree of polarity within the bond, causing one atom to acquire a relatively negative charge, $\delta-$, and the other a relatively positive charge, $\delta+$ (*see* page 35).

Consider the carbon–chlorine bond in which the chlorine atom has the higher electronegativity value.

$$
\begin{array}{ccc}
\diagdown & \diagdown & \diagdown \\
-\text{C}^{\delta+}\!-\!\text{Cl}^{\delta-} & -\text{C}\!\rightarrow\!\text{Cl} & -\text{C} \quad\quad \text{Cl} \\
\diagup & \diagup & \diagup \\
\text{I} & \text{II} & \text{III}
\end{array}
$$

I clearly indicates the different relative charges on the two atoms. In II, the arrow along the bond indicates the direction of the attractive force, and in III the more heavily shaded part illustrates the region in which the effective electron density is greatest. For convenience it is usually preferable to use either I or II.

Inductive Effect

Permanent polarizing effects in *single bonds*, as exemplified by the carbon–chlorine bond, are known as INDUCTIVE (I) EFFECTS.

If the carbon atom attached to the polarizing atom or group is itself attached to further carbon atoms, the inductive effect is transmitted along the chain, although it tends to be insignificant beyond the second carbon.

$$
\begin{array}{cccc}
-\text{C}\!-\!\text{C}\!\rightarrow\!\text{C}\!\rightarrowtail\!\text{Cl} \\
3 \quad\; 2 \quad\; 1 \quad -I
\end{array}
$$

The inductive effect of C_1 upon C_2 is significantly less than the effect of the Cl atom upon C_1. Most atoms or groups tend to be *electron-withdrawing* with respect to the carbon atom to which they are attached, and exert an inductive effect in the same direction as chlorine. Such atoms or groups are said to exert a $-I$ effect.

However, certain groups, notably alkyl groups, exert an inductive effect in the opposite direction, i.e. they are *electron-donating* and exert a $+I$ effect. Tertiary alkyl groups exert a greater $+I$ effect than secondary which in turn exert a greater effect than primary

$$\underset{\text{Tertiary}}{\underset{(3\,°)}{\overset{\text{CH}_3}{\underset{\text{CH}_3}{\text{CH}_3\text{—C—}}}}} > \underset{\text{Secondary}}{\underset{(2\,°)}{\overset{\text{CH}_3}{\underset{\text{CH}_3}{\text{CH—}}}}} > \underset{\text{Primary}}{\underset{(1\,°)}{\text{CH}_3\text{CH}_2\text{—}}} > \text{CH}_3\text{—}$$

Mesomeric Effect

The shift of π electrons in multiple bonds towards the more electronegative atom is referred to as the MESOMERIC (M) EFFECT, and is analogous to the inductive effects in single bonds. The carbonyl group, $>C=O$, in which the effective electron density is greater in the region of the more electronegative oxygen atom, provides a simple example:

$$>C \text{———} O$$

The structure can also be represented as a RESONANCE HYBRID between two CANONICAL FORMS, either of which may be used to illustrate the polarization in the bond,

$$>C\overset{\frown}{=}O \longleftrightarrow >\overset{+}{C}\text{—}\overset{-}{O}$$

although it is probably generally more convenient simply to indicate the relative charge on each atom, thus:

$$>\overset{\delta+}{C}=\overset{\delta-}{O}$$

The effect is transmitted along a chain in a way similar to the inductive effect.

The mesomeric effect is of paramount importance in *conjugated* chains of carbon atoms (i.e. systems in which multiple bonds occur between alternate carbon atoms, as in buta-1,3-diene, $CH_2=CH.CH=CH_2$), and it is for this reason that it is sometimes referred to as the CONJUGATIVE EFFECT.

Electromeric Effect

The ELECTROMERIC (E) EFFECT is a *temporary polarizability* which occurs in unsaturated systems as they are approached by the reagent. It is as a result of this effect that the halogens direct predominantly to the 2- and 4-positions in the benzene ring despite the fact that they are electron-withdrawing (*see* 'Orientation of substitution in a monosubstituted benzene nucleus', page 137).

Steric Factors

The spatial distribution of atoms or groups in a molecule may alter, or in some cases completely prevent, a reaction occurring despite favourable electronic effects. The most commonly encountered steric effect is that of hindrance or blocking, and it is particularly effective when the reaction site is crowded with large bulky groups. For example, the rate of esterification of ethanoic (acetic) acid with propan-2-ol (isopropyl alcohol) is half that of the rate with ethanol.

$$CH_3\overset{\displaystyle O}{\overset{\|}{C}}\!\!-\!OH + CH_3CH_2OH \underset{}{\overset{H^+ \text{ catalyst}}{\rightleftharpoons}} CH_3\overset{\displaystyle O}{\overset{\|}{C}}\!\!-\!OCH_2CH_3 + H_2O$$

Ethanoic acid   Ethanol   Ethyl ethanoate
(Acetic acid)   (Ethyl ethanoate)

$$CH_3\overset{\displaystyle O}{\overset{\|}{C}}\!\!-\!OH + \underset{CH_3}{\overset{CH_3}{\diagup\!\!\!\!\diagdown}}CHOH \underset{}{\overset{H^+ \text{ catalyst}}{\rightleftharpoons}} CH_3\overset{\displaystyle O}{\overset{\|}{C}}\!\!-\!OCH\underset{CH_3}{\overset{CH_3}{\diagup\!\!\!\!\diagdown}} + H_2O$$

Propan-2-ol   1-Methylethyl ethanoate
(Isopropyl alcohol)   (Isopropyl acetate)

In the reaction with propan-2-ol, the reaction rate is retarded by the presence of the two methyl groups on the α-carbon atom of the alcohol. (The α-carbon atom is the one to which the functional group is directly attached.)

Steric factors do not always inhibit the rate of reaction since they sometimes promote more favourable electronic effects by donating or withdrawing electrons to or from the reaction site.

QUESTIONS

1. Which one of the following best describes the type of species formed as a result of heterolytic fission?

   A atoms
   B free radicals
   C electrophiles and nucleophiles
   D acids
   E bases

2. Which one of the following is an *inaccurate* description of a nucleophile?

   A an acidic reagent
   B a basic reagent
   C an electron-rich species
   D a species which often contains a lone pair of electrons
   E a reagent which attacks electron-deficient sites in molecules

3. Mesomeric effects are only operative in molecules which

   A are saturated
   B are unsaturated
   C are highly polar
   D contain oxygen
   E contain electron-donating groups

4. The reaction

$$\underset{CH_3}{\overset{CH_3}{\diagup\!\!\!\!\diagdown}}C=O + HCN \rightarrow CH_3\!-\!\underset{CH_3}{\overset{OH}{\underset{|}{\overset{|}{C}}}}\!-\!CN$$

   is best described as

   A substitution
   B elimination
   C addition
   D addition–elimination
   E rearrangement

8

The Mechanism, Energetics and Kinetics of a Reaction

Conventional stoichiometric equations indicate the reactants taking part and the products formed in a chemical reaction, but do not say anything about what takes place during this change. A *detailed description of a chemical reaction outlining each separate stage* is called a MECHANISM.

This is based upon experimental data, which are seldom complete, about transition states and unstable intermediates. Therefore, mechanisms for reactions are continually under review and being constantly modified as more information is gained about them. In some cases, information is obtained that makes a particular mechanism invalid and an entirely new one has to be proposed.

The following outlines the mechanism for the alkaline hydrolysis of bromomethane (a gas) to form methanol:

| Bromomethane | Transition state | Methanol |

In this reaction a TRANSITION STATE is formed in which the entering hydroxyl group and the leaving halogen are both partially bonded to the same carbon atom. The reaction is concluded by the bromine atom being completely cleaved from the carbon and the new bond with the —OH group being formed.

Energetics of Reaction

The full course of a reaction is usually too complex to follow in detail, but a study of the energetics of a particular reaction may contribute evidence as to whether or not any form of reaction intermediate is formed.

Energy, usually in the form of heat, must be provided to the reactants to enable the necessary bonds to be broken. The reactant molecules become activated owing to their greater energy content and are referred to as the TRANSITION STATE or ACTIVATED COMPLEX which corresponds to the peak of the curve shown (Fig. 8.1). The complex is the least stable state through which the reactants pass before forming the products. The quantity of energy required to raise the reactant molecules to this state is referred to as the ACTIVATION ENERGY, E_a, for the reaction. It is, in fact, this energy which is the most influential in *determining the rate at which a reaction proceeds*.

The use of a catalyst often brings about an increase in the rate of reaction by enabling the products to be formed by an alternative path, each stage having a lower activation energy than the uncatalysed reaction.

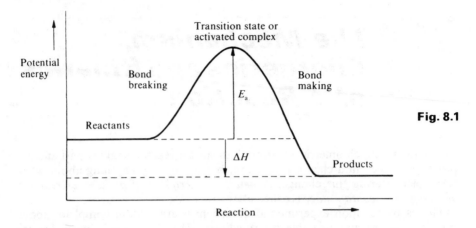

Fig. 8.1

Once the reactants have absorbed sufficient energy to get them over this peak, energy is evolved as the new bonds are made in forming the stable products. For reactions at constant pressure, the difference between the amount of energy provided to break the bonds of the reactants and that evolved during the formation of new molecules is termed the ENTHALPY OF REACTION, ΔH. When more energy is evolved than absorbed, the reaction is EXOTHERMIC, i.e. ΔH is *negative* (Fig. 8.1), and when less energy is evolved than absorbed, the reaction is ENDOTHERMIC, i.e. ΔH is positive (Fig. 8.2).

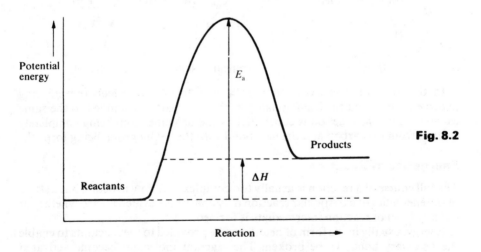

Fig. 8.2

Products formed via an exothermic process have a lower energy content than the reactants from which they are formed, whereas products formed via an endothermic process have a higher energy content than the parent reactants. Exothermic compounds are, therefore, generally more stable than endothermic compounds.

In certain reactions the activated complex exists as an UNSTABLE INTERMEDIATE which in many instances may actually be isolated. This is observed in a reaction profile as a trough in the activated peak of the curve, resulting in a double hump.

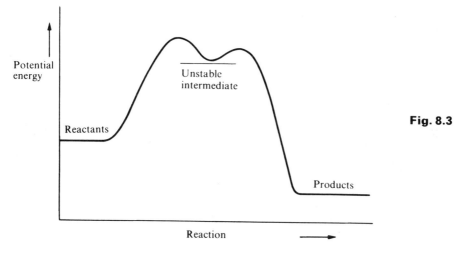

Fig. 8.3

As the minimum in the trough becomes more marked, i.e. as the intermediate becomes more stable, the greater the likelihood of being able to separate the intermediate from the reaction mixture during the course of the reaction.

The profiles outlined here describe only simple mechanisms, and many reactions occur in which there are several transition states, and which may involve the formation of more than one unstable intermediate.

Rates of Reaction

In chemistry, there are two fundamental questions relating to all reactions.
(1) Will the reaction take place?
(2) If it does, how long will it take in order for the reaction to reach completion?

The first of these questions may be answered by the application of thermodynamic principles, and the second by CHEMICAL KINETICS. Chemical kinetics makes probably the largest contribution towards the determination of reaction mechanisms. Three other important procedures that contribute to providing information for the description of mechanisms are the study of steric effects, product analysis and the use of isotopes.

Clues to the mechanism of a reaction may sometimes be obtained by examining the effect of temperature on the rate, and also the effect of the medium, since a large proportion of organic reactions are carried out in solution. For example, the extent to which ionic species are involved in the reaction may be determined by using solvents of different polarities. If such species are involved to any appreciable extent, then it would be expected that a more polar solvent would enhance the rate of reaction.

Order of Reaction

Consider the hydrolysis of haloalkanes, RX, to alcohols.

$$RX + {}^-OH \longrightarrow ROH + X^-$$

Primary haloalkanes, e.g. bromomethane, CH_3Br, and bromoethane, CH_3CH_2Br, are not hydrolysed appreciably in neutral aqueous solutions but in an alkaline medium hydrolysis proceeds rapidly. An increase in the concentration of either the haloalkane or the hydroxide ions causes a proportional increase in the rate of reaction. This may be expressed as

$$\text{Rate} \propto \text{[haloalkane][hydroxide ions]}$$
$$= k\text{[haloalkane][hydroxide ions]}$$

where k *is the rate constant for the reaction.*

Reactions of this type, where the sum of the powers of the reactant concentrations is equal to two, are referred to as SECOND ORDER REACTIONS.

However, kinetic studies have shown the rate of hydrolysis of tertiary haloalkanes, e.g. 2-bromo-2-methylpropane (*tert*-butyl bromide), $(CH_3)_3CBr$, to be proportional only to the concentration of the haloalkane and independent of the hydroxide ion concentration.

$$\text{Rate} = k\text{[haloalkane]}$$

Reactions of this type, where the rate is directly proportional to one of the reactant concentrations, are referred to as FIRST ORDER REACTIONS.

Such studies warn against generalizing too readily from insufficient evidence, since these apparently similar reactions must necessarily proceed via different mechanisms. The mechanisms of these reactions, together with the kinetic evidence for them, are discussed in Chapter 15.

THIRD ORDER REACTIONS, in which the rate is proportional to the third power of the reactant concentrations also occur, but are comparatively rare and invariably involve nitrogen oxide (nitric oxide).

The order of a reaction need not necessarily be a whole number. Many of the orders which best fit the experimentally measured rate–concentration relationship are FRACTIONAL.

Rate of Reaction and the Energy Curve

The majority of organic reactions are complex and proceed via the formation of intermediates, which correspond to a trough in the activated part of the reaction profile. The first peak in the curve, arising from the breaking of bonds in the reactant molecules, is usually higher than any subsequent peak, and it is this stage in the reaction that generally proceeds more slowly than any other. Since a reaction cannot proceed more rapidly than its slowest stage, it is this RATE-DETERMINING STEP that governs the rate of the overall reaction. A kinetic study of a reaction will sometimes allow the reacting species participating in this rate-determining step to be predicted reasonably accurately.

Molecularity of Reaction

The MOLECULARITY of the reaction describes the number of species involved in bond cleavage in the rate-determining step, whereas the order of reaction is reserved solely for a description of the kinetics. Reactions in which only one molecule is involved in bond cleavage during this step, that is,

$$AB \longrightarrow A + B$$

are described as UNIMOLECULAR, and those in which two molecules are involved, that is,

$$AB + C \longrightarrow A + BC$$

are described as BIMOLECULAR.

The molecularity must, by necessity, be a whole number.

As the hydrolysis of a primary haloalkane is both bimolecular and second order and the hydrolysis of a tertiary haloalkane is both unimolecular and first order, it might, at first sight, appear that the terms 'first order' and 'second order' are interchangeable with the terms 'unimolecular' and 'bimolecular'. This is not necessarily so. For example, if in a bimolecular reaction one of the reactants is also the solvent and present in large excess, then the order of reaction will be independent of this reagent as its concentration will remain effectively constant during the reaction. In other words, the kinetics observed for reactions taking place under these conditions will be those of a first order reaction.

QUESTIONS

1. For the reaction

$$2A + B + C \rightarrow 3D + E$$

the experimentally determined rate equation is given by

$$\text{Rate} = k[A][B]$$

Which of the following statements is *not* applicable to this reaction?

A the reaction is first order with respect to A

B the reaction is first order with respect to B

C the reaction is first order with respect to C .

D the reaction is second order overall

E there would be a fourfold increase in the rate if the concentration of both A and B were doubled

2. Which one of the following statements is a completely false description of the rate-determining step of a reaction?

A it governs the rate of the overall reaction

B it usually corresponds to the highest activation peak in the reaction profile

C it corresponds to the slowest stage of the reaction

D it necessarily involves molecules of all reactants

E it generally involves the breaking of bonds in the reactant molecules

3. Sketch a reaction profile for an exothermic reaction involving the formation of a single unstable intermediate which could, under special conditions, actually be isolated.

4. Briefly explain the difference between the meaning of the terms 'order' and 'molecularity' of a reaction.

9 Identification of Organic Compounds

The main procedures employed in identifying an organic compound are:
(1) ISOLATION AND PURIFICATION OF THE COMPOUND
(2) QUALITATIVE ANALYSIS
    (a) Test for elements
    (b) Test for functional groups
(3) QUANTITATIVE ANALYSIS
    (a) Combustion experiments to determine the respective quantities of the elements present
    (b) Determination of empirical formula
    (c) Determination of relative molecular mass
    (d) Determination of molecular formula
(4) DETERMINATION OF STRUCTURE
    (a) Utilization of information obtained from tests for functional groups
    (b) Spectroscopic analysis
        (i) Ultra-violet spectroscopy
        (ii) Infra-red spectroscopy
        (iii) Nuclear magnetic resonance spectroscopy
        (iv) Mass spectroscopy
    (c) Degradation reactions
    (d) Synthesis of the compound from simpler substances of known structure
    (e) Preparation of crystalline derivatives

When analysing an unknown organic compounds it is not usually necessary to carry out all these procedures nor is it always desirable to adhere to this sequence.

When identification of a mixture of compounds is required, it is usual practice to separate them into their respective components and then analyse them separately.

Isolation

Most organic compounds can normally be isolated and purified by at least one of the various techniques mentioned below.

The purity of a solid may be checked by performing a melting point determination. A pure compound has a sharp melting point whereas impure substances melt over a range of several degrees. A further check can be made by carrying out a 'mixed melting point' determination. In the vast majority of cases the presence of a 'foreign substance' causes a lowering of the melting point of a pure organic compound. If, for example, the compound under investigation has a melting point of 121 °C and is suspected of being benzenecarboxylic (benzoic) acid, then this may be tested for by intimately mixing together a sample of this compound with an equal amount of an authentic specimen of benzenecarboxylic acid; if the melting point is still 121 °C, then the original compound is benzenecarboxylic acid, but if any depression in the melting point is observed, then the two components of the mixture cannot be identical.

A pure liquid has a sharp and constant boiling point at any particular pressure, and evaporates leaving no residue. However, a sharp boiling point is not by itself necessarily a criterion for the purity of a liquid as there is always the possibility that it may in fact be an azeotropic (constant boiling point) mixture. This can be tested for by redistilling at a different pressure; a mixture will then give a distillate of different composition which would exhibit a different boiling point when distilled again at the original pressure.

Techniques available for isolation and purification include the following.

Filtration under normal or reduced pressure is one of the simplest and most common modes of separation. Particles must be sufficiently large to prevent them passing through the pores of the filter paper, sintered glass, Gooch fibre etc.

Centrifuging is generally used as an alternative to filtration. Modern ultracentrifuges, which can generate up to 250 000 times the acceleration due to gravity, are capable of bringing about the separation of even colloidal mixtures.

Recrystallization provides a useful means of removing insoluble solid impurities from a solid dissolved in a suitable solvent.

Sublimation provides a means of separating solids capable of exhibiting this phenomenon, which are comparatively few. These include benzenecarboxylic (benzoic) acid, naphthalene and cyclohexadiene-1,4-dione (quinone).

Fractional crystallization is suitable for separating a mixture of solids of different solubilities. Careful control of temperature is necessary and complete separation usually requires repetition of the process several times.

Simple distillation is used for separating a liquid from solid or non-volatile liquid impurities. Reduced pressure, which lowers the normal boiling point, is used for processes involving substances likely to decompose on heating.

Fractional distillation is used for separating mixtures of liquids with different boiling points. This usually requires the use of a special fractionating column, of which there are several types, all serving to increase the effective surface area of the column.

Steam distillation is most effective when one of the components to be separated, either solid or liquid, is either insoluble or immiscible with water, has a high vapour pressure at about 100 °C, or has a high relative molecular mass. It is especially useful for purifying substances that decompose at or near their boiling points, since the substance usually distils over at temperatures well below this value.

In practice, steam is passed through the mixture and the required substance, together with water, is collected from the distillate before being isolated by one of the other techniques, e.g. filtration, fractional distillation, solvent extraction etc.

Solvent extraction uses a semi-continuous partition process, *countercurrent distribution*, for separating materials that distribute themselves between two immiscible solvents. After separating the two layers, the less dense fraction is transferred to another tube containing the denser solvent while more of the less dense solvent is added to the residual heavier fraction. The process is repeated many times, usually by fully automatic machines containing, say, 100 tubes. The development of zones is similar in principle to that outlined below for gas chromatography.

Molecular (evaporative) distillation uses the principle that the molecules of a gas or vapour are in random motion and undergo frequent collisions with each other and with the walls of the container. The mean free path, i.e. the average distance travelled by the molecules between collisions, can be increased from about 10^{-4} mm (i.e. 10^{-7} m) to a few centimetres by simply reducing the pressure to about 10^{-3} mm Hg(0.13 Pa). The mean free path of larger molecules is shorter than that of smaller ones.

Molecular distillation requires a receiving surface being placed at a distance of less than the mean free path from a heated liquid film. The molecules from this film are then able to travel to and condense on the receiving surface, provided they have sufficient kinetic energy to detach themselves from the liquid surface and traverse the intervening space. Using this technique, liquid mixtures can be separated at temperatures 100–150 °C below their normal boiling points. The rate of separation of any one component depends upon its relative molecular mass and its vapour pressure at the distillation temperature, although there are other contributory factors.

Chromatography (Gr. 'colour writing')

Chromatography provides a very sensitive method of separating extremely small samples of mixtures and is especially useful for those whose components approach each other in physical properties. Although the term suggests that these components should be coloured, this is by no means an essential criterion for separation.

Separation is brought about by the differential movement of the components of a mixture between two immiscible phases, one of which is a solid or liquid phase and the other a mobile liquid or gas phase.

The student has probably already encountered simple *paper chromatographic techniques* for separating, say, the different coloured pigments (chlorophyll, xanthophyll etc.) from grass and leaves.

Adsorption Column Chromatography

This technique involves a solid, white, adsorbent stationary phase, carefully packed into a vertical column (it is introduced into the column in the form of a slurry) and a mobile liquid phase.

Suitable adsorbents are activated aluminium oxide, magnesium carbonate, sodium carbonate, activated magnesium silicate, starch, talc, sucrose etc.

Suitable eluants are petroleum ether, benzene, tetrachloromethane (carbon tetrachloride), absolute ethoxyethane (ether), anhydrous propanone (acetone), ethanol, methanol, glacial ethanoic (acetic) acid, cyclohexane, trichloromethane (chloroform), ethyl ethanoate (acetate) etc.

On introducing the sample, dissolved in a suitable solvent, into the top of the column, an equilibrium is established between the solute in solution and that adsorbed on the surface of the solid. A continuous process of separation can be established by the subsequent addition of further quantities of solvent (which may be the original solvent or some other suitable liquid), referred to in this context as the ELUANT. Since each component of the sample will possess different adsorption affinities for the solid stationary phase, those being more strongly adsorbed moving much more slowly than those less strongly adsorbed, a complete separation may be achieved, with each component occupying distinctive bands in the CHROMATOGRAM.

The components may be recovered by progressively washing each band out of the column or, alternatively, the whole column may be pushed out of the column and the bands cut out with a knife. The separated compounds can then be taken back into solution and recovered from it.

An important extension of the column technique is ION-EXCHANGE CHROMATOGRAPHY in which an ion-exchange resin replaces the more con-

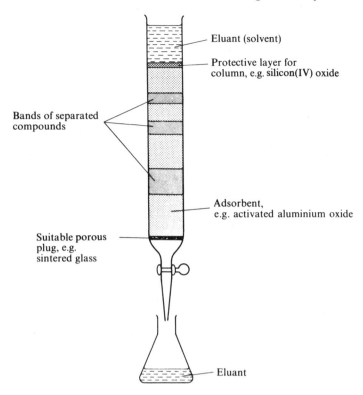

Eluant (solvent)

Protective layer for
column, e.g. silicon(IV) oxide

Bands of separated
compounds

Adsorbent,
e.g. activated aluminium oxide

Suitable porous
plug, e.g.
sintered glass

Eluant

Fig. 9.1 Apparatus for adsorption column chromatography

ventional adsorbent. The method proves extremely useful for the selective concentration of certain ionic components.

Partition (Liquid–Liquid) Chromatography

This technique requires that the components of the sample become partitioned between water, which serves as a stationary second solvent supported by an inert porous medium, and a mobile organic solvent. Materials suitable as a supporting medium include Celite (a proprietary brand of kieselguhr, which is a form of silicon(IV) oxide), aluminium oxide, cellulose and moist silica gel. The principles may be implemented on sheets of filter paper (paper chromatography), in columns (partition column chromatography), or on a glass sheet coated with an inert support (thin layer chromatography).

Paper chromatography, which can be adopted as either an ascending or descending process, is capable of separating microgram quantities. For the ascending technique, the sample is spotted on to the paper, which is suspended vertically in a glass tank with the bottom edge of the paper dipping into a suitable partitioning solvent. The spot should be located just above the surface of the solvent. The components become partitioned between water in the cellulose fibres of the paper ('dry' paper may contain 2–3 per cent by mass of water intermolecularly hydrogen bonded to the cellulose, together with more which may be absorbed by capillary action) and the mobile organic solvent.

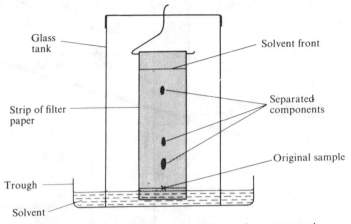

Fig. 9.2 Apparatus for ascending paper chromatography

After a period of time, when the solvent has nearly reached the end of the paper, the paper is removed from the tank and dried, the position of the solvent front having first being marked. The chromatogram is then developed with a suitable reagent, e.g. ninhydrin/butanol, or by irradiating with ultra-violet light.

The position of each component is noted and can then be identified from its R_F value. This is a constant for each compound, for a particular solvent system on a particular stationary phase, and is defined as the distance travelled by the compound relative to the distance travelled by the solvent front.

$$R_F = \frac{\text{Distance travelled by the compound}}{\text{Distance travelled by the solvent}}$$

Gas Chromatography

Gas chromatography is usually employed as a partition technique (gas/liquid chromatography, g.l.c.) for examining gases, volatile liquids or solids in the gaseous state, although it may also be carried out in adsorption columns (gas/solid chromatography).

In order to save space, g.l.c. columns, which may be as long as 5 metres with a bore of 2–10 mm, are generally wound into the form of a coil and evenly lined with finely ground Celite or firebrick, which acts as an inert support for the non-volatile stationary phase, e.g. a hydrocarbon grease. In special capillary techniques, columns may be up to 300 metres in length and as small as 0.1 mm in diameter.

The column is contained in a thermostatically controlled jacket maintained at a predetermined elevated temperature, and a steady stream of an inert gas, e.g. hydrogen, nitrogen, carbon dioxide, helium or argon, is passed through it. The choice of carrier gas and the temperature of the column depends upon the nature of the sample. Carrier gases have to be of exceptionally high purity and should preferably be dried before using. The rate of flow is carefully controlled by means of a flowmeter.

Gaseous and volatile liquid samples (as little as a few micrograms is sometimes all that is necessary for analytical work) are injected into the carrier gas from a microsyringe or some other device. Less volatile liquids and solids can often be

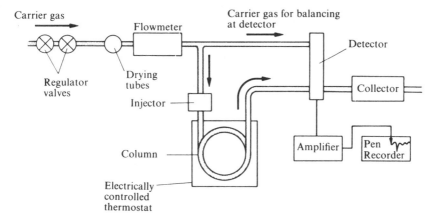

Fig. 9.3 Schematic diagram of apparatus for gas chromatography

dissolved in a suitable solvent and introduced in the same way. The point of injection is heated electrically to promote vaporization of the sample.

On its initial contact with the column, each component of the sample establishes an equilibrium between that in solution in the non-volatile liquid phase and that retained as vapour in the interstices of the inert support. As the carrier gas sweeps the mixture through, the equilibrium position of each component is disturbed so that the material in solution moves out into the vapour phase to form a new equilibrium further along. Since the components are retained by the stationary phase to varying degrees, by the time they reach the end of the column they emerge at discrete intervals, separated by zones of the carrier gas.

The degree of separation is related to the volatility of each component, the more volatile compounds passing through the column at the greater rate. The actual speed of the process is further governed by the nature and amount of the stationary liquid phase and of the solid, inert support.

The most common type of detector is the differential type, which determines the composition of the effluent gases by measuring the difference in their thermal conductivity. The chromatogram is recorded as a series of peaks on a chart by a pen, plotting vapour concentration versus time (minutes). In some cases, a complete separation may take several hours.

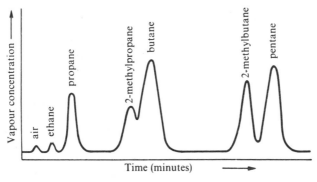

Fig. 9.4 Chromatogram showing the vapour phase separation of a petroleum fraction into its component gases

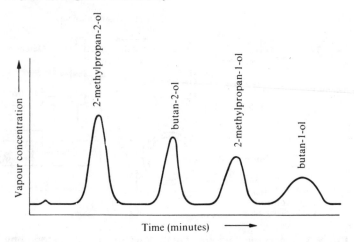

Fig. 9.5 Chromatogram showing the vapour phase separation of a mixture of isomeric alcohols, C_4H_9OH

One of the most widely used and sensitive detectors is the HYDROGEN FLAME IONIZATION DETECTOR. (Its use depends upon hydrogen being used as the carrier gas.) It consists of a metal jet, which acts as a negative electrode, at which the issuing gases are burnt, and a platinum gauze, which acts as a positive electrode, suspended 1–2 cm above the flame. A positive potential of 50–250 volts is maintained between the electrodes.

Burning the component gases causes them to ionize and to conduct an electric current, the conductivity being proportional to the number of ions and hence to the concentration of each component. There will be a small ionization current due to hydrogen ions formed as the carrier gas is burnt but this can easily be balanced out.

Another popular form of ionization detector is the ARGON TYPE.

In order that only small amounts of the injected sample are consumed by the detector, a by-pass, consisting of two concentric tubes with a volume ratio in the order of 1:20 (variable), is inserted, conserving the larger quantity for further analysis by directing it into special traps.

G.l.c. instruments can be linked directly with an infra-red spectrometer (*see* page 67) by means of special units, enabling structural information to be obtained more rapidly and efficiently.

Information about identity can also often be gleaned from the RETENTION TIMES. For a given flow rate, the time taken for a particular component to emerge from the column is a characteristic of that compound.

In addition to its uses as an analytical technique, g.l.c. *can also be used preparatively*. For this purpose, the only additional unit required is a series of collectors or traps into which the effluent gases can be condensed at low temperatures. Quantities ranging from 10 milligrams to 100 grams can be used in this context, although the apparatus may have to be scaled up to enable it to cope with the larger samples, for which nitrogen is the only safe and economic carrier gas.

In preparative work, it is important to volatilize a comparatively large quantity of material in a short period of time. This is achieved by placing a special heater at the head of the column.

Qualitative Analysis

Element Tests

Normally it is only necessary to test for nitrogen, sulphur, the halogens and phosphorus. This may be done by carrying out a *Lassaigne* sodium fusion test. The presence of carbon and hydrogen is assumed since very few organic compounds do not contain hydrogen. Oxygen is usually detected, if present, in later tests for functional groups.

Lassaigne Sodium Fusion Test

A little of the substance (about 50 mg or 2 drops) is added to a small pellet of sodium in an ignition tube and then heated, gently at first but then more strongly, to dull redness. The tube, while still hot, is plunged into about 10–15 cm^3 cold distilled water in an evaporating basin. The mixture is boiled for a short time, stirring with the unbroken portion of the tube and then filtered through a fluted filter paper. The filtrate, which should be both clear and colourless, is ready to be examined for the presence of nitrogen, sulphur and halogens. (Safety precautions are essential for this exercise as, in addition to the hazard of shattering glass, the reaction with certain compounds, particularly those containing chlorine, may be explosive.)

Test for Nitrogen (Cyanide Test)

The Lassaigne test converts any nitrogen present in the compound to sodium cyanide.

About 0.5 cm^3 of a cold saturated solution of iron(II) sulphate, that has been boiled momentarily to ensure the presence of some iron(III) salt, is added to a portion (4 cm^3) of the filtrate. The mixture is boiled for about one-half to one minute, cooled rapidly, and then acidified by adding concentrated hydrochloric acid (or 3M sulphuric acid) drop-wise. The formation of a Prussian blue (bluish-green) precipitate indicates the presence of nitrogen.

If the proportion of nitrogen is low, only a greenish solution may result, but when this is filtered and the paper washed, any blue precipitate present is usually visible.

Test for Sulphur (Sulphide Test)

The Lassaigne test converts any sulphur present in the compound to sodium sulphide.

This can be recognized by adding a few drops of a cold, freshly prepared, dilute solution of sodium pentacyanonitrosylferrate(II) (nitroprusside) to a portion of the filtrate. The presence of sulphur is indicated by the production of a rich purple colouration. (This test is very sensitive.)

Test for Halogens

The presence of halogens is tested for in the usual way by acidifying a portion of the filtrate with dilute nitric acid and adding silver(I) nitrate solution. Halogens are indicated by the formation of a white or yellow precipitate.

If nitrogen and/or sulphur have been detected, the solution must be boiled for a couple of minutes to expel HCN and H$_2$S, which interfere with the test, before adding the silver(I) nitrate solution.

If a positive test is obtained, further examination is required in order to distinguish between the halogens.

A further portion of the alkaline filtrate is acidified with 2M hydrochloric acid before adding about 1 cm³ of tetrachloromethane (carbon tetrachloride) and a few drops of chlorine water. The colour of the tetrachloromethane layer, after shaking, enables the halogen to be identified. If the tetrachloromethane layer is colourless, *chlorine* is indicated; brown, *bromine* is indicated; or violet, *iodine* is indicated.

BEILSTEIN'S TEST provides an alternative means of detecting halogens, but is not particularly reliable. A clean copper wire is heated in a flame until the green colour is no longer apparent and then dipped, while still hot, into a portion of the compound being analysed. Halogens are indicated by a green or bluish-green flame (due to the volatile copper halide).

Test for Phosphorus

About 2 cm³ of concentrated nitric acid is added to about 1 cm³ of the filtrate and boiled in order to convert any phosphorus present into phosphate(V) ions. The solution is then cooled and ammonium molybdate(VI) added. The formation of a yellow precipitate on gently warming to no more than 50 °C indicates the presence of phosphate(V) ions. (Arsenate(V) ions give a similar precipitate if present but only if the solution is boiled.)

Middleton's Test

In the interest of safety, this test is preferable to Lassaigne's test.

As in the Lassaigne test, Middleton's test depends upon heating the compound with an excess of a metallic reducing agent, in this case, zinc, so that the nitrogen forms cyanide ions, sulphur forms sulphide ions, and the halogens form halide ions. *The detection of these ions is similar for both processes.*

Middleton's mixture comprises two parts of zinc to one part of sodium carbonate. A small quantity of this mixture is then heated strongly in an ignition tube with a small amount of the organic compound under investigation. The tube is heated until red-hot and then plunged into an evaporating basin containing about 15 cm³ of cold distilled water. The ensuing procedure is then similar to that for Lassaigne's test.

Test for Metals

Metals can be detected in the compound by igniting a small portion of it on a piece of porcelain. A residue of the oxide or carbonate of the metal (other than volatile metals such as As, Sb, and Hg) may be identified by means of a semi-micro qualitative analysis scheme.

Functional Group Tests

Element tests may be followed by tests for the different functional groups, e.g. unsaturated, hydroxyl, aldehydic, keto, carboxylic, amino etc., present in compounds. These are detected by carrying out suitable reactions, described in textbooks of Organic Qualitative Analysis, which are characteristic of the group.

Tests for functional groups are not always considered essential, particularly if modern spectroscopic instruments are available, but, nonetheless, they do provide additional information which often enables a more precise analysis of the compound to be made. One of the main disadvantages of incorporating group analysis into the scheme is that comparatively large amounts of the substance are required.

Quantitative Analysis

The relative amounts of the different elements present in a compound are obtained mainly by combustion techniques. These results are interpreted to provide the empirical formula of the compound, which, when used in conjunction with the measured relative molecular mass, enables the molecular formula to be resolved.

Carbon and Hydrogen

A small, accurately weighed sample of the compound is heated to $700\,^\circ C$ in a stream of pure dry oxygen, and in the presence of pure copper(II) oxide, which ensures complete combustion of the vapours.

The hydrogen is oxidized to steam and the carbon to carbon dioxide. The amount of steam present is determined by passing it through a previously weighed tube of calcium chloride, and the carbon dioxide by passing it through a previously weighed wash-bottle (or preferably a potash bulb) of concentrated potassium hydroxide.

The mass of hydrogen present in the original sample will be 1/9 the increase in mass of the calcium chloride, and the mass of carbon will be 3/11 the increase in mass of the potassium hydroxide.

$$C_xH_y + \left(x+\frac{y}{4}\right)O_2 \longrightarrow xCO_2 + \frac{y}{2}H_2O$$

$$(12x+y) \qquad\qquad 44x \quad 18\,\frac{y}{2}$$

Nitrogen

Dumas Method

A known mass of the compound is heated with excess copper(II) oxide, with the exclusion of air. The effluent gases are passed over heated copper, which decomposes any oxides of nitrogen into the gaseous element. Carbon, hydrogen and sulphur are converted into their oxides and dissolved, together with any free halogen, in concentrated potassium hydroxide solution. The volume of nitrogen is collected in a NITROMETER and estimated.

Kjeldahl's Method

The nitrogen in the compound is converted into ammonium sulphate by boiling a known mass of it with concentrated sulphuric acid and anhydrous sodium sulphate until the solution becomes colourless. The mixture is then treated with excess sodium hydroxide, and the ammonia evolved is dissolved in a known volume of standard acid and estimated by back-titration.

Halogens *Carius' Method*

A known mass of the compound is heated at 200 °C in a sealed tube with a mixture of fuming nitric acid and solid silver(I) nitrate. After cooling, the precipitated silver(I) halide is filtered off, washed, dried and then weighed.

Sulphur *Carius' Method*

A known mass of the compound is heated with fuming nitric acid, which oxidizes any sulphur present to sulphuric acid. After cooling, the sulphate can be estimated by precipitating with barium chloride solution.

In a similar manner, phosphorus can be estimated by converting to phosphoric(V) acid.

Oxygen

The percentage composition of oxygen in a compound is difficult to determine directly and is usually found by elimination.

Determination of Empirical Formula

Once the percentage composition of a compound has been determined, the EMPIRICAL FORMULA can be calculated. This procedure is probably best exemplified by an illustrative example.

An organic compound was shown on quantitative analysis to contain 40.0 per cent carbon, 6.7 per cent hydrogen and 53.3 per cent oxygen. (Relative atomic masses: C = 12, H = 1, O = 16.)

The ratio of the number of constituent atoms in a molecule of the compound is given by:

$$\frac{Per\ cent\ of\ element\ by\ mass}{Relative\ atomic\ mass}$$

Since the molecule must contain an integral number of atoms, the ratio is determined by dividing through by the smallest number and correcting all values to the nearest whole number. The substance therefore contains carbon, hydrogen and oxygen in the ratio 1:2:1 respectively.

Element	$\dfrac{Per\ cent\ mass\ of\ element}{Relative\ atomic\ mass}$
Carbon	$\dfrac{40.0}{12} = 3.33$
Hydrogen	$\dfrac{6.7}{1} = 6.7$
Oxygen	$\dfrac{53.3}{16} = 3.33$

Empirical formula is CH_2O.

Determination of Relative Molecular Mass

Four of the most commonly applied methods for determining relative molecular masses are:

(1) VAPOUR DENSITY MEASUREMENTS, e.g. gas syringe, Victor Meyer's, Dumas' and Regnault's methods.

$$\text{Relative molecular mass} = \text{Vapour Density} \times 2$$

(2) MEASUREMENT OF THE DEPRESSION OF FREEZING POINT (CRYOSCOPIC METHOD)

(3) MEASUREMENT OF THE ELEVATION OF BOILING POINT (EBULLIOSCOPIC METHOD)

(4) HIGH RESOLUTION MASS SPECTROMETRY, which also provides a great deal of information about the structure of the compound (*see* 'Mass Spectrometry', page 80).

Having determined the relative molecular mass and empirical formula, the molecular formula of the compound can be found.

$$\text{Molecular formula} = (\text{Empirical formula})_n$$

For example, if the relative molecular mass of the compound of empirical formula CH_2O is 60, then the MOLECULAR FORMULA is $C_2H_4O_2$.

The molecular formula of gaseous hydrocarbons can usually be determined by eudiometry (gas explosion reactions). A known volume of the gas is repeatedly sparked in excess oxygen in a eudiometer until no further change in volume is observed. After cooling to the ambient temperature, the volume is noted and the amount of carbon dioxide determined by dissolving in potassium hydroxide. The remaining gas is excess oxygen.

Example

30 cm^3 of a gaseous hydrocarbon, C_xH_y, were mixed with 140 cm^3 of oxygen (an excess) and exploded. After cooling to room temperature the residual gases occupied 95 cm^3. By absorption with potassium hydroxide solution a diminution of 60 cm^3 was produced, and the remaining gas was shown to be oxygen. Determine the formula of the hydrocarbon (pressure constant at one atm).

$$C_xH_y + \left(x+\frac{y}{4}\right)O_2 \longrightarrow xCO_2 + \frac{y}{2}H_2O$$

$$\text{1 molecule} \quad \left(x+\frac{y}{4}\right)\text{molecules} \quad x \text{ molecules} \ \frac{y}{2} \text{ molecules}$$

So, by the converse of Avogadro's hypothesis:

$$\text{1 volume} \quad \left(x+\frac{y}{4}\right)\text{volumes} \quad x \text{ volumes} \ \frac{y}{2} \text{ volumes}$$

As the measurements are all made at room temperature, the steam will condense to water and occupy negligible volume.

The potassium hydroxide solution absorbs the volume of carbon dioxide produced, i.e. 60 cm^3.

∴ volume of excess oxygen is $(96-60) \text{ cm}^3 = 35 \text{ cm}^3$.

∴ 30 cm^3 of C_xH_y combines with $(140-35) \text{ cm}^3$, i.e. 105 cm^3, of oxygen to give 60 cm^3 of carbon dioxide.

Now, $30\,cm^3$ of $C_xH_y \equiv 1$ volume.

∴ $105\,cm^3$ of oxygen

$$\equiv \frac{105}{30} \text{ volumes}$$

$$= 3.5 \text{ volumes}$$

and $60\,cm^3$ of carbon dioxide

$$\equiv \frac{60}{30} \text{ volumes}$$

$$= 2 \text{ volumes}$$

$$\text{i.e. } x = 2$$

Equating to the coefficient for the volume of oxygen used:

$$x + \frac{y}{4} = 3.5$$

$$\therefore y = 6$$

giving the molecular formula of the hydrocarbon as C_2H_6 (ethane).

Determination of Structure

Having determined the molecular formula, all that there remains to do is to ascertain the structural arrangement of the atoms. Much of this information may be known already from the functional group analysis, and a good deal more can be learnt from the spectroscopic measurements discussed in the next section.

Large molecules can often be broken down into simpler and smaller ones, e.g. by oxidation, reduction, hydrolysis etc., and by working back through the various stages of degradation much information can be obtained about the structure of the original molecule.

In order to minimize the risk of an incorrect conclusion being made, it is advisable to attempt to synthesize the compound from simpler molecules of known structure or, alternatively, to prepare at least two crystalline derivatives and then check their melting points with those quoted in the literature. Sometimes it may be found necessary to prepare a liquid derivative.

Use of Molecular Spectra as Aids in the Identification of Organic Structures

The absorption of electromagnetic radiation by some part of the molecule may be used to help gain precise information about structure. In the case of ultra-violet and infra-red spectroscopy, the radiation is passed through the sample under analysis and the spectrum is recorded.

During the early stages of analysis, it is often found advantageous to study first the infra-red spectrum, and then the ultra-violet, bearing in mind the evidence already obtained from the infra-red spectrum. Consideration of the molecular formula will often allow the rejection of a number of alternative interpretations consistent with the same piece of spectroscopic evidence.

Whenever possible, this type of analysis should be carried out in conjunction with chemical tests. Final identification of the substance is often most readily achieved by preparing a crystalline derivative which has a sharp melting point.

The Basic Spectrometer

The optical features of an ultra-violet/visible and infra-red spectrometer are basically very similar.

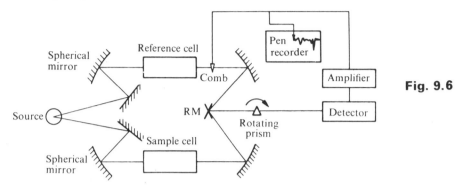

Fig. 9.6

Radiation from the source is split into two separate beams by a system of mirrors. One beam is passed through a cell containing the sample. If the sample is contained in solution, then the other beam is passed through an exactly similar cell containing a sample of the solvent, which acts as a blank and automatically compensates for any absorption by the solvent containing the compound.

A null point is reached when the two beams have the same intensity and the compensating comb is fully withdrawn from the reference beam. At wavelengths where the sample absorbs some of the radiation, the comb moves into the reference beam, reducing its energy until the beams are again equal. The movement of the comb is a measure of the absorption by the sample and is linked mechanically to the pen of the recorder, which draws out a plot of the intensity of the transmitted light versus the wavelength, quoted in nanometres (nm) or in wave numbers (cm^{-1}).

RM is a pair of reciprocating mirrors, mounted one above the other, which, by rotating, are used to send alternate pulses from the two beams to the detector.

The recorder is governed to respond linearly to either the wavelength or the wave number of the incident radiant energy.

Ultra-violet Spectroscopy

The ULTRA-VIOLET SPECTRUM is recorded over the wave number range 50050–25000 cm^{-1} (185–400 nm). The 25000 12000 cm^{-1} (400–800nm) region records absorption in the VISIBLE REGION.

The position of the spectrum is set in the region at which absorption of energy is to occur. This is referred to as the specific absorption. Absorption of electromagnetic radiation in these regions involves the promotion of electrons from the ground state to higher energy states, i.e. excited states.

The intensity of absorption depends upon how tightly the electrons are coupled within the molecule as a whole; for example, the elevation of the more firmly held electrons in σ bonds requires a considerable amount of energy, corresponding to a high wave number (low wavelength) of about 83 300 cm^{-1}, which is too high for normal ultra-violet measurements. The excitation of the more accessible and less firmly held π electrons usually falls well within the ultra-violet/visible range.

Although ultra-violet/visible spectroscopy has certain analytical limitations, it can prove extremely useful in detecting the presence of multiple bonds in molecules, especially when a conjugated system of double bonds is present, e.g. —C≡C—C≡C—, benzene rings etc. Conjugation loosens the coupling of the π electrons, which results in the formation of strong absorption bands.

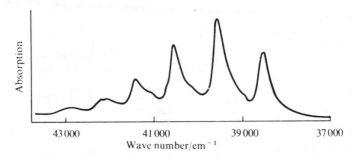

Fig. 9.7 Ultra-violet spectrum of benzene in ethanol solution

The substance under analysis is dissolved in a suitable solvent, e.g. 95 per cent ethanol, water or hexane, which does not absorb light in the region under investigation. The use of different solvents may cause a shift in the absorption bands of a particular compound. A narrow beam of light from a source of radiation, e.g. a hydrogen discharge tube or a tungsten filament lamp, is passed through the sample contained in the cell, the latter being transparent to light in the given region. Although ordinary glass is satisfactory for work in the visible region, it absorbs ultra-violet light; hence quartz cells must be used for studying spectra in this region.

Infra-red Spectroscopy

Either wave numbers or wavelength is used to plot the positions of the absorption bands in the infra-red spectrum, which in the ordinary region extends from $4000-667 \, \text{cm}^{-1}$ ($2500-15000 \, \text{nm}$).

In contrast to the relatively few absorption peaks observed in the visible and ultra-violet spectrum, the infra-red region possesses a much greater array of characteristic bands which provide a wealth of structural information about the molecule. Furthermore, all organic compounds absorb light in this part of the spectrum, converting the absorbed radiation into vibrational energy.

There are two fundamental vibrations in molecules, *stretching* and *bending*. Different modes of vibration of atoms W and X about C are illustrated below.

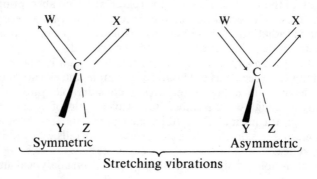

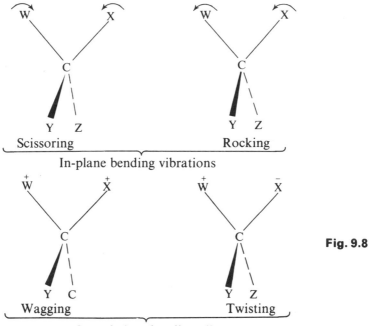

Fig. 9.8

These vibrations occur at certain quantized frequencies, and when infra-red radiation of that frequency is incident upon the molecule, energy is absorbed and the amplitude of that vibration is increased. Many groups of atoms give rise to absorption bands in approximately the same part of the spectrum irrespective of the nature of the molecule, although small deviations, brought about by the interaction between adjacent groups of atoms, may slightly alter the location of a band. However, this displacement can sometimes be utilized to give additional information about the nature of the rest of the molecule.

The absorption bands are readily identified using literature tables which specify the characteristic wave numbers. The task of identifying particular absorption bands has become immeasurably easier in recent years owing to the development of a large library of spectra which serve as 'fingerprints' for the identification of an unknown. This proves especially useful in the 1430–$910 \, \text{cm}^{-1}$ region, or FINGERPRINT REGION, which is extremely rich in absorption bands, the latter being due mainly to bending vibrations.

It is sometimes found necessary to calibrate a recorded spectrum as it is not always possible to place the recorder paper, which in the ordinary spectrometer is fitted on a cylindrical drum, in precisely the same position every time. One of the several absorption peaks of poly(phenylethene) (polystyrene) is commonly used for this purpose.

Optical prisms or gratings are used to obtain almost monochromatic light from an infra-red source, e.g. a Nernst glower (transition metal oxides heated to $1500 \, ^\circ\text{C}$).

Analysis requires less than a milligram of the sample, which may be a gas, liquid, solid or solution, and is in most cases recoverable. Gases have to be handled in special cells which have path lengths of between one and ten centimetres. As glass and quartz are not transparent to infra-red light, the cells or plates are made of rock salt (sodium chloride) or potassium bromide.

Certain solids may be examined by melting and allowing to solidify on rock salt plates. Those solids which are not easily melted are ground into a mull with Nujol (an inert, liquid hydrocarbon with a very simple infra-red spectrum) or compressed into a disc with potassium bromide before being inserted into the path of the beam. Only when the work is of a quantitative nature is it necessary to examine the substance in solution.

Some Characteristics of Absorption of Infra-red Spectra

C—H stretching vibrations	*Wave number range*$/cm^{-1}$
(1) Alkane	2962–2853
(2) Alkene, monosubstituted	3040–3010 and 3095–3075
disubstituted	3095–3010
trisubstituted	3040–3010
(3) Alkyne	~ 3300
(4) Aromatic	~ 3030

C—H bending vibrations

(1) Alkane, C—H	~ 1340
—CH_2—	1485–1445
—CH_3	1470–1430
(2) Alkene, monosubstituted	995–985, 915–905 and 1420–1410
disubstituted (*cis*)	~ 690
disbustituted (*trans*)	970–960 and 1310–1295
trisubstituted	840–790
—$(CH_2)_n$—, when $n \geqslant 4$	~ 750
(3) Alkyne	~ 630
(4) Aromatic, benzene	~ 671
monosubstituted	770–730
disubstituted	883–735
trisubstituted	865–760
tetrasubstituted	870–800

C—C multiple bond stretching vibrations	*Wave number range*$/cm^{-1}$
(1) Alkene, non-conjugated	1680–1620
monosubstituted	~ 1645
disubstituted	1680–1650
trisubstituted	~ 1669
tetrasubstituted	~ 1669
(2) Alkyne, monosubstituted	2140–2100
disubstituted	2260–2190
(3) Aromatic	~ 1600

Carbonyl stretching vibrations

(1) Aldehyde, aliphatic, saturated	1470–1720
aromatic	1715–1695
(2) Ketone, R—CO—R′	1725–1705
R—CO—Ar	1700–1680
Cyclic, saturated (precise absorption depends on number of carbons in ring)	1775–1705

(3) Carboxylic acid, R—COOH (dimer)   1725–1700
                   Ar—COOH   1700–1680
   (O——H---O, intermolecularly   2700–2500
          hydrogen bonded)   (several bands)
(4) Ester, R—COOR′   1750–1735
         Ar—COOR   1730–1715
         R—COOAr   1800–1730

O—H stretching vibrations   *Wave number range/cm^{-1}*

Alcohols and Phenols,
    Free O—H   3650–3590
    intermolecularly hydrogen bonded— 3550–3450
    single bridge
    (varies according to dilution)

O—H bending and C—OH stretching vibrations

(1) Primary alcohols   ~1050 and 1350–1260
(2) Secondary alcohols   ~1100 and 1350–1260
(3) Tertiary alcohols   ~1150 and 1410–1310
(4) Phenols   ~1200 and 1410–1310

C—X stretching vibrations

(1) C—F   1400–1000
(2) C—Cl   800–600
(3) C—Br   600–500
(4) C—I   ~500

Hexane, $CH_3CH_2CH_2CH_2CH_2CH_3$

2960 cm^{-1} ⎫
2920 cm^{-1} ⎬   C—H stretching (CH$_3$ and CH$_2$)
2870 cm^{-1} ⎭

1460 cm^{-1} C—H bending (CH$_2$)

1380 cm^{-1} C—H bending (CH$_3$)

 725 cm^{-1} C—H bending (—(CH$_2$)$_n$—, when $n \geqslant 4$)

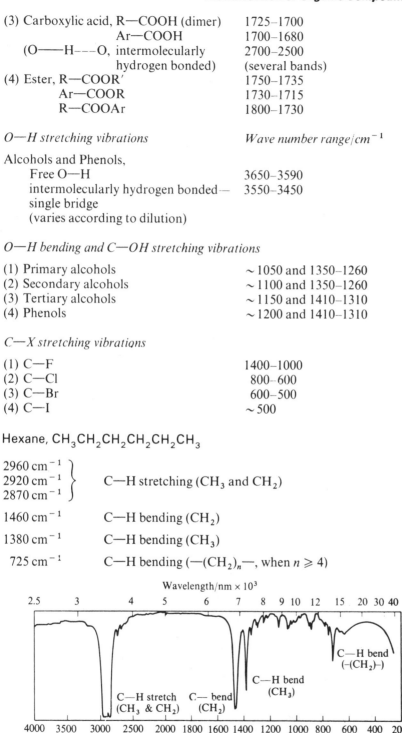

Fig. 9.9 I.R. spectrum of hexane, $CH_3CH_2CH_2CH_2CH_2CH_3$

Cyclohexane

$$2910 \text{ cm}^{-1} \atop 2840 \text{ cm}^{-1} \Big\}$$ C—H stretching (symmetrical and asymmetrical CH_2)

1445 cm^{-1} C—H bending (CH_2)

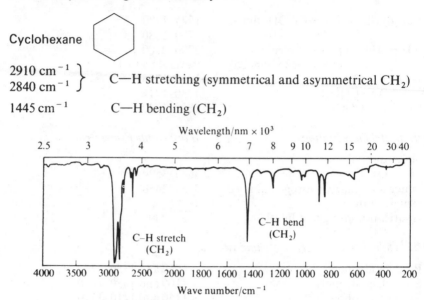

Fig. 9.10 I.R. spectrum of cyclohexane, C_6H_{12}

Nujol

$$2920 \text{ cm}^{-1} \atop 2850 \text{ cm}^{-1} \Big\}$$ C—H stretching (CH_3 and CH_2)

1460 cm^{-1} C—H bending (alkane CH_2 and C—CH_3 bending)

1375 cm^{-1} C—H bending (alkane C—CH_3)

$$720 \text{ cm}^{-1} \atop 635 \text{ cm}^{-1} \Big\}$$ Weak bending vibrations of the —$(CH_2)_n$—, when $n \geqslant 4$

When Nujol is used as a mulling agent, very little information can be derived about absorptions of the sample in these regions.

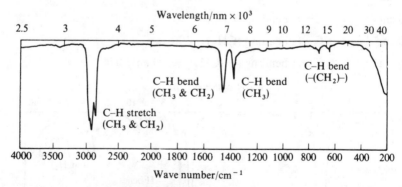

Fig. 9.11 I.R. spectrum of nujol

Poly(phenylethene) (polystyrene)

$$2850 \text{ cm}^{-1} \atop 1603 \text{ cm}^{-1} \atop 906 \text{ cm}^{-1} \Bigg\}$$ Any one of these absorptions is often used to calibrate a spectrum.

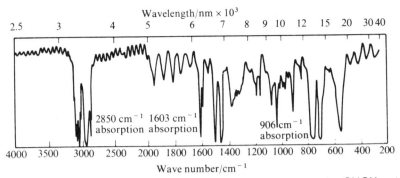

Fig. 9.12 I.R. spectrum of poly(phenylethene) (polystyrene), $\left(\begin{array}{c}-CHCH_2-\\ \mid\\ C_6H_5\end{array}\right)_n$

Trichloromethane (chloroform), $CHCl_3$

$3020\,cm^{-1}$	C—H stretching (CH)
$1215\,cm^{-1}$	C—H bending (shifted to lower frequency by electronegative Cl atoms)
$755\,cm^{-1}$	C—Cl stretching

The most commonly used solvents in infra-red spectroscopy are tri-chloromethane, tetrachloromethane (carbon tetrachloride) and carbon disul-phide. The spectrum of the solution should always be compared with a blank of the solvent in order to eliminate the unwanted absorption due to the solvent.

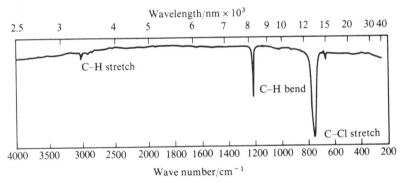

Fig. 9.13 I.R. spectrum of trichloromethane (chloroform), $CHCl_3$

Methylbenzene (toluene)

$3020\,cm^{-1}$	C—H stretching (aromatic)
$2910\,cm^{-1}$	C—H stretching (CH_3)
$\left.\begin{array}{l}1945\,cm^{-1}\\1855\,cm^{-1}\\1800\,cm^{-1}\\1730\,cm^{-1}\end{array}\right\}$	Absorptions characteristic of monosubstituted benzene derivatives.

$\left.\begin{array}{l} 1600 \text{ cm}^{-1} \\ 1495 \text{ cm}^{-1} \end{array}\right\}$ Carbon–carbon stretching of aromatic nucleus

$\left.\begin{array}{l} 725 \text{ cm}^{-1} \\ 690 \text{ cm}^{-1} \end{array}\right\}$ C—H out-of-plane bending of monosubstituted benzene derivative.

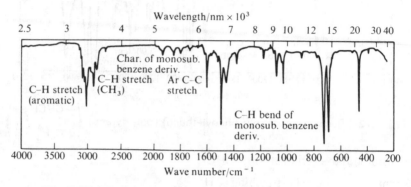

Fig. 9.14 I.R. spectrum of methylbenzene (toluene), $C_6H_5CH_3$

Methanol, CH_3—OH

3340 cm^{-1} O—H---O stretching (intermolecularly hydrogen bonded)

$\left.\begin{array}{l} 2940 \text{ cm}^{-1} \\ 2830 \text{ cm}^{-1} \end{array}\right\}$ C—H stretching (CH_3)

1450 cm^{-1} (in-plane)   O—H bending (in-plane)

1410 cm^{-1} C—H bending (symmetrical CH_3)

$\left.\begin{array}{l} 1110 \text{ cm}^{-1} \\ 1025 \text{ cm}^{-1} \end{array}\right\}$ C—OH stretching

The broad absorption at 3340 cm^{-1} in the spectrum of the liquid (due to O—H stretching of the intermolecularly hydrogen bonded species) decreases in intensity with dilution, with a resultant increase in the free O—H stretching at $3660–3590 \text{ cm}^{-1}$. The intensity of the free hydroxyl absorption is most pronounced in the vapour phase spectra of alcohols (illustrated in the vapour phase spectrum of ethanol).

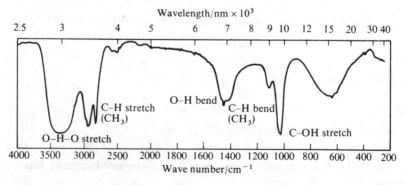

Fig. 9.15 I.R. spectrum of methanol (liquid phase), CH_3OH

Ethanol (vapour phase), CH_3CH_2—OH

3655 cm^{-1}	O—H stretching (free O—H)
2980 cm^{-1}	C—H stretching (asymmetric CH_2)
2970 cm^{-1}	C—H stretching (symmetric CH_3)
2900 cm^{-1}	C—H stretching (symmetric CH_2)
1405 cm^{-1}	O—H bending (in-plane)
1250 cm^{-1}	C—H bending (symmetric CH_3)

$\left.\begin{array}{l} 1070 \text{ cm}^{-1} \\ 890 \text{ cm}^{-1} \end{array}\right\}$ C—OH stretching (characteristic of R—CH_2OH)

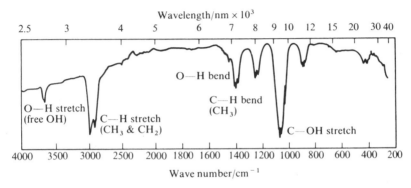

Fig. 9.16 I.R. spectrum of ethanol (vapour phase), CH_3CH_2OH

Ethoxyethane (diethyl ether), CH_3CH_2—O—CH_2CH_3

$\left.\begin{array}{l} 2985 \text{ cm}^{-1} \\ 2860 \text{ cm}^{-1} \end{array}\right\}$ C—H stretching (CH_3 and CH_2)

1450 cm^{-1}	C—H bending (CH_2 and C—CH_3)
1385 cm^{-1}	C—H bending (C—CH_3)
1120 cm^{-1}	C—O stretching

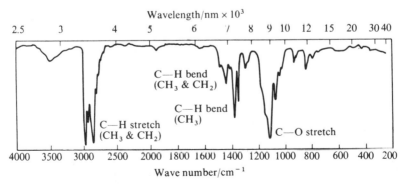

Fig. 9.17 I.R. spectrum of ethoxyethane (diethyl ether), $CH_3CH_2OCH_2CH_3$

Propanone (acetone), $(CH_3)_2C=O$

Propanone exists in dynamic equilibrium with its tautomer, the enol, the latter being present in only small proportions.

$$CH_3-CH=CH-OH \rightleftharpoons \begin{matrix} CH_3 \\ \diagdown \\ C=O \\ \diagup \\ CH_3 \end{matrix}$$

This phenomenon gives rise to infra-red absorptions for both isomers.

$3410\ cm^{-1}$	Could be either O—H stretching or C—H stretching of H—C=C
$3000\ cm^{-1}$	C—H stretching (CH_3)—shifted owing to adjacent C=O group
$1720\ cm^{-1}$	C=O stretching of aliphatic ketone
$1420\ cm^{-1}$	C—H deformation—displaced owing to adjacent C=O groups
$1360\ cm^{-1}$	C—H bending $(CH_3$ adjacent to C=O group)
$\left.\begin{matrix} 1220\ cm^{-1} \\ 1095\ cm^{-1} \\ 900\ cm^{-1} \end{matrix}\right\}$	Probably C—H bending of $>C=CH_2$, which is present in small amounts

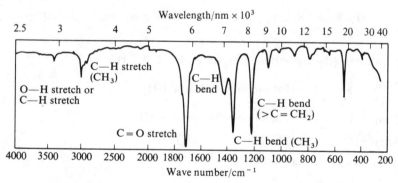

Fig. 9.18 I.R. spectrum propanone (acetone), $(CH_3)_2C=O$

The highly polar carbonyl group produces a strong absorption band, although it is sometimes obscured by other strong absorptions in the same region.

Ethylethanoate (acetate), $CH_3-\overset{\overset{\displaystyle O}{\|}}{C}-O-CH_2CH_3$

$2980\ cm^{-1}$	C—H stretching (asymmetric CH_3) $\Big]$ shifted owing to
$2940\ cm^{-1}$	C—H stretching (asymmetric CH_2) $\Big\}$
$2910\ cm^{-1}$	C—H stretching (symmetric CH_2) $\Big]$

$$\begin{matrix} O \\ \diagup\diagup \\ -C-O-\ \text{group} \end{matrix}$$

1740 cm^{-1}	C=O stretching of esters
1470 cm^{-1}	C—H bending (CH$_2$ scissoring)
1450 cm^{-1}	C—H bending (asymmetric CH$_3$)
1370 cm^{-1}	C—H bending (symmetric CH$_3$)
1240 cm^{-1}	C—O stretching (asymmetric C—O—C of esters)
1045 cm^{-1}	An absorption characteristic of esters

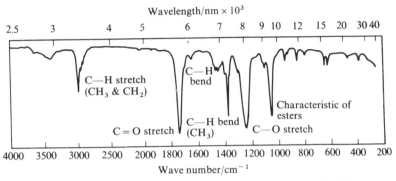

Fig. 9.19 I.R. spectrum of ethyl ethanoate (acetate), CH$_3$COOCH$_2$CH$_3$

Nuclear Magnetic Resonance (NMR) Spectroscopy

The organic chemist uses NMR as a complementary tool to both infra-red and ultra-violet spectroscopy, enabling him to gather much more information about molecular structure.

The principal components of an NMR spectrometer are: a highly homogenous permanent magnet or electromagnet, which may be anything between one and five tonnes in mass; a resonance (field) sweep; a radio frequency source to obtain the appropriate frequency; a detector and a recorder.

A sample of the compound in a suitable solvent is placed in a precision tube between the pole faces of the magnet and the spectrum determined. The effective

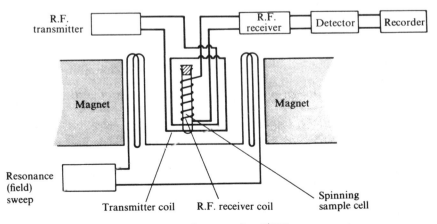

Fig. 9.20 Schematic diagram of an NMR spectrometer

homogeneity of the field is enhanced by spinning the sample tube several hundred times a minute about a vertical axis. It is then 'swept' in the absorption region, maintaining the frequency oscillator at a constant value and varying the magnetic field slightly.

Fundamental requirements for NMR are that the nucleus must have spin and magnetic properties. A spinning, positively charged nucleus possesses a magnetic moment which is capable of interacting with an externally applied field.

In order to produce an NMR spectrum, the nucleus must have a net spin. The criterion for this is that the nucleus must contain an odd mass number. Nuclei such as ^1H, ^{13}C, ^{19}F and ^{31}P are therefore suitable, whereas atoms of even mass number, such as ^{12}C and ^{16}O are not. By far the most important element encountered in organic chemistry which displays NMR properties is hydrogen.

The environment of each nucleus in a molecule is different, being dependent upon the orbital and bonding electrons, and the absorption of energy by the nucleus is in accordance with its environment. This enables the hydrogens in a methyl group, $-CH_3$, to be distinguished from those in the methylene, $-CH_2-$, and hydroxyl, $-OH$, groups and also from other hydrogens in different environments.

For example, consider the different environments of the hydrogen atoms in the ethanol molecule, CH_3CH_2OH. The frequency at which absorption occurs for the hydrogen atoms in the $-CH_3$ groups is different from that for those in the $-CH_2-$ group, which in turn is different from that for the one in the $-OH$ group. As a result, the NMR spectrum of ethanol shows three absorption peaks, caused by the hydrogens in each of these three groups.

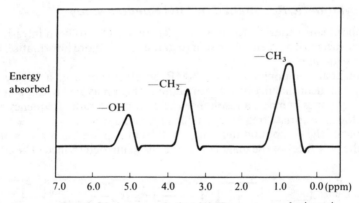

Fig. 9.21 Low resolution NMR spectrum of ethanol

The relative areas enclosed by the pen in recording the absorption spectrum are proportional to the number of hydrogen atoms of each type; e.g. in the case of ethanol they are in the ratio 3:2:1 for the $-CH_3$, $-CH_2-$ and $-OH$ groups respectively.

Modern instruments automatically integrate the spectrum so as to determine the relative number of protons causing each absorption. The integral tracing rises to a height which is proportional to the area enclosed by the peak, indicating at a glance the number of protons responsible for that absorption. In the spectrum for ethanol, the integral tracing rises to heights in accordance with the ratio 3:2:1 for the $-CH_3$, $-CH_2-$ and $-OH$ groups respectively.

The spectrum is calibrated against a standard, which is usually tetramethyl-silane (TMS), $Si(CH_3)_4$, and then interpreted. All twelve protons in this

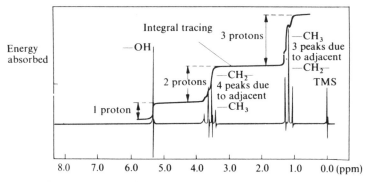

Fig. 9.22 High resolution NMR spectrum of ordinary ethanol

compound are equivalent and resonate at a single frequency, $v_{TMS} = 0$. The units chosen are parts per million (ppm) for the change in magnetic field, represented by the symbol, δ. The arbitrary value chosen for the absorption of TMS is 10 and the peak positions are given in τ (Tau) units, where $\tau = (10 - \delta)$ ppm. The value of δ or τ for a particular peak in the spectrum is referred to as the CHEMICAL SHIFT of the proton.

If a high resolution instrument is employed, it is found that these peaks show fine structure, each being subdivided into groups of peaks. This splitting is due to the magnetic field experienced by one group being affected by the spin arrangements of the protons on the adjacent group. The multiplicity of the split depends upon the number of hydrogen atoms in the adjacent groups. For n equivalent and adjacent hydrogen atoms, the peak is split into $(n + 1)$ peaks.

This results in the two hydrogens in the —CH_2— group (i.e. $n = 2$) splitting the methyl absorption into a triplet and the three hydrogens of the methyl group (i.e. $n = 3$) splitting the methylene absorption into a quartet.

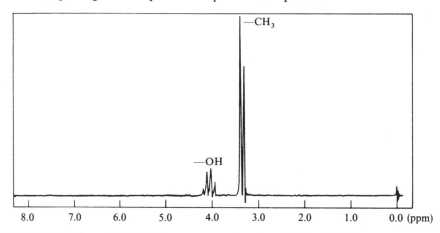

Fig. 9.23 High resolution NMR spectrum of methanol, CH_3OH (CCl_4 solvent)

The relative areas enclosed by the split peaks are given by the coefficients of the binomial expansion

$$1, n, \frac{(n-1),}{2!} \frac{n(n-1)(n-2),}{3!} \cdots \cdots$$

where n is the number of nuclei in the adjacent group. It follows that the areas enclosed by the three split peaks of the methyl absorption are in the ratio of $1:2:1$ and that those enclosed by the four methylene peaks are in the ratio of $1:3:3:1$.

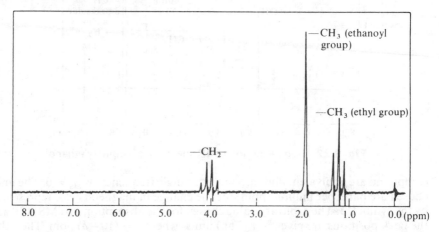

Fig. 9.24 High resolution NMR spectrum of ethyl ethanoate (acetate), $CH_3COOCH_2CH_3$ (CCl_4 solvent)

From this very elementary and simplified discussion it may be seen that an NMR spectrum can give rise to information about the types of hydrogen atoms present in a molecule, the numbers of each type and also which types of hydrogen are adjacent to one another.

Mass Spectrometry

Unlike the different types of electromagnetic spectroscopy already discussed, mass spectrometry separates the different species, in the form of positively charged ions, according to their mass.

The bombardment of atoms and molecules with free electrons can be used as a means of raising them to the state of positively charged ions by completely removing outer electrons. The mass spectrometer is an instrument for measuring the mass/charge ratio of these positively charged ions.

In the case of organic compounds, the ions formed are generally singly charged owing to the loss of only one outer electron,

$$M + e \longrightarrow M^+ + 2e$$

although doubly charged ions occasionally occur.

The sample under investigation is introduced into the spectrometer in the gaseous phase, so it is therefore essential that liquid and solid samples are sufficiently volatile, although modern instruments will operate at temperatures as high as 350 °C. Furthermore, the substance must not undergo decomposition during analysis as this would likely lead to a completely misleading interpretation of the spectrum. In order to avoid interference from air molecules the main spectrometer tube operates at extremely low pressure, about 10^{-7} mm Hg (1.3×10^{-5} Pa).

The sample can be drawn from a reservoir, maintained at about 10^{-5} mm Hg (1.3×10^{-3} Pa), into the spectrometer tube where it is bombarded with electrons from a heated filament, causing the sample molecules to be ionized. During this process, the parent molecules are simultaneously broken down into smaller fragments which themselves become ionized on collision with free electrons. The ions are then accelerated between slits in negatively charged plates before passing through a magnetic field in which the ions are deflected along circular paths. The degree of deflection depends upon the relative mass to charge ratios of the individual ions, the ions of largest mass being deflected least, and *vice versa*.

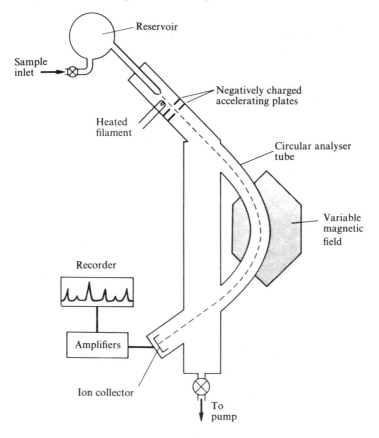

Fig. 9.25 Schematic diagram of a mass spectrometer

The separated streams of ions are made to fall one by one on to a detector by scanning the magnetic field before being amplified and recorded. Pen recorders can be employed to plot the abundance of each ion present as a peak against the corresponding mass/charge ratio, although these tend to be rather slow in action and it is often more convenient to use an oscilloscope or data system method of recording. Another important operating factor is that conditions remain steady during the analysis as the accuracy depends upon the constancy of the ion population during that period.

The relative molecular mass of a particular substance, which is not necessarily a whole number, is indicated by the mass number of the ion of the parent molecule. The presence of isotopes of different atoms in the molecule gives rise to peaks at different mass/charge values, depending upon the mass numbers of the different isotopes. These can be interpreted in conjunction with the other mass numbers indicated for the parent ion to give an accurate relative molecular mass of the sample.

The relative intensities of the peaks, due to the different isotopes present in the naturally occurring element, are usually expressed as a percentage of the most intense one and are proportional to the amount of each isotope present. For example, naturally occurring chlorine contains 75.4 per cent of ^{35}Cl and 24.6 per cent of ^{37}Cl, and therefore the relative intensities of the two peaks at mass/charge values of 35 and 37 are about 3:1 respectively. The presence of isotopes of elements is thus readily recognizable.

In addition to measuring mass numbers and identifying isotopes, the mass spectrum also provides some useful information about the structure of the molecules of the sample. Molecules and ions generally rupture preferentially at the weakest point in their structure, and a significant amount of information may be gleaned from the abundance of the fragments into which the parent molecule is broken down. Solid samples may be introduced directly into the mass spectrometer for the purpose of obtaining structural information.

Consider the mass spectrum of the simplest organic compound, methane, illustrated below. The molecules of this compound fragment into the ions CH_4^+,

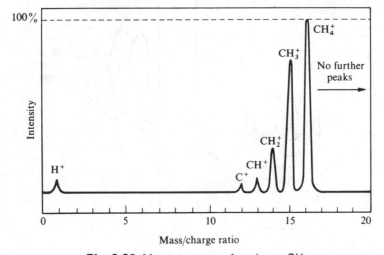

Fig. 9.26 Mass spectrum of methane, CH_4

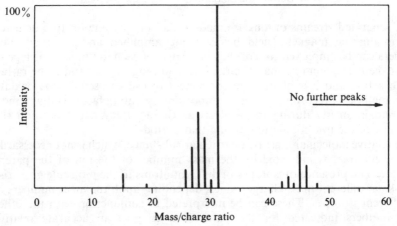

Fig. 9.27 Schematic mass spectrum of ethanol, CH_3CH_2OH

CH_3^+, CH_2^+, CH^+, C^+ and H^+, and their relative abundance in the spectrometer is illustrated by the intensity of the peaks; the parent molecule ion, CH_4^+, and the methyl ion, CH_3^+, being by far the most common. The peak at mass/charge value 16 corresponds to that of the ion of the parent molecule CH_4^+.

For simplicity and ease of interpretation, spectra can be illustrated schematically using vertical lines to represent the different peaks. This is exemplified on page 82, showing the mass spectrum of ethanol.
The main peaks are identified in the following table.

Mass/charge ratio	15	26	27	28	29	31	43	45	46
Nature of ion	CH_3^+	$C_2H_2^+$	$C_2H_3^+$	$C_2H_5^+$	$C_2H_4^+$	CH_3O^+	$C_2H_3O^+$	$C_2H_5O^+$	$C_2H_6O^+$

The peak at mass/charge value 46 corresponds to that of the ion of the parent molecule, $CH_3CH_2OH^+$.

QUESTIONS

1. Which one of the following gases makes the least suitable carrier gas for gas/liquid chromatography?

   A hydrogen
   B nitrogen
   C carbon dioxide
   D sulphur dioxide
   E argon

2. Determine the most likely structure for a compound of molecular formula C_3H_8O which gives a liquid phase infra-red absorption maximum at $3940 \, cm^{-1}$ but none in the $3330 \, cm^{-1}$ and $1725 \, cm^{-1}$ regions.

3. Which one of the following pure samples is most likely to produce the above schematic mass spectrum shown in Fig. 9.28, given the following relative atomic masses: $H = 1$, $C = 12$, $O = 16$, $Cl = 35.5$?
   A methanol, CH_3OH
   B chloroethane, CH_3CH_2Cl
   C butan-1-ol, $CH_3(CH_2)_3OH$
   D hexan-1-ol, $CH_3(CH_2)_5OH$
   E 1-chlorohexane, $CH_3(CH_2)_5Cl$

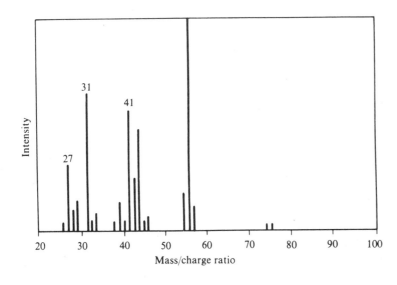

Fig. 9.28

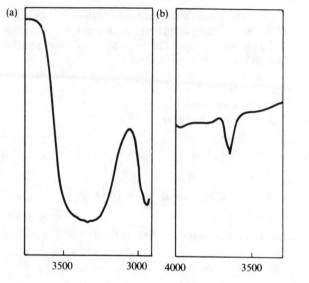

Fig. 9.29

4. Explain the significance of the infra-red absorption bands shown in Fig. 9.29, which have been extracted from the spectra of different compounds. The units are quoted in wave numbers/cm^{-1}.

5. State the number of major groups of peaks due to protons given by the NMR spectrum of each of the following:

A $C_6H_5CH_3$
B $(CH_3)_2CO$
C CH_3CHO
D $CH_3CH_2CH_2OH$

6. Indicate how using a high resolution instrument would affect the multiplicity of the splitting in the peaks for ethanal (acetaldehyde).

Part II

10 *Alkanes (Paraffins)*

The alkanes form a homologous series of saturated hydrocarbons and correspond to a general molecular formula, C_nH_{2n+2}. Successive members differ in composition by the increment CH_2.

All carbon atoms are sp^3 hybridized and are consequently tetrahedrally surrounded by hydrogen and other carbon atoms. They are normally very stable compounds (the name paraffin means 'little affinity'), and are relatively unreactive in comparison with their unsaturated counterparts.

Nomenclature

With the exception of the first four members of the series, methane, ethane, propane and butane, the straight-chain alkanes are named by taking the Greek prefix appropriate to the number of carbon atoms and adding the ending '-ane'.

For branched alkanes, the largest unbranched chain of carbon atoms is selected and named accordingly. The names of the alkyl substituents prefix the name of the main chain, the position of substitution being indicated by the appropriate number.

$$CH_3-CH_2-CH_2-CH_3 \qquad CH_3-CH_2-CH_2-CH_2-CH_3$$

Butane · Pentane

$$CH_3-\overset{\displaystyle |}{\underset{\displaystyle CH_3}{CH}}-CH_2-CH_3 \qquad CH_3-\overset{\displaystyle |}{\underset{\displaystyle CH_3}{CH}}-CH_2-CH_2-CH_3$$

2-Methylbutane · · · · · · · · · · · · 2-Methylpentane
(Isopentane) · · · · · · · · · · · · · · · · · (Isohexane)

$$CH_3-\overset{\displaystyle CH_3}{\underset{\displaystyle CH_3}{\overset{\displaystyle |}{\underset{\displaystyle |}{C}}}}-CH_3$$

2,2-Dimethylpropane
(Neopentane)

Structural Isomerism in Alkanes

Methane, ethane and propane have no structural isomers, butane has two, pentane has three, and each of the following higher homologues of the series have a progressively greater number. For example there are 75 compounds corresponding to the formula $C_{10}H_{22}$ and 366319 correspond to the formula $C_{20}H_{42}$. All isomers are due to branching of the hydrocarbon chain and are referred to as CHAIN or BRANCHED-CHAIN ISOMERS.

Two butanes. C_4H_{10}

$CH_3—CH_2—CH_2—CH_3$

Butane

$$\begin{array}{c} CH_3—CH—CH_3 \\ \quad\;| \\ \quad\; CH_3 \end{array}$$

2-Methylpropane
(Isobutane)

Three pentanes, C_5H_{12}

$CH_3—CH_2—CH_2—CH_2—CH_3$

Pentane

$$\begin{array}{l} CH_3—CH—CH_2—CH_3 \\ \qquad\;\;| \\ \qquad\;\; CH_3 \end{array}$$

2-Methylbutane
(Isopentane)

$$\begin{array}{c} CH_3 \\ | \\ CH_3—C—CH_3 \\ | \\ CH_3 \end{array}$$

2,2-Dimethylpropane
(Neopentane)

Classification of Carbon and Hydrogen Atoms

A carbon atom is classified according to the number of other carbons to which it is attached.

A PRIMARY (1°) carbon is one which is attached to *no more than one other carbon atom*; a SECONDARY (2°) carbon is one which is attached to *two other carbon atoms*, and a TERTIARY (3°) carbon is one which is attached to *three other carbon atoms*.

$$\begin{array}{cccc} 1° & 2° & 2° & 1° \\ CH_3— & CH_2— & CH_2— & CH_3 \end{array}$$

$$\begin{array}{ccc} 1° & 3° & 1° \\ CH_3— & CH— & CH_3 \\ & | & \\ & CH_3 & \\ & 1° & \end{array}$$

It follows then that a $—CH_3$ group is a primary group, a $—CH_2—$ group is a secondary group and a $\rangle\!—CH$ group is a tertiary group.

Hydrogen atoms are classified according to the nature of the carbon atom to which they are attached.

Physical Properties

The straight-chain alkanes, C_1 to C_4, are gases, C_5 to C_{17} are liquids, and the remaining higher homologues are all solids at 20 °C.

Boiling points and melting points increase with increasing relative molecular mass, although branched-chain isomers are more volatile than their straight-chain counterparts; furthermore, the greater the degree of branching in an isomer, the greater is its volatility.

The density of the alkanes increases with increasing relative molecular mass, although branching in an isomer contributes to reducing this factor. The viscosity of the liquid members follows a similar pattern. All alkanes are less dense than water.

Being non-polar compounds, the alkanes are predictably immiscible with water but soluble in non-polar organic solvents such as trichloromethane (chloroform), ethoxyethane (ether), benzene etc. ('like dissolves like'). Methane shows a slight tendency to dissolve in water, but this is attributed mainly to the very small size of its molecules.

Natural Sources of Methane

The anaerobic ('without air') decomposition of the large, complicated organic molecules of vegetable matter ultimately produces methane as an end product. The gas is often encountered in the atmosphere surrounding swamps, marshes and stagnant ponds from which it can sometimes be seen bubbling to the surface. Hence the popular name, MARSH GAS.

Methane is the main constituent of NATURAL GAS (often more than 90 per cent by volume). Progressively smaller quantities of ethane, propane and some of the higher alkanes make up most of the remaining gases present. For many years, the only abundant sources of natural gas suitable for large scale exploitation or industrial and domestic levels were in the United States, but with the advent of off-shore drilling for potential oil wells, new sources of natural gas are being discovered. As a result of this, 'North Sea Gas' is now being piped into the industries and homes of Britain.

Coal mines provide a natural source of methane where it is known as 'fire damp'. A mixture of this gas with air in certain proportions is explosive, and was the cause of innumerable accidents before Davy invented his safety lamp.

Methane is formed when coal or wood is heated strongly in the absence of air, and is therefore present in coal gas (approximately 30–35 per cent by volume), which is manufactured by the destructive distillation of coal.

If the gas is required pure from natural sources, it must be separated by fractional distillation, but as most of it is consumed as fuel, this process is rarely necessary.

Crude petroleum is a dark brown or sometimes green liquid containing mainly straight-chain, branched and cyclic alkanes. The latter are also known as naphthenes. Altogether, in the region of 150 different compounds have been isolated from crude petroleum.

Fractional Distillation of Petroleum

The crude petroleum is fractionally distilled, and the fractions are collected over a range of boiling points.

The carbon content of each of the alkanes in each fraction corresponds approximately to a definite range, with the simpler, more volatile homologues distilling over first. However, the carbon content of lighter fractions is enhanced by a certain proportion of the more volatile branched compounds of higher relative molecular mass. In practice, this is of little consequence, as the uses to which each fraction are applied depend almost essentially upon their volatility and viscosity rather than upon their respective constituents.

Fraction	Distillation temperature range/°C	Approximate carbon content
Gas	Below 20	C_1-C_4
Light petroleum (petroleum ether)	20–60	C_5-C_6
Ligroin (light naphtha)	60–100	C_6-C_7
Petrol (gasoline)	40–205	C_5-C_{12} (+cyclo-alkanes)
Paraffin (kerosene)	175–325	$C_{12}-C_{18}$ (+aromatics)
Gas oil	275–400	$C_{12}-C_{25}$
Lubricating oil	Non-volatile liquids	—
Asphalt (bitumen)	Residue	—

Uses of the Fractions

The more volatile fractions are used mainly as fuel.

Fraction	Uses
Gas	Heating
Light petroleum (petroleum ether)	Organic solvent
Ligroin (light naphtha)	Organic solvent
Petrol (gasoline)	Fuel for internal combustion engines requiring volatile liquids
Paraffin (kerosene)	Heating fuel and for engines requiring less volatile liquids, e.g., tractors, jet engines
Gas oil	Heating fuel and for Diesel engines
Lubricating oil	Lubricant
Asphalt (bitumen)	Road construction and roofing

The lubricating oil fraction often contains long-chain alkanes ($C_{20}-C_{34}$) of high melting point which may form solid waxes when cold. If these were allowed to remain in the fraction, they would tend to block the oil pipes in the refinery, particularly in cold weather. Instead, they are separated out by cooling the fraction and filtering. The solid is sold as PARAFFIN WAX (m.p. 50–55 °C) or used to make PETROLEUM JELLY (VASELINE).

Petroleum fractions also provide useful compounds for preparing other chemicals, and the more volatile ones, containing up to five carbons, provide probably the most important source of raw materials for large-scale preparations of aliphatic compounds.

Knocking

The higher compression ratio of the modern internal combustion engine has made it more efficient but at the same time it has created other problems. The normal, smooth combustion of the petrol-air mixture in the cylinder of the engine is more likely to be replaced by a series of sharp detonations causing the engine to lose power. This phenomenon is known as KNOCKING.

Octane Rating

The problem of knocking has been successfully overcome by adding an 'anti-knock' additive, tetraethyllead(IV), $Pb(C_2H_5)_4$, to the fuel and by the more careful selection of the hydrocarbons in the petrol. The more careful this selection is, the higher the OCTANE RATING given to the petrol.

This rating is based on an arbitrary 'knocking-scale', for which heptane, which causes severe knocking, is given a value of zero, and 2,2,4-trimethylpentane (an octane), which causes little knocking is given a value of 100. Even so, modern fuels are available with octane ratings of greater than 100.

$$
\begin{array}{c}
\quad\quad CH_3 \quad\quad CH_3 \\
\quad\quad | \quad\quad\quad | \\
H_3C-C-CH_2-CH-CH_3 \\
\quad\quad | \\
\quad\quad CH_3
\end{array}
$$

2,2,4-Trimethylpentane

The octane rating of the petrol is related to the compression ratio of the engine, so no additional benefit is gained by using a higher grade of petrol in the engine than that specified by the manufacturer. However, if a grade lower than the one recommended is used, it is likely that a lack of performance will be encountered.

Synthetic Preparation

Hydrogenation of Alkenes

The hydrogenation of alkenes provides one of the most important methods of preparing specific alkanes. A mixture of the alkene and hydrogen is passed over finely divided platinum, palladium or nickel catalyst. Nickel is the least active of these catalysts and requires an elevated temperature and pressure, whereas platinum and palladium function adequately at ordinary temperatures and pressures.

$$C_nH_{2n} + H_2 \xrightarrow{\text{Pt, Pd or Ni cat.}} C_nH_{2n+2}$$

Alkene   Alkane

Reduction of Haloalkanes

Haloalkanes may be obtained prior to the preparation (*see* page 151)

$$ROH + HX \longrightarrow RX + H_2O$$

Alcohol   Haloalkane

and then employed in any of the following preparations, or they may simply be hydrogenated at room temperature using a zinc–copper couple in aqueous alcohol.

$$2RX + Zn + 2H^+ \xrightarrow{\text{Zn–Cu/aq. alcohol}} 2RH + Zn^{2+} + X^-$$

Alkane

Grignard Reaction

The GRIGNARD REAGENT (*see* page 199) is prepared by adding a dry ethereal (ethoxyethane) solution of an haloalkane to metallic magnesium. The magnesium dissolves, with the liberation of heat, to form a cloudy solution of the ALKYLMAGNESIUM HALIDE, RMgX.

The reagent, on treatment with aqueous hydrochloric or sulphuric acid, liberates the alkane.

$$RX + Mg \xrightarrow[\text{(C}_2\text{H}_5)_2\text{O}]{\text{dry}} RMgX$$
$$\text{Alkylmagnesium halide}$$

$$RMgX + H_2O \xrightarrow[\text{H}_2\text{SO}_4]{\text{aq. HCl or}} R\text{—}H + Mg(OH)X$$

Wurtz Synthesis

The alkane is prepared by the synthesis of metallic sodium and the haloalkane in a dry ethereal (ethoxyethane) solution.

$$2\,RX + 2\,Na \xrightarrow[\text{(C}_2\text{H}_5)_2\text{O}]{\text{dry}} R\text{—}R + 2NaX$$

The reaction is limited in its application, giving only low yields with haloalkanes of low relative molecular mass, although much better yields are obtained with those of higher relative molecular mass. A more versatile coupling reaction of this type is the Corey-Hause reaction involving the haloalkane and a lithium dialkylcopper.

$$RX + R_2'CuLi \longrightarrow R\text{—}R' + R'Cu + LiX$$

Kolbé Synthesis

The sodium salt of a monocarboxylic acid is electrolysed in aqueous methanolic solution.

$$CH_3COONa \longrightarrow CH_3COO^- + Na^+$$

At Pt anode: $$2CH_3COO^- \longrightarrow CH_3CH_3 + 2CO_2 + 2e$$

Hydrogen is evolved at the cathode.

This reaction is only suitable for symmetrical alkanes, i.e. those of the type, R—R.

Methods Specific to Methane

In addition to the general methods of preparation, methane may also be prepared by treating *aluminium carbide with hot water or dilute acid,*

$$Al_4C_3 + 12HCl \longrightarrow 3CH_4 + 4AlCl_3$$

or by *decarboxylating sodium ethanoate (acetate)* by fusing it with 'sodalime' (calcium oxide slaked with sodium hydroxide).

$$CH_3COONa + NaOH \xrightarrow{\text{fuse}} CH_4 + Na_2CO_3$$
Sodium   Sodalime
ethanoate

Reactions

The alkanes, particularly the straight-chain alkanes, are comparatively inert relative to the alkenes and alkynes. Practical reactions require a fairly high temperature and/or a photochemical (photolytic) or peroxide initiator. They are also resistant to mineral acids and oxidizing agents.

Cracking Alkanes

Pyrolysis ('cleavage by heat') of alkanes is referred to as CRACKING, particularly where petroleum is involved. Alkanes, particularly from the paraffin (kerosene) fraction, in the vapour state are passed through a metal chamber heated to 400–700°C. This usually contains various metallic oxides which function as a catalyst. The starting alkanes are broken down into a mixture of smaller alkanes, alkenes and some hydrogen.

$$\text{Alkane} \xrightarrow{400-700\,°C} \text{Smaller alkanes} + \text{Alkenes} + H_2$$

e.g. $2CH_3CH_2CH_3 \xrightarrow{400-700\,°C} CH_4 + CH_3CH{=}CH_2 + CH_2{=}CH_2 + H_2$

    Propane   Propene   Ethene

Mechanism

The reaction proceeds via a free-radical mechanism, with homolytic fission taking place between carbon–carbon atoms, although some hydrogen is produced, probably from the rupture of carbon–hydrogen bonds. A possible mechanism, indicating *some* of the different stages, for the cracking of propane is:

(1) $CH_3\overset{\frown}{CH_2}{-}CH_3 \longrightarrow CH_3CH_2{\cdot} + CH_3{\cdot}$ Chain initiation

(2) $CH_3CH_2{\cdot} \longrightarrow CH_2{=}CH_2 + H{\cdot}$

(3) $CH_3CH_2CH_3 + H{\cdot} \longrightarrow H_2 + CH_3\overset{\cdot}{C}HCH_3$ Chain propagation

(4) $CH_3CH_2CH_3 + CH_3{\cdot} \longrightarrow CH_4 + CH_3\overset{\cdot}{C}HCH_3$

(5) $2CH_3CH_2{\cdot} \longrightarrow CH_2{=}CH_2 + CH_3CH_3$ Chain

(6) $2CH_3\overset{\cdot}{C}HCH_3 \longrightarrow CH_3CH{=}CH_2 + CH_3CH_2CH_3$ termination

The cracking of non-volatile petroleum alkanes results in the formation of smaller, volatile products which have good anti-knock properties, and these are utilized in high-grade petrols.

Reactions of this type are called CHAIN REACTIONS as they involve a series of steps, each of which forms a reactive product that initiates the next step. Stages (2), (3) and (4), which are only examples of the many propagation reactions that occur, are described as being SELF PROPAGATING.

The formation of a single free radical in the initiation step can cause the chain propagating reactions to be repeated several thousand times. The number of times reactions (2), (3) and (4) are repeated in this process before the chain is terminated is referred to as the CHAIN LENGTH. This is a term used in chemical kinetics and should not be confused with the same term used to describe the number of carbon atoms in a linear hydrocarbon.

Chlorination of Alkanes

Alkanes undergo chlorination in the presence of ultra-violet light or at a temperature of 250–400 °C, yielding a mixture of products. For example, methane yields a mixture of chloromethane, CH_3Cl, dichloromethane, CH_2Cl_2, trichloromethane (chloroform), $CHCl_3$ and tetrachloromethane (carbon tetrachloride), CCl_4.

$$CH_4 \xrightarrow[h\nu \text{ (light energy)}]{Cl_2} \text{Mixture of } CH_3Cl, CH_2Cl_2, CHCl_3 \text{ and } CCl_4$$

Mechanism

The reaction is initiated by homolytic fission of chlorine molecules producing highly reactive chlorine free radicals. These react with methane molecules, and abstract a hydrogen atom from each of them to form hydrogen chloride molecules. Methyl groups, each with an unpaired electron (methyl radicals) are also formed. The methyl radicals then react with other chlorine molecules to form chloromethane and more chlorine radicals.

(1) $Cl\frown Cl \xrightarrow[\text{energy)}]{h\nu \text{ (light}} 2Cl\cdot$ Chain initiation

(2) $CH_4 + Cl\cdot \longrightarrow CH_3\cdot + HCl$

(3) $CH_3\cdot + Cl_2 \longrightarrow CH_3Cl + Cl\cdot$ Chain propagation

Steps (2) and (3) are repeated to give the further products CH_2Cl_2, $CHCl_3$ and CCl_4.

The *chain termination* processes for the reaction for the formation of chloromethane are:

(4) $CH_3\cdot + Cl\cdot \longrightarrow CH_3Cl$

(5) $CH_3\cdot + CH_3\cdot \longrightarrow CH_3CH_3$

(6) $Cl\cdot + Cl\cdot + S \longrightarrow Cl_2 + S*$

Analogous chain termination reactions occur for the subsequent formation of the other major products. The compounds formed by the chain termination are present in the final mixture in only trace amounts.

In the chain termination processes, the combination of two chlorine free radicals occurs with a great evolution of energy. If the radicals are to remain intact after collision, this energy has to be dissipated to a 'third body', S, which can be any of the other molecules present in the system e.g. Cl_2, CH_4, CH_3Cl etc. The presence of a 'third body' is not necessary for the combination of methyl radicals as this process is not so highly exothermic.

Methane undergoes bromination (but not iodination) by a similar mechanism. Fluorination of methane is violent.

The halogenation of all higher alkanes takes place at a slower rate than those reactions involving methane.

The dependence of these processes upon a photochemical initiator is indicated by the fact that halogenation of alkanes *does not occur in the dark*.

Halogenation using Sulphur Dichloride Dioxide (Sulphuryl Chloride)

The alkane is refluxed with sulphur dichloride dioxide at 40–80 °C using di(benzenecarbonyl)peroxide (di(benzoyl)peroxide) as a catalyst.

$$RH + SO_2Cl_2 \xrightarrow[\substack{\text{catalyst} \\ 40\text{--}80\,°C}]{\text{di(benzenecarbonyl)peroxide}} RCl + HCl + SO_2$$

Sulphur dichloride   Haloalkane
dioxide

Nitration of Alkanes

Vapour-phase nitration of alkanes using nitric acid takes place at 150–400 °C via a free-radical mechanism, forming the nitroalkane.

$$RH + HNO_3 \xrightarrow{150\text{--}400\,°C} RNO_2 + H_2O$$

Reactions involving higher alkanes yield a mixture of smaller nitro products which result from the 'cracking' of the larger molecules.

Nitroalkanes are useful commercial solvents.

Combustion

Alkanes burn exothermically in excess oxygen with a *non-smoky flame*, producing carbon dioxide and steam.

$$C_nH_{2n+2} + \tfrac{3n+1}{2}O_2 \xrightarrow{\text{burn}} nCO_2 + (n+1)H_2O \quad \Delta H = -Q$$
$$\text{Excess}$$

The reaction proceeds via a high temperature free-radical mechanism.

Tetrachloromethane (Carbon Tetrachloride), CCl₄

Tetrachloromethane provides one of the most important organic solvents, and industrially is used on a large scale to manufacture chlorofluoromethanes (*see* page 304).

The bulk of it is manufactured from carbon disulphide and chlorine,

$$CS_2 + 3Cl_2 \xrightarrow[30\,°C]{\text{anhyd. FeCl}_3} CCl_4 + S_2Cl_2$$
$$CS_2 + 2S_2Cl_2 \xrightarrow[60\,°C]{\text{anhyd. FeCl}_3} CCl_4 + 6S$$

although smaller quantities are obtained by the high temperature (600 °C) CHLORINOLYSIS of propane and by the chlorination of methane.

$$C_3H_8 + 8Cl_2 \xrightarrow{600\,°C} CCl_4 + CCl_2{=}CCl_2 + 8HCl$$
$$\text{Tetrachloroethene}$$

The Cycloalkanes

Saturated hydrocarbons in which the carbons are arranged to form rings are referred to as CYCLOALKANES.

e.g.

$$
\begin{array}{ccc}
CH_2{-}CH_2 & CH_2{-}CH_2 & CH_2{-}CH_2 \\
\diagdown\ \diagup & | \quad | & | \quad | \\
CH_2 & CH_2{-}CH_2 & CH_2 \quad CH_2 \\
& & \diagdown\ \diagup \\
& & CH_2
\end{array}
$$

Cyclopropane   Cyclobutane   Cyclopentane

$$
\begin{array}{c}
CH_2 \\
\diagup \qquad \diagdown \\
CH_2 \qquad\quad CH_2 \\
| \qquad\qquad | \\
CH_2 \qquad\quad CH_2 \\
\diagdown \qquad \diagup \\
CH_2
\end{array}
$$

Cyclohexane

Cycloalkanes are slightly denser and boil at temperatures 10–20 °C higher than their straight-chain counterparts. Chemically, they bear a close resemblance to the alkanes, although cyclopropane and cyclobutane tend to be considerably more reactive.

Orientation of Cycloalkanes

Cyclopropane must, by necessity, adopt a planar structure, having the three carbon atoms inclined at 60° to each other. Since this is a long way removed from the desired regular tetrahedral bond angle of 109° 28', the molecule is *highly strained*. The four-membered ring of cyclobutane adopts a square planar arrangement (carbon–carbon bond angles are 90°) and is also highly strained, albeit to a lesser extent. Cyclopentane is likewise planar, but since the internal angles of a regular pentagon (108°) approach the regular tetrahedral bond angle, this structure is only slightly strained. Although puckering of the ring is possible for both cyclobutane and cyclopentane, this would serve only to increase the degree of strain and is therefore not favoured.

All larger cyclic molecules, however, adopt puckered structures, the simplest example of this being the *boat and chair conformations of cyclohexane* (page 33).

QUESTIONS

1. Give the IUPAC name for

A $CH_3CHCH_2CH_3$ B $CH_3CHCH_2CHCH_3$ C $CH_3CHCH_2CCH_2CH_3$

      CH_3 CH_3 CH_2CH_3 CH_3 CH_3

(with C bearing a $CH_2CH_2CH_3$ group)

2. Give the structural formula for

   A   2,4-dimethylpentane
   B   1,1,3-trimethylcyclopentane
   C   2,5-dimethyl-5-ethylheptane
   D   2,2,4-trimethylpentane

3. Formulate and name all the structural isomers of hexane, C_6H_{14}.

4. Which of the following does *not* represent an alkane?

A C_6H_{14}
B $C_{13}H_{28}$
C $C_{18}H_{36}$
D $C_{19}H_{40}$
E $C_{38}H_{78}$

5. How many straight-chain dichloro-alkanes correspond to the formula $C_4H_8Cl_2$?

A 4
B 5
C 6
D 7
E 8

6. Which one of the following alkanes does *not* contain a secondary carbon atom?

A $CH_3CH_2CH_3$
B $(CH_3)_2CHCH_2CH_3$
C $(CH_3)_2CHCH_2CH(CH_3)_2$.
D $(CH_3)_3CCH_2CH_3$
E $(CH_3)_3CCH(CH_3)_2$

7. Which one of the following groups of products is formed when methane and chlorine are mixed in the dark?

A carbon powder and hydrogen chloride
B chloromethane, dichloromethane, tri-chloromethane and tetrachloromethane
C chloromethane and hydrogen chloride
D tetrachloromethane and hydrogen chloride
E no products are formed

8. Without referring to data tables, list the following alkanes in decreasing order of volatility

A hexane
B heptane
C 2-methylhexane
D octane
E 2,2,4-trimethylpentane
F 2,3-dimethylbutane
G 2,2-dimethylbutane

9. Write the mechanism for the bromi-nation of methane in light, indicating the initiation, propagation and termination for the formation of bromomethane.

11 *Alkenes (Olefins)*

The alkenes form a homologous series of unsaturated hydrocarbons containing a carbon–carbon double bond and corresponding to a general molecular formula, C_nH_{2n}.

The unsaturated carbon atoms are sp^2 hybridized and are attached to each other by a σ bond, resulting from the overlapping of two of the hybrid orbitals (i.e. one from each carbon), and a π bond which is formed from the overlapping of the non-hybridized p orbitals. The latter lie at right angles to the plane of the hybrid orbitals (*see* page 19).

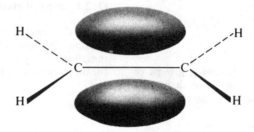

Fig. 11.1 The ethene (ethylene) molecule

The remaining sp^2 hybrid orbitals form σ bonds with other carbon or hydrogen atoms.

The π electrons are much more exposed than those in the σ bond and are therefore more vulnerable to any attacking species, particularly electrophiles. This availability of electrons in the double bond makes the alkenes generally much more reactive than the alkanes.

Nomenclature

In accordance with the IUPAC system, an alkene is named by dropping the ending '-ane' from the name of the corresponding alkane and replacing it with the suffix '-ene'. Where required, the position of the double bond is specified by placing the appropriate number between the stem of the name and the '-ene'. Ethene and propene are still sometimes referred to by their common names, ethylene and propylene respectively.

Formula	IUPAC name	Common name
$CH_2{=}CH_2$	Ethene	Ethylene
$CH_3{-}CH{=}CH_2$	Propene	Propylene

Formula	IUPAC name	Common name
$^4CH_3—^3CH_2—^2CH=^1CH_2$	But-1-ene	1-Butylene
$^4CH_3—^3CH=^2CH—^1CH_3$	But-2-ene	2-Butylene
$CH_3—CH_2—\underset{\underset{C_6H_5}{\mid}}{CH}—CH=CH_2$	3-Phenylpent-1-ene	—

Structural Isomerism in Alkenes

Ethene and propene have no structural isomers, but there are three butenes (butylenes), C_4H_8.

Of these, two are straight-chain structures with the difference being in the position of the double bond in the molecules. These are described as POSITIONAL ISOMERS.

$$CH_3—CH_2—CH=CH_2 \qquad\qquad CH_3—CH=CH—CH_3$$

But-1-ene But-2-ene

The third butene is a BRANCHED-CHAIN ISOMER, 2-methylpropene (iso-butene).

$$CH_3—\underset{\underset{CH_3}{\mid}}{C}=CH_2$$

2-Methylpropene

Prevention of free rotation about the double bond (refer to the section on rotation about carbon–carbon bonds, pages 23 and 27) creates the phenomenon of GEOMETRICAL ISOMERISM. An alkene having a formula RCH=CHR can have two stereoisomers, depending upon whether the two alkyl groups are on the same or different sides of the double bond. If they are both on the same side, then

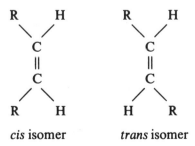

cis isomer *trans* isomer

it is referred to as the *cis* ISOMER and if they are on different sides, then it is called the *trans* ISOMER.

Higher alkenes have a progressively greater number of isomers, corresponding to these three categories.

Physical Properties

Name	Formula	State at 20°C
Ethene	$CH_2{=}CH_2$	Gas
Propene	$CH_2{=}CHCH_3$	Gas
But-1-ene	$CH_2{=}CHCH_2CH_3$	Gas
Pent-1-ene	$CH_2{=}CH(CH_2)_2CH_3$	Liquid
Hex-1-ene	$CH_2{=}CH(CH_2)_3CH_3$	Liquid
Hept-1-ene	$CH_2{=}CH(CH_2)_4CH_3$	Liquid
Oct-1-ene	$CH_2{=}CH(CH_2)_5CH_3$	Liquid

Higher members with more than fifteen carbons are solids, but as in the case of the alkanes, branching enhances the volatility. The boiling points of the alkenes correspond very closely with those of their alkane counterparts, although they are generally marginally lower.

The alkenes are virtually insoluble in water but soluble in non-polar organic solvents such as trichloromethane (chloroform), ethoxyethane (ether), benzene etc.

Unsymmetrical alkanes are very slightly polar owing to the electron-donating properties of the alkyl group(s).

$$\begin{array}{ccc} R & & H \\ & \diagdown\;\diagup & \\ & C & \\ & \| & \\ & C & \\ & \diagup\;\diagdown & \\ H & & H \end{array}$$

Industrial Source

Large qualities of alkenes are obtained by the cracking of petroleum.

$$\begin{array}{c} \quad \underset{H\;H}{\overset{H\;H}{\underset{|\;|}{\overset{|\;|}{-C-C-}}}} \;\xrightarrow{\text{pyrolysis}}\; \underset{}{\overset{H\;H}{\underset{}{\overset{|\;|}{-C{=}C-}}}} + H_2 \end{array}$$

The simplest members can be separated in the pure form by fractional distillation.

Ethene is occasionally prepared industrially by passing ethanol vapour over an aluminium oxide catalyst at 350 °C.

$$CH_3CH_2OH \xrightarrow[350\,°C]{Al_2O_3 \text{ catalyst}} CH_2{=}CH_2 + H_2O$$

$$\text{Ethanol} \qquad\qquad\qquad \text{Ethene}$$

Synthetic Preparations

The great majority of synthetic preparations of alkenes involve ELIMINATION of atoms or groups from two adjacent carbon atoms, mainly from alcohols and haloalkanes.

$$\underset{\underset{\text{H} \quad \text{OH}}{|\quad\ |}}{-\text{C}-\text{C}-} \longrightarrow \overset{|\quad\ |}{-\text{C}=\text{C}-} + H_2O$$

Alcohol   Alkene

Ease of dehydration of alcohols: 3° alcohol > 2° alcohol > 1° alcohol

$$\underset{\underset{\text{H} \quad \text{Cl}}{|\quad\ |}}{-\text{C}-\text{C}-} \longrightarrow \overset{|\quad\ |}{-\text{C}=\text{C}-} + HCl$$

Haloalkane   Alkene

Ease of dehydrohalogenation of haloalkanes: 3° > 2° > 1°.

Dehydration of Ethanol using Concentrated Sulphuric Acid

The heating of ethanol with excess concentrated sulphuric acid at 170 °C provides what is probably the most commonly employed preparation of ethene.

$$CH_3CH_2OH \xrightarrow[170\,°C]{\text{conc. } H_2SO_4} CH_2{=}CH_2 + H_2O$$

In practice, a certain amount of oxidation by the acid produces small quantities of carbon dioxide and sulphur dioxide which are removed by passing the gases through a concentrated solution of potassium hydroxide.

Dehydrohalogenation

Despite the fact that haloalkanes are often prepared from the corresponding alcohol, their use in the preparation of alkenes is sometimes preferred to the direct dehydration of alcohols as the overall process proves to be less complicated.

Dehydrohalogenation of haloalkanes is carried out by heating them in an alcoholic solution of potassium hydroxide.

$$\underset{\underset{\text{H} \quad \text{X}}{|\quad\ |}}{-\text{C}-\text{C}-} \xrightarrow[\text{alc. KOH}]{\text{heat}} \overset{|\quad\ |}{-\text{C}=\text{C}-} + HX$$

This reaction proceeds much more easily with secondary and tertiary haloalkanes than with primary. In fact, a very simple primary haloalkene like iodoethane gives only about a 2 per cent yield of ethene.

Mixed Products

A mixture of alkenes is usually produced when preparing higher homologues, the relative proportion of which depends on the respective stabilities of the individual alkenes (*see* page 108).

$$CH_3CH_2CHCH_3 \xrightarrow[-H_2O]{\text{conc. } H_2SO_4} CH_3CH=CHCH_3 + CH_3CH_2CH=CH_2$$
$$|$$
$$OH$$

But-2-ene   But-1-ene
Major product

$$CH_3CH_2CHCH_3 \xrightarrow[-HX]{\text{alc. KOH}} CH_3CH=CHCH_3 + CH_3CH_2CH=CH_2$$
$$|$$
$$X$$

The more stable the alkene, the more readily it is formed.

Reactions

Alkenes are highly reactive compounds in comparison with alkanes. The π electrons in the double bond act as a source of electrons, i.e. it functions as a base. Their reactions are therefore characterized by ELECTROPHILIC (electron-deficient or acidic species) ADDITION across the double bond. These additions can proceed through an ionic or free-radical mechanism. In this chapter a greater emphasis is placed upon the former.

Ionic Addition

Ionic addition across the alkene double bond is initiated by the more electropositive component of the attacking reagent attaching itself to one of the unsaturated carbons and inducing a positive charge on the other. The resulting transition state contains a positively charged 'three valent carbon', which is referred to as a CARBOCATION (CARBONIUM ION).

$$>C=C< \quad A^{\delta+} - Y^{\delta-} \longrightarrow -\overset{|}{\underset{A}{C}}-\overset{+}{\underset{|}{C}}- \xrightarrow{Y^-} -\overset{|}{\underset{A}{C}}-\overset{Y}{\underset{|}{C}}-$$

Carbocation (Carbonium ion)

The reaction is completed by the subsequent attack of the anion on the carbocation, yielding a saturated product.

For the ionic addition of halogens, a further transition state has been proposed which involves the formation of the HALONIUM ION.

$$\underset{\text{Halonium ion}}{>C\overset{\overset{\displaystyle X}{\diagup \overset{+}{} \diagdown}}{\rule{1.2cm}{0.4pt}}C<} \qquad X = \text{Halogen atom}$$

Certain reactions are favoured by the presence of a polar catalyst which enhances the degree of polarity of the attacking reagent.

Addition of Halogens

Ionic addition of bromine or chlorine takes place readily in tetrachloromethane (carbon tetrachloride) or ethanoic (acetic) acid at room temperature and in the absence of light. (In the presence of light, free-radical addition takes place.)

Consider the addition of a bromine molecule.

The dipole is first induced in the bromine molecule before it approaches the alkene. Evidence for this is the fact that the reaction does not take place if the bromine/tetrachloromethane mixture is perfectly dry, nor if the surface of the reaction vessel is coated with a non-polar material, e.g. paraffin wax. Traces of water and the surface of the glass vessel, which functions as a surface catalyst, probably contribute to instigating the dipole in the bromine. As the relatively positive, $\delta +$, end of the dipole approaches the proximity of the π electrons in the double bond, this polar effect is enhanced by the repulsive force between the π electrons of the alkene and the electrons in the bromine–bromine bond. The more positive bromine then forms a σ bond with one of the unsaturated carbons and breaks from the other bromine, which forms an ion. The process is completed by the subsequent attack by this ion upon the carbocation.

This reaction provides a useful *test for unsaturation*, the red-brown colour of the bromine being rapidly discharged as the colourless dibromo compound is formed.

The addition of bromine water ('bromic(I) acid', BrOH), hydrogen bromide, concentrated sulphuric acid and water, all proceed via a similar mechanism in which the more electropositive atom or group attaches itself to the alkene first.

Addition of Bromine Water

Bromine and chlorine dissolve in water forming a solution which contains some halic(I) (hypohalous) acid.

$$H_2O + Br_2 \longrightarrow BrOH + HBr$$
$$\text{Bromic(I)}$$
$$\text{acid}$$

This reacts readily with the alkene at room temperature to form the halo-alcohol.

Bromoalcohol
(Alkene bromohydrin)

The red-brown colour of the bromine is discharged as the bromoalcohol is formed and this reaction, like the previous one, can be used to test for the presence of an unsaturated carbon–carbon linkage in a molecule.

Reactions involving gaseous alkenes are performed by bubbling them through the solution.

Chloric(I) (hypochlorous) acid polarizes, $HO^{\delta+}-Cl^{\delta-}$, and the mechanism proceeds with the initial attack of the electron-deficient hydroxyl group upon the alkene double bond.

Addition of Hydrogen Bromide

Hydrogen bromide, generated by the action of concentrated sulphuric acid on sodium bromide, reacts rapidly with alkenes at room temperature yielding the bromoalkane.

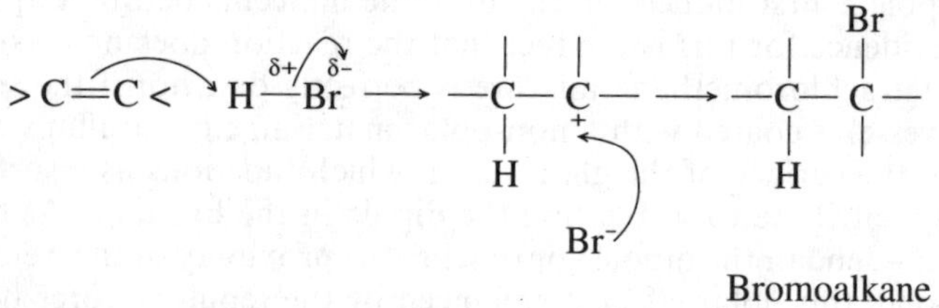

Bromoalkane

Addition of Concentrated Sulphuric(VI) Acid

Simple alkenes react with cold (0–15 °C), concentrated sulphuric acid to form alkyl hydrogensulphates, $ROSO_2OH$, which dissolve in the acid layer to form a colourless solution. Gaseous alkenes may be bubbled through the acid. This may then be hydrolysed to the alcohol by heating with water.

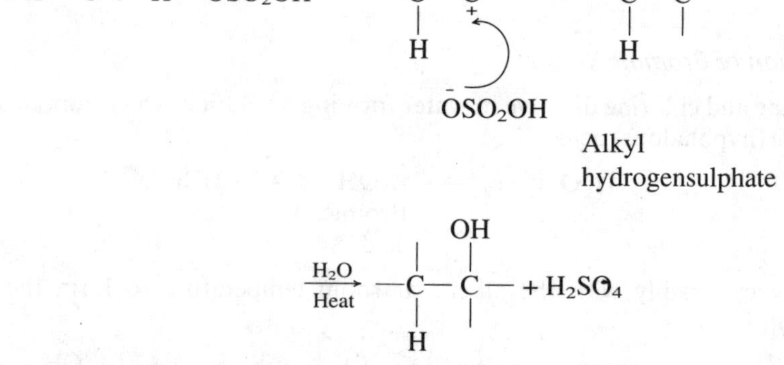

Alkyl
hydrogensulphate

$$\xrightarrow[\text{Heat}]{H_2O} \quad + H_2SO_4$$

The principles of this reaction have been utilized for many years to provide most of the world's supply of ethanol. However, this has gradually been superseded by direct hydrolysis of ethene, although the absorption–hydrolysis technique still plays an important rôle in manufacturing propan-2-ol and certain other higher alcohols. The most modern industrial preparation of ethanol uses a catalyst of phosphoric(V) acid on Celite at 300 °C and about 68–70 atmospheres pressure (*see* page 109).

Hydroxylation

An alkene (excess) readily decolorizes an alkaline solution of purple *potassium manganate(VII) (permanganate)* producing a diol (a glycol).

$$> C{=}C < \xrightarrow{\text{aq. KMnO}_4/\text{OH}^-} \begin{array}{cc} | & | \\ -C{-}{-}C- \\ | & | \\ \text{OH} & \text{OH} \end{array}$$

Diol

Oxidation can also be brought about by using aqueous sulphuric acid instead of alkali, but the reaction tends to proceed further to give some carboxylic acid. These reactions may be used as a simple qualitative test for unsaturated carbon–carbon systems.

Hydroxylation may be performed by using *osmium(VIII) oxide (osmium tetraoxide)*, OsO_4, in an ethereal solution. The reaction is completed by hydrolysis using aqueous sodium sulphite.

$$> C{=}C < \xrightarrow[\text{(2) aq. Na}_2\text{SO}_3]{\text{(1) OsO}_4/\text{(C}_2\text{H}_5)_2\text{O}} \begin{array}{cc} | & | \\ -C{-}{-}C- \\ | & | \\ \text{OH} & \text{OH} \end{array}$$

Diol

Hydroxylation by peroxoacid oxidation may be brought about by warming the alkene with *hydrogen peroxide and ethanoic (acetic) acid*,

$$> C{=}C < \xrightarrow[80\text{--}100\,°\text{C}]{\text{H}_2\text{O}_2,\text{CH}_3\text{COOH}} \begin{array}{cc} | & | \\ -C{-}{-}C- \\ | & | \\ \text{OH} & \text{OH} \end{array}$$

or by the action of *benzeneperoxocarboxylic (peroxobenzoic) acid*, C_6H_5COOOH, on the alkene, which yields the oxide, followed by high temperature hydrolysis.

$$> C{=}C < \xrightarrow{\text{C}_6\text{H}_5\text{COOOH}} \begin{array}{c} | \;\; | \\ -C{-}C- \\ \diagdown\!\diagup \\ O \end{array} \xrightarrow[160\,°\text{C}]{\text{H}_2\text{O}} \begin{array}{cc} | & | \\ -C{-}{-}C- \\ | & | \\ \text{OH} & \text{OH} \end{array}$$

Epoxyalkane (Alkene oxide)

With Trioxygen (Ozonolysis)

Trioxygen (ozone) is bubbled through a solution of the alkene in tetrachloromethane at a temperature below 20°C to form the ozonide.

$$\text{R}{-}\text{CH}{=}\text{CH}{-}\text{R}' \xrightarrow[<20\,°\text{C}]{\text{O}_3,\ \text{CCl}_4} \begin{array}{c} \text{O} \\ \diagup \quad \diagdown \\ \text{R}{-}\text{CH} \qquad \text{CH}{-}\text{R}' \\ \diagdown \qquad \diagup \\ \text{O}{-}\text{O} \end{array}$$

An ozonide

The subsequent hydrolysis of the ozonide, using zinc and ethanoic (acetic) acid, may be used in the determination of the structure of alkenes, since analysis of the products indicates the position of the double bond in a carbon chain. (Using these reagents, carboxylic acids, as opposed to aldehydes, may be produced.)

$$R-CH \underset{O-O}{\overset{O}{\diagdown\diagup}} CH-R'+H_2O \xrightarrow[\text{acid}]{\text{Zn dust/ethanoic}} RCHO + R'CHO + H_2O_2$$

$$\text{Aldehydes}$$

Addition of Alkanes

In the presence of an acid catalyst, alkanes add across alkenes to form a higher alkane.

$$>C{=}C< \ + \ RH \xrightarrow{H^+ \text{ cat.}} \underset{\underset{H \quad R}{|\quad|}}{-C-C-}$$

$$\text{Alkene} \qquad \text{Alkane} \qquad\qquad \text{Higher alkane}$$

Addition of Hydrogen

Alkenes are hydrogenated by passing them over a finely divided platinum, palladium or nickel catalyst in an atmosphere of hydrogen. Platinum and palladium function satisfactorily at ordinary temperatures and pressures, but the use of nickel as a catalyst requires heat and an elevated pressure.

$$>C{=}C< \ + \ H_2 \xrightarrow{\text{Pt, Pd or Ni cat.}} \underset{\underset{H \quad H}{|\quad|}}{-C-C-}$$

$$\text{Alkane}$$

This provides a useful method for preparing alkanes.

Polymerization

The process by which many simple molecules join together to form very large molecules is known as POLYMERIZATION. The relative molecular mass of the polymer is theoretically an integral multiple of that of the monomer.

Simple alkenes polymerize to form a family of long-chain ADDITION POLYMERS.

POLY(ETHENE) (polythene) is manufactured by various techniques, some of which are discussed in more detail on page 302.

$$nCH_2{=}CH_2 \longrightarrow \ {\sim}CH_2{-}CH_2{-}CH_2{-}CH_2{\sim}$$

$$\text{Poly(ethene)}$$

Propene polymerizes in a similar manner to form POLY(PROPENE) (polypropylene). These polymers are strong, flexible solids with a seemingly infinite number of domestic and commercial applications.

POLY(TETRAFLUOETHENE) (PTFE, Teflon, Fluon) is obtained by the polymerization of tetrafluoroethene (*see* page 304).

$$nCF_2{=}CF_2 \longrightarrow \ {\sim}CF_2{-}CF_2{-}CF_2{-}CF_2{\sim}$$

$$\text{Tetrafluoroethene} \qquad\qquad \text{PTFE, Teflon}$$

It is resistant to chemicals and possesses an extremely low coefficient of friction, which makes it particularly suitable for making non-stick cooking utensils.

Simple Tests for Unsaturation

The presence of carbon–carbon multiple bonds in compounds can be recognized by their ability to undergo addition reactions. Bromine in tetrachloromethane or in water and potassium manganate(VII) (permanganate) in acidic solution readily lose their characteristic colour in forming their respective addition products. The reaction with manganate(VII) is not by itself distinctive, since decolorization is also brought about by reducing agents, and should be carried out in conjunction with one of the other tests. If the solution is neutral or only mildly alkaline, black manganese(IV) oxide is precipitated. In strongly alkaline solution, green manganate(VI) ions, MnO_4^{2-}, are formed.

Unsaturated compounds burn with a luminous, smoky flame, but since this is also a characteristic property of aromatic systems, a chemical test should also be performed in order to distinguish between them.

Orientation of Addition to Alkenes

As ethene is symmetrical about the double bond, it is of no consequence which way round the attacking reagent adds across it.

However, in the case of propene and other unsymmetrical alkenes, two modes of addition are possible in theory.

For reactions involving *ionic addition*, the predominant products in the process illustrated below is II, indicated by reaction (1). This is in accordance with MARKOWNIKOFF'S RULE which states:

In the addition of an unsymmetrical reagent to an unsymmetrical alkene, the more electronegative atom or group becomes attached to the more highly substituted carbon atom, i.e. the carbon atom containing fewer hydrogen atoms.

The orientation of addition is determined by consideration of the relative stabilities of the intermediate carbocations (carbonium ions).

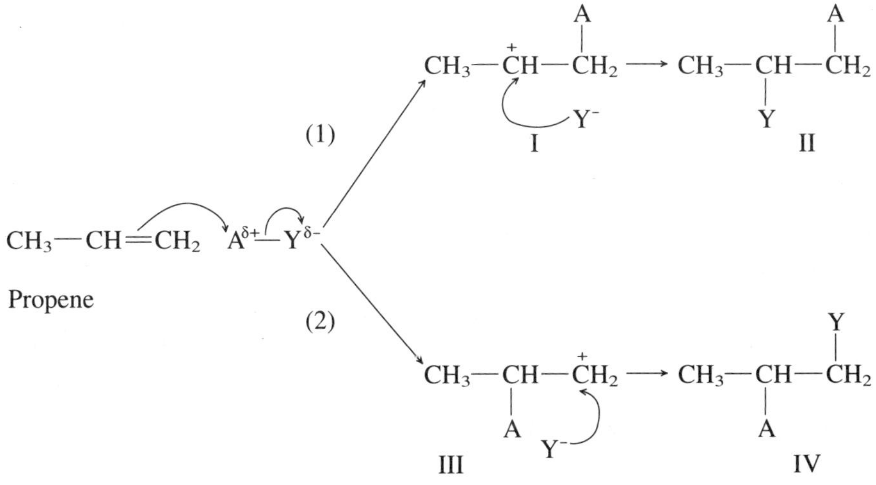

The stability of a carbocation is enhanced by its attachment to electron-donating groups. Hence, the formation of such an ion is facilitated by the presence of electron-donating alkyl groups which exert this property by inductive effects. Generally, the greater the number of alkyl groups present, the more stable is the carbocation intermediate and ultimately the resultant alkene. The attachment of a benzene ring also exerts a similar effect owing to its own great stability.

Consider the addition of HX to 2-methylpropene:

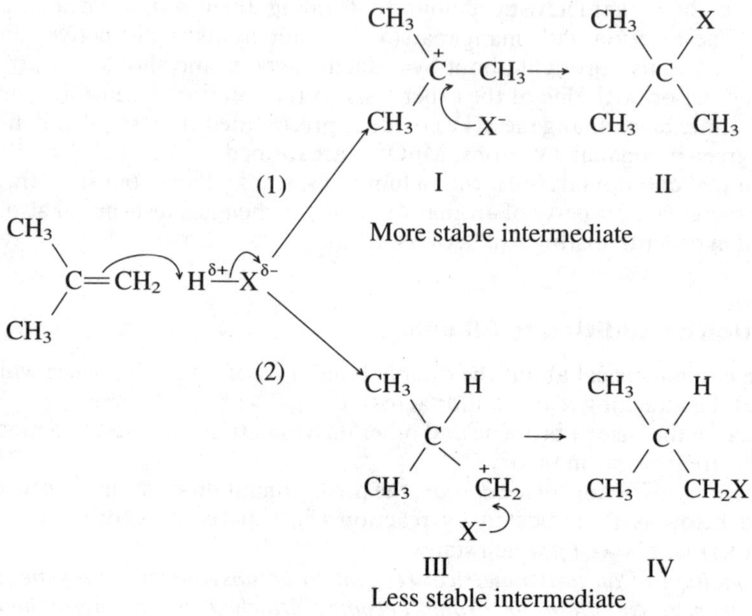

(1)

I

More stable intermediate

(2)

III   IV

Less stable intermediate

The intermediate carbocation I is stabilized by three electron-donating methyl groups whereas III is stabilized by the inductive effects of only two methyl groups.

For simple alkenes of the type $CH_3CH=CH_2$, Markownikoff's rule may read: IN THE ADDITION OF AN UNSYMMETRICAL REAGENT ACROSS THE DOUBLE BOND OF AN UNSYMMETRICAL ALKENE, THE HYDROGEN ATOM (PROTON), OR THE MORE ELECTROPOSITIVE ATOM OR GROUP, BECOMES ATTACHED TO THE CARBON ATOM OF THE DOUBLE BOND POSSESSING THE GREATER NUMBER OF HYDROGEN ATOMS.

Stability of Alkenes

The stabilizing effects of alkyl and other electron-donating groups are illustrated by the study of the kinetics of various addition reactions. The more highly alkylated alkenes undergo addition at a greater rate than their less highly substituted counterparts.

The relative rates at which alkylated alkenes undergo addition decreases in the order:

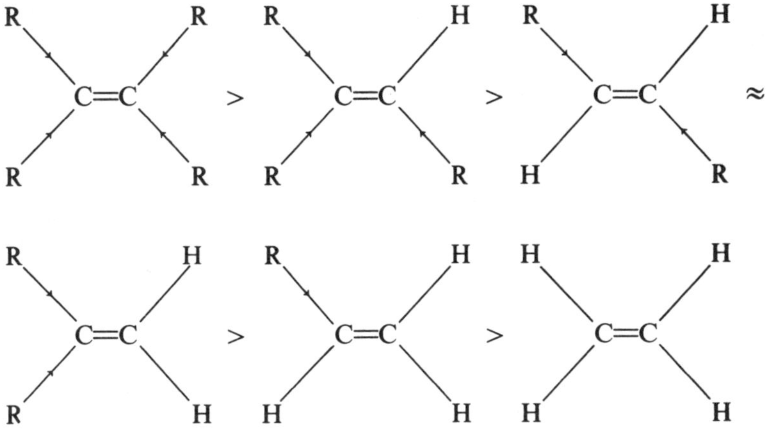

In certain circumstances, the anti-Markownikoff product may be obtained. This is usually a result of one or more of the following three factors:

(1) the presence of strong electron-withdrawing substituents, such as fluorine, in the alkene;

(2) steric hindrance preventing the completion of the reaction by the attachment of a larger, more electronegative species at a highly substituted carbon atom;

(3) addition may take place via a free-radical mechanism, particularly when organic peroxides, e.g. di(benzenecarbonyl)peroxide (di(benzoyl)peroxide), are present, or when the reaction is carried out at high temperatures.

For example, if propene is reacted with hydrogen bromide in the presence of di(benzenecarbonyl)peroxide, the anti-Markownikoff product is formed.

$$CH_3CH{=}CH_2 + HBr \longrightarrow CH_3CH_2CH_2Br$$

Propene

1-Bromopropane
Anti-Markownikoff product

The Rôle of Simple Alkenes in the Petrochemical and Natural Gas Industries

The abundant supply of simple alkenes from petroleum and natural gas makes them one of the most important starting reagents for large scale industrial processes.

ETHANOL is manufactured nowadays mainly by the direct hydrolysis of ethene. This involves passing a stream of ethene and water vapour over a phosphoric(V) acid on Celite catalyst at a temperature of 300 °C and 68–70 atmospheres pressure.

$$CH_2{=}CH_2 + H_2O \xrightarrow[\text{cat., 300 °C, 68-70 atm}]{\text{phosphoric(V) acid on Celite}} \underset{\underset{\text{H} \quad \text{OH}}{|\qquad|}}{CH_2{-}CH_2}$$

Ethanol

Some is still obtained by absorbing ethene in concentrated sulphuric acid 80°C and 25–30 atmospheres and then hydrolysing the ethyl sulphate with an equal volume of warm water, although this technique is gradually becoming out-moded and will eventually become obsolete.

Ordinary commercial alcohol is a constant-boiling mixture of alcohol (95.6 per cent by mass) and water (4.4 per cent), which boils at 78.2 °C (pure ethanol has a boiling point of 78.3 °C).

PROPAN-2-OL (isopropyl alcohol) is generally prepared by absorbing pro-pene in about 75–85 per cent concentrated sulphuric acid at 20–30 °C and 20–30 atmospheres, and then hydrolysing. Although it undergoes direct hydrolysis more easily than ethene, the process is accompanied by a certain amount of polymerization which can cause quite serious problems.

$$CH_3CH=CH_2 + H_2SO_4 \xrightarrow[\text{20–30 atm}]{\text{20–30 °C}} CH_3CH-CH_3$$

75–85
per cent

$$OSO_2OH$$

$$\xrightarrow[\text{35–40 °C}]{\text{H}_2\text{O}} CH_3-CH-CH_3 + H_2SO_4$$

OH
Propan-2-ol

A useful by-product of this reaction is 2,4-dimethylpentan-3-ol (diisopropyl alcohol) which has an octane rating of 98. Propan-2-ol is used in the manufacture of propanone (acetone) (*see* page 224).

Other important uses of propene include the manufacture of epoxypropane (propene oxide), butanols, phenol, 1-chloroprop-2-ene (allyl chloride), pro-penenitrile (acrylonitrile) (*see* page 309), and both high and low relative molecular mass polymers (*see* page 303).

1,2-DICHLOROETHANE (ethylene dichloride) is a colourless liquid (b.p. 83.8 °C), and is manufactured by either the liquid or vapour phase interaction of ethene and chlorine. In the liquid phase reaction, a concentrated stream of ethene is required and is reacted with the chlorine in a 1,2-dichloroethane or 1,2-dibromoethane (ethylene dibromide) solvent in the presence of a metal chloride catalyst at 50 °C and under a *slight* pressure.

$$CH_2=CH_2 + Cl_2 \xrightarrow[\substack{\text{CH}_2\text{Cl.CH}_2\text{Cl solvent,} \\ \text{50 °C, slight press.}}]{\text{metal chloride cat.}} CH_2-CH_2$$

Cl   Cl

1,2-Dichloroethane

The vapour phase reaction utilizes a lower concentration of ethene and the catalyst comprises a metal chloride on an inert support.

It is an excellent extracting solvent, and is used as a solvent in the manufacture of poly(chloroethene) (polyvinyl chloride, PVC). Certain 'anti-knock' com-pounds contain about 9 per cent 1,2-dichloroethane.

EPOXYETHANE (ethylene oxide) is a volatile, colourless, low boiling point (11 °C) liquid and is usually prepared by direct combination of fairly pure ethene and oxygen (from the air) at 300 °C in the presence of a silver catalyst.

$$CH_2{=}CH_2 \xrightarrow[\text{silver cat. 300 °C}]{[O]} \underset{\underset{\displaystyle O}{\diagdown\diagup}}{CH_2{-}CH_2}$$

Epoxyethane
(Ethylene oxide)

It is also formed as an intermediate compound in the preparation of ethane-1,2-diol ('glycol').

Alcoholysis of epoxyethane produces a series of monoalkyl ethers which are known by the trade name of *Cellosolve*.

$$\underset{\underset{\displaystyle O}{\diagdown\diagup}}{CH_2{-}CH_2} + CH_3OH \xrightarrow[\text{cat.}]{H_2SO_4} \underset{\underset{\displaystyle OH \quad OCH_3}{|\qquad|}}{CH_2{-}CH_2}$$

Methanol   Methyl Cellosolve

These compounds provide useful solvents for varnishes and lacquers.

Epoxyethane dimerizes in the presence of an acid catalyst to form *Dioxan*, which is a useful organic solvent and has the advantage that it is also miscible with water.

$$2\ \underset{\underset{\displaystyle O}{\diagdown\diagup}}{CH_2{-}CH_2} \xrightarrow{H^+ \text{ catalyst}} \begin{array}{c} CH_2{-}CH_2 \\ \diagup \qquad\qquad \diagdown \\ O \qquad\qquad\qquad O \\ \diagdown \qquad\qquad \diagup \\ CH_2{-}CH_2 \end{array}$$

Dioxan

ETHANE-1,2-DIOL (ethylene glycol, 'glycol') was prepared originally by the hydrolysis of 1,2-dichloroethane, but nowadays it is best manufactured by treating 2-chloroethanol (ethylene chlorohydrin) with sodalime to form epoxyethane and then hydrolysing with steam and dilute hydrochloric acid.

$$\underset{\underset{\displaystyle OH \quad Cl}{|\qquad|}}{CH_2{-}CH_2} \xrightarrow{\text{sodalime}} \underset{\underset{\displaystyle O}{\diagdown\diagup}}{CH_2{-}CH_2} \xrightarrow[\text{dil. HCl}]{\text{steam}} \underset{\underset{\displaystyle OH \quad OH}{|\qquad|}}{CH_2{-}CH_2}$$

2-Chloroethanol
(Ethylene
chlorohydrin)

Alternatively, the 2-chloroethanol may be hydrolysed directly by boiling with sodium carbonate solution.

$$\underset{\underset{\displaystyle OH \quad Cl}{|\qquad|}}{CH_2{-}CH_2} \xrightarrow[\text{solution}]{Na_2CO_3} \underset{\underset{\displaystyle OH \quad OH}{|\qquad|}}{CH_2{-}CH_2}$$

Ethane-1,2-diol

Ethane-1,2-diol is a colourless, viscous liquid (f.p. $-13\,°C$, b.p. $197\,°C$) and is used as an antifreeze agent. An aqueous mixture containing 60 per cent ethane-1,2-diol freezes at $-40\,°C$. One of its main industrial uses is in the manufacture of Terylene (*see* page 310).

CHLOROETHENE (vinyl chloride), $CH_2{=}CHCl$, is an unreactive gaseous compound which is probably best considered as an addition product of ethyne (*see* page 117), although it can be obtained by heating 1,2-dichloroethane at $500\,°C$.

$$CH_2Cl.CH_2Cl \xrightarrow{\text{Heat, } 500\,°C} CH_2{=}CHCl + HCl$$

In the presence of a peroxide initiator, it polymerizes into POLY(CHLOROETHENE) (polyvinyl chloride, PVC) which is a plastic with widespread uses in industry. This process is dealt with in Chapter 12, and also in more detail in Chapter 26, 'Polymers'.

Other important uses of ethene include the manufacture of poly(ethene) (*see* page 302), phenylethene (styrene) and thence poly(phenylethene) (polystyrene) (*see* page 304).

QUESTIONS

1. Give the IUPAC name for:

A $CH_3C{=}CHCH_2CHCH_3$
$\quad\quad |\quad\quad\quad\quad\quad |$
$\quad\quad CH_3\quad\quad\quad CH_3$

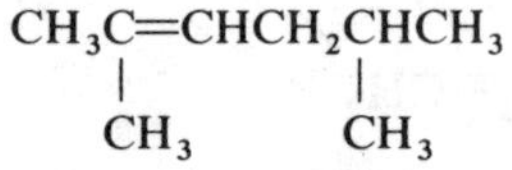

B
$$CH_3{\searrow}\quad\quad{\swarrow}CH_3$$
$$C{=}C$$
$$\quad{\swarrow}\quad\quad{\searrow}$$
$$H\quad\quad\quad H$$

C $CH_3CCH{=}CH_2$
$\quad\quad |\ (Cl)$
$\quad\quad CH_3$

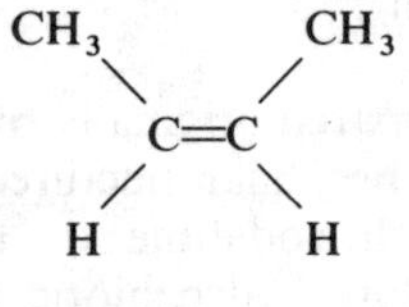

with Cl above the central C.

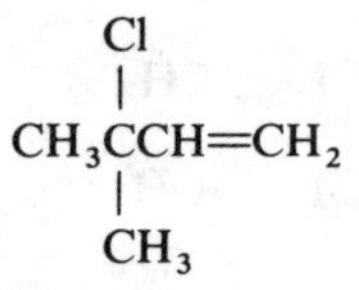

D
$$CH_3CH_2{\searrow}\quad\quad{\swarrow}H$$
$$C{=}C$$
$$\quad{\swarrow}\quad\quad{\searrow}$$
$$H\quad\quad\quad CH_2CH_2Cl$$

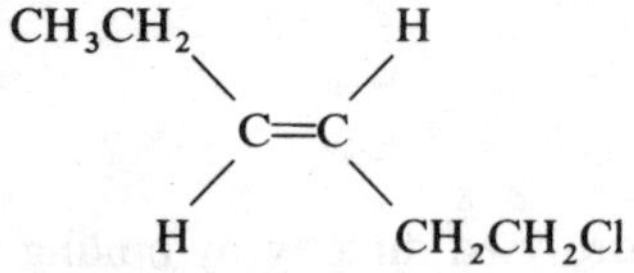

2. Give the structural formula for:

A 4-bromopent-1-ene
B 3-ethylpent-1-ene
C 2,2-dimethylhex-3-ene
D *trans*-2-methylhept-3-ene

3. Which one of the following reagents does *not* undergo a reaction with ethene?

A acidified potassium manganate(VII)
B hydrogen bromide
C aqueous ammonia
D bromine in tetrachloromethane
E hydrogen chloride

4. An organic compound, C_6H_{12}, on ozonolysis and subsequent treatment with zinc dust and ethanoic acid, gave two different products, one of which was identified as propanone.

Which one of the following structures best represents this organic compound?

A $CH_3CH_2CH{=}C(CH_3)_2$
B $(CH_3)_2C{=}C(CH_3)_2$
C $CH_3CH{=}C(CH_3)CH_2CH_3$
D $CH_2{=}CHCH(CH_3)CH_2CH_3$
E $CH_2{=}CHCH_2CH(CH_3)_2$

5. In which one of the following properties will *cis*-hex-3-ene *not* differ from *trans*-hex-3-ene?

A boiling point
B melting point
C dipole moment
D product of hydrogenation
E infra-red spectrum

6. Give the structural formula and IUPAC name of the product of each of the following reactions.

A $CH_3CH{=}CH_2 + HI \longrightarrow$

B $(CH_3)_2C{=}CH_2 + HCl \xrightarrow{\text{peroxide init.}}$

C $(CH_3)_2C{=}CH_2 + HBr \longrightarrow$

D

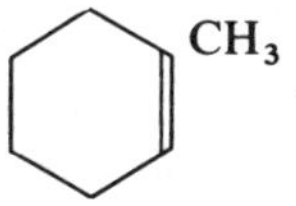

$+ HBr \longrightarrow$

7. Write the mechanism for the addition of the following reagents to propene and name the products.

A chlorine in tetrachloromethane
B chlorine water
C bromine water

8. Briefly discuss the rôle of ethene and propene in the petrochemical and natural gas industries.

12 Alkynes (Acetylenes)

The alkynes form a homologous series of unsaturated hydrocarbons containing a carbon–carbon triple bond and corresponding to a general molecular formula, C_nH_{2n-2}.

The unsaturated carbon atoms are *sp* hybridized and attached to each other by a σ bond and two π bonds. The σ bond results from the overlapping of two hybrid orbitals, and the two π bonds are formed from the separate overlapping of the two *p* orbitals from the two adjacent carbon atoms. The π bonds lie in two different planes at right angles to each other (*see* page 20).

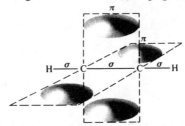

Fig. 12.1 The ethyne (acetylene) molecule

The other *sp* hybrid orbital of each of the unsaturated carbon atoms forms a σ bond with another carbon or hydrogen atom. The simplest molecule, ETHYNE (acetylene), is linear, allowing the hybrid orbitals to be as far apart as possible.

The availability of π electrons in the multiple bonds makes them prone to addition reactions, which, like those of the alkenes, characterize the reactions of the alkynes.

Nomenclature

The IUPAC names of alkynes are afforded by taking the stem of the name of the corresponding alkane and replacing the ending '-ane' of the alkane with the suffix '-yne'. The position of the triple bond is indicated by inserting the appropriate number between the stem and the ending.

Formula	IUPAC name	Common name
$CH{\equiv}CH$	Ethyne	Acetylene
$CH_3C{\equiv}CH$	Propyne	Methylacetylene
$\overset{4}{C}H_3\overset{3}{C}H_2\overset{2}{C}{\equiv}\overset{1}{C}H$	But-1-yne	Ethylacetylene
$\overset{4}{C}H_3\overset{3}{C}{\equiv}\overset{2}{C}\overset{1}{C}H_3$	But-2-yne	Dimethylacetylene
$\overset{5}{C}H_3\overset{4}{C}H_2\overset{3}{C}H\overset{2}{C}{\equiv}\overset{1}{C}H$ $\quad\quad\;\;\vert$ $\quad\quad\;C_6H_5$	3-Phenylpent-1-yne	—

Physical Properties

Name	Formula	State at 20°C
Ethyne	$CH{\equiv}CH$	Gas
Propyne	$CH{\equiv}CCH_3$	Gas
But-1-yne	$CH{\equiv}CCH_2CH_3$	Gas
Pent-1-yne	$CH{\equiv}C(CH_2)_2CH_3$	Liquid
Hex-1-yne	$CH{\equiv}C(CH_2)_3CH_3$	Liquid
Hept-1-yne	$CH{\equiv}C(CH_2)_4CH_3$	Liquid
Oct-1-yne	$CH{\equiv}C(CH_2)_5CH_3$	Liquid

Boiling points increase with increasing relative molecular mass but, as for the previous series, symmetry in a molecule contributes to its stability and causes a slight elevation in boiling point. Conversely, branching enhances the volatility.

The alkynes are virtually insoluble in water but soluble in the usual non-polar organic solvents.

Industrial Source

By far the most important and useful alkyne is ETHYNE (acetylene), which is nowadays manufactured primarily from natural gas and higher alkanes obtained from petroleum.

In the SACHSE or BASF (Badische Anilin und Soda Fabrik) PROCESS the heat evolved by the highly exothermic partial combustion of methane in air, or preferably oxygen, using special burners, is used to elevate the reaction temperature for the cracking of further quantities of gas to the optimum 1500 °C.

$$CH_4 + O_2 \longrightarrow CO_2 + 2H_2 \qquad \text{Exothermic}$$
$$2CH_4 + 3O_2 \longrightarrow 2CO + 4H_2O \qquad \text{Exothermic}$$
$$2CH_4 \xrightarrow{1500\,°C} CH{\equiv}CH + 3H_2$$

Ethyne

The resulting gases, which contain about 8 per cent ethyne, are cooled rapidly by injecting water. The ethyne is dissolved in a selective solvent, methylpyrrolidone, under pressure. (Water was originally used for this purpose.)

A further development of this technique is the SBA–KELLOGG PROCESS which uses specially modified burners and employs liquid ammonia as the selective solvent for the gas.

In the WULFF PROCESS the alkanes are cracked at 900–1300 °C in regenerative furnaces, each containing refractory tiles and arranged in pairs to allow the process to operate continuously, using steam as a diluent.

An alternative technique is the HULS PROCESS which involves heating methane or natural gas to 1500–1600 °C in an electric arc and then suddenly cooling by quenching with water sprays.

$$2CH_4 \xrightarrow[\text{electric arc}]{1500\,°C} CH{\equiv}CH + 3H_2$$

At one time, virtually all ethyne was manufactured by treating calcium dicarbide with water. The calcium dicarbide was obtained by reducing quicklime, obtained from limestone, with coke in an electric furnace at 2000–3000 °C. This technique is now obsolete owing to high electrical costs involved in maintaining the high temperatures in the furnace.

$$CaCO_3 \xrightarrow{\quad heat \quad} CaO \qquad + CO_2$$
Calcium carbonate   Calcium oxide
(Limestone)   (Quicklime)

$$CaO + 3C \xrightarrow{\quad 2000-3000\,°C \quad} CaC_2 \quad + CO$$

Calcium
dicarbide

$$CaC_2 + 2H_2O \xrightarrow{\hspace{3cm}} CH{\equiv}CH + Ca(OH)_2$$

Ethyne

This reaction still provides a simple and convenient laboratory preparation of ethyne, although it is generally found necessary to employ a dilute acid instead of water.

Synthetic Preparations

As in the preparation of compounds containing carbon–carbon double bonds, reactions requiring the formation of triple bonds invariably involve the elimination of atoms or groups from adjacent carbon atoms.

$$-\underset{|}{\overset{|}{C}}-\underset{|}{\overset{|}{C}}- \longrightarrow -\overset{|}{C}{=}\overset{|}{C}- \longrightarrow -C{\equiv}C-$$

Ethyne may be prepared by boiling 1,2-dibromoethane (ethylene dibromide) with an alcoholic solution of potassium hydroxide.

$$\underset{\underset{Br}{|}}{CH_2}-\underset{\underset{Br}{|}}{CH_2} + 2KOH \xrightarrow{\quad alcohol \quad} CH{\equiv}CH + 2KBr + 2H_2O$$

The action of dilute acid upon calcium dicarbide is often employed, but the product sometimes contains small amounts of phosphine, arsine and hydrogen sulphide impurities if commercial dicarbide is used. These impurities can be removed by bubbling the gas through an acidified solution of copper(II) sulphate before collecting.

Reactions

The availability of π electrons in the multiple bonds makes the alkynes, like the alkenes, vulnerable to characteristic addition reactions. In certain reactions they tend to be more reactive than the alkenes, notably when undergoing NUCLEOPHILIC ADDITIONS, which are virtually unknown for the alkenes; but in others they tend to be less reactive, notably when undergoing ELECTROPHILIC ADDITIONS. Addition of halogens, X_2, and hydrogen halides, HX, upon alkynes is initiated by electrophilic attack whereas the addition of hydrogen cyanide, HCN, is initiated by nucleophilic attack.

For the addition of unsymmetrical reagents across unsymmetrical alkynes, MARKOWNIKOFF'S RULE applies in a similar way as it does for alkenes, although light or peroxide catalysed reactions again tend to result in the formation of the ANTI-MARKOWNIKOFF product.

Alkynes can undergo DOUBLE ADDITION involving two molecules of the attacking reagent which add on successively across the triple and then the double bond.

$$-C\equiv C- \xrightarrow{YZ} \underset{\underset{Z}{|}}{\overset{\overset{Y}{|}}{-C}}=\underset{\underset{Z}{|}}{\overset{\overset{Z}{|}}{C}}- \xrightarrow{YZ} \underset{\underset{Y}{|}}{\overset{\overset{Y}{|}}{-C}}-\underset{\underset{Z}{|}}{\overset{\overset{Z}{|}}{C}}-$$

In many reactions the intermediate alkene product can be isolated and polymerized to form several products such as poly(chloroethene) (polyvinyl chloride, PVC), poly(ethenyl ethanoate) (polyvinyl acetate, PVA) etc.

Addition of Hydrogen

Ethyne, when heated with hydrogen in the presence of a finely divided Pt, Pd or Ni catalyst is reduced to ethane, the reaction being too difficult to stop in order to isolate ethene. Pt and Pd operate at ordinary temperatures, but nickel requires heating (125 °C–250 °C).

$$CH\equiv CH + H_2 \xrightarrow[\text{catalyst}]{\text{Pt, Pd or Ni}} \underset{\text{Ethene}}{CH_2{=}CH_2} \xrightarrow{+H_2} \underset{\text{Ethane}}{CH_3{-}CH_3}$$

In the reduction of certain higher alkynes, the intermediate alkene can be isolated using a poisoned catalyst (a Lindlar catalyst). e.g. $Pd/CaCO_3$ plus quinoline.

Addition of Halogens

Chlorine and bromine give addition products with ethyne in the presence of a metallic halide or kieselguhr (silicon(IV)oxide) catalyst at ordinary temperatures, the reaction taking place via an electrophilic addition mechanism.

$$CH\equiv CH + X_2 \xrightarrow[\text{catalyst}]{\text{metallic halide}} \underset{\underset{\underset{\text{dihalide)}}{\text{(Acetylene}}}{\text{1,2-Dihaloethene}}}{\overset{\overset{X\ \ X}{|\ \ \ |}}{CH{=}CH}} \xrightarrow{+X_2} \underset{\underset{\underset{\text{tetrahalide)}}{\text{(Acetylene}}}{\text{1,1,2,2-Tetrahaloethane}}}{\overset{\overset{X\ \ X}{|\ \ \ |}}{\underset{\underset{X\ \ X}{|\ \ \ |}}{CH{-}CH}}}$$

Under controlled conditions, the intermediate dihalide can be isolated without difficulty.

In the absence of a catalyst, chlorine reacts explosively with ethyne yielding hydrogen chloride and carbon.

$$CH\equiv CH + Cl_2 \longrightarrow 2HCl + 2C$$

Addition of Hydrogen Halides

Alkynes undergo addition of hydrogen halides in the presence of light or a metallic halide catalyst, e.g. $HgCl_2$ or $CuCl$, either in the gaseous phase or in solution (e.g. in benzene).

$$CH{\equiv}CH + HX \xrightarrow[\substack{\text{metallic halide} \\ \text{catalyst}}]{\text{u.v. light or}} \underset{\substack{| \quad | \\ H \quad X}}{CH{=}CH} \xrightarrow{+HX} \underset{\substack{| \quad | \\ H \quad X}}{\overset{\substack{H \quad X \\ | \quad |}}{CH{-}CH}}$$

Haloethene   1,1-Dihaloethane
(Vinyl halide)   (Ethylidene dihalide)

Rate of reaction: $HI > HBr > HCl$

HALOETHENES (vinyl halides) can be isolated and polymerized. Haloethenes are peculiarly unreactive, especially when compared with the highly reactive haloalkanes (*see* page 153).

Addition of Water

Ethyne can be hydrated by bubbling the gas through dilute sulphuric acid at 60 °C in the presence of a mercury(II) sulphate catalyst. The reaction is initiated by *nucleophilic* attack.

$$CH{\equiv}CH \xrightarrow[\substack{HgSO_4 \text{ catalyst} \\ 60\,°C}]{\text{dil. } H_2SO_4,} \underset{\substack{| \quad | \\ H \quad OH}}{CH{=}CH} \underset{\xleftarrow{\hspace{1cm}}}{\xrightarrow{\text{rearranges}}} \overset{\displaystyle CH_3}{\underset{\displaystyle H}{\diagdown C{=}O \diagup}}$$

Ethenol   Ethanal
(Vinyl alcohol)   (Acetaldehyde)

Ethenol (vinyl alcohol) is an ENOL which is far too unstable to be isolated, but exists in dynamic equilibrium with the ethanal (acetaldehyde), the equilibrium lying very much towards the right-hand side. This phenomenon where *a pair of isomers are in dynamic equilibrium with each other* is termed TAUTOMERISM. In cases where the migration of a hydrogen atom is concerned, which is the most commonly encountered form, it is referred to as PROTOTROPY or PROTOTROPIC ISOMERISM.

Addition of Hydrogen Cyanide

The addition of hydrogen cyanide to ethyne takes place under pressure and in the presence of a barium cyanide catalyst. The reaction is initiated by *nucleophilic* attack.

$$CH{\equiv}CH + HCN \xrightarrow[\text{catalyst}]{Ba(CN)_2} \underset{\substack{| \quad | \\ H^+ \quad CN}}{\overline{C}H{=}CH} \longrightarrow \underset{\substack{| \quad | \\ H \quad CN}}{CH{=}CH}$$

Propenonitrile
(Acrylonitrile or
vinyl cyanide)

Dimerization of Ethyne

Ethyne dimerizes in a solution of copper(I) chloride and ammonium chloride in hydrochloric acid.

$$CH{\equiv}CH + CH{\equiv}CH \xrightarrow[\text{in HCl}]{\text{CuCl, NH}_4\text{Cl}} CH_2{=}CHC{\equiv}CH$$

1-Buten-3-yne
(Vinyl acetylene)

2-Chlorobuta-1,3-diene (chloroprene), $CH_2{=}CHCCl{=}CH_2$, can be prepared by treating 1-buten-3-yne with HCl and polymerized into a poly(2-chlorobuta-1,3-diene) (*neoprene* rubber) (*see* page 301).

Addition of Methanal (Formaldehyde)

Addition of methanal (formaldehyde) takes place under high pressure and in the presence of a copper(I) dicarbide catalyst. Hydrogenation, followed by dehydration, results in the formation of BUTA-1,3-DIENE, which is an important reagent in the preparation of synthetic rubbers (*see* page 301).

$$CH{\equiv}CH + 2HCHO \xrightarrow[\text{high pressure}]{\text{Cu}_2\text{C}_2 \text{ catalyst}} HOCH_2C{\equiv}C\,CH_2OH$$

Methanal
(Formaldehyde)

Butyne-1,4,-diol

$$\downarrow \text{H}_2 \quad \text{Pt catalyst}$$

$$CH_2{=}CHCH{=}CH_2 \xleftarrow[-2\text{H}_2\text{O}]{\text{Al}_2\text{O}_3, 270\,^\circ\text{C}} HOCH_2CH_2CH_2CH_2OH$$

Buta-1,3-diene

Butane-1,4-diol

Polymerization of Ethyne

Ethyne polymerizes to benzene when passed through a heated tube containing a complex organo-nickel catalyst.

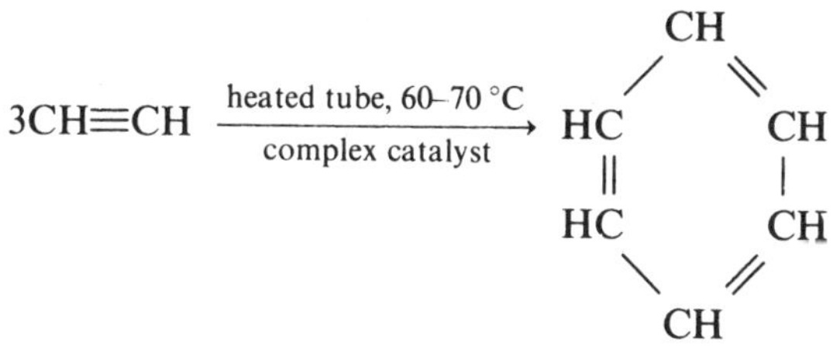

$$3CH{\equiv}CH \xrightarrow[\text{complex catalyst}]{\text{heated tube, 60–70 }^\circ\text{C}}$$

Benzene

Substitution Reactions

Formation of Heavy Metal Dicarbides (Acetylides)

Alkynes which have the triple bond at the end of the chain (*terminal alkynes*) react with the Cu^+ ions in an aqueous ammoniacal solution of copper(I) chloride and the Ag^+ ions in a solution of $AgNO_3$ to form the insoluble heavy metal dicarbides (acetylides). These reactions take place at room temperature.

$$CH\equiv CH + 2Cu^+ \xrightarrow{NH_3 \cdot H_2O} CuC\equiv CCu \qquad + 2H^+$$

Copper(I) dicarbide
(Copper(I) acetylide)
red precipitate

$$CH\equiv CH + 2Ag^+ \longrightarrow AgC\equiv CAg \qquad + 2H^+$$

Silver(I) dicarbide
(Silver(I) acetylide)
white precipitate

Alkynes of the type $RC\equiv CR$ do not react and therefore these reactions can be used *to test for the terminal triple bond.*
These heavy metal dicarbides are dangerously sensitive explosives.

Formation of Ethenylsodium (*Sodium Acetylide*)

Ethyne reacts with sodium in liquid ammonia to form ethenylsodium (sodium acetylide),

$$2CH\equiv CH + 2Na \xrightarrow{\cdot \text{liquid } NH_3} 2CH\equiv CNa \qquad + H_2$$

Ethenylsodium
(Sodium acetylide)

which can be used to synthesize the higher methyl homologue by reacting it with iodomethane.

$$CH\equiv CNa + CH_3I \longrightarrow CH\equiv CCH_3 \qquad + NaI$$

Propyne
(Methylacetylene)

Simple Tests for Unsaturation in Alkynes

Unsaturation in alkynes can be detected by employing the same simple tests as used for alkenes, i.e. decolorization of bromine and potassium manganate(VII) (permanganate) solutions, although in this case the reactions proceed rather more slowly.

Ethenylation (Vinylation) Reactions in the Plastics and Synthetic Fibres Industry

Monosubstituted ethenes (vinyl compounds) are very important monomers that can be easily polymerized into plastics and synthetic fibres, which have innumerable practical applications.

COPOLYMERS can be formed by mixing two or more unsaturated monomers and allowing them to react together and, thus, in certain cases, allowing the beneficial properties of the polymers of the individual monomers to be utilized, e.g. Vinyon.

These reactions and the nature of the products are discussed in Chapter 26, 'Polymers' (*see* page 297).

QUESTIONS

1. Give the IUPAC name for:

   A $CH \equiv CCH_2CH_2Cl$

   B $CH_3CH_2CHC \equiv CCH_3$
   $\qquad \quad |$
   $\qquad \quad CH_3$

   C $CH_3C \equiv CCH_2CHC \equiv CH$
   $\qquad \qquad \qquad \quad |$
   $\qquad \qquad \qquad \quad CH_3$

   D $CH_3CH_2CHC \equiv CH$
   $\qquad \quad |$
   $\qquad \quad CH_2CH_3$

2. Which of the following compounds will form a white precipitate with an aqueous solution of silver(I) nitrate?

   A $CH_2 = CHCH_2CH_3$
   B $CH \equiv CH_2CH_2CH_3$
   C $CH_3CH = CHCH_3$
   D $CH_3C \equiv CCH_3$
   E $CH_2 = CHCH = CH_2$

3. Propyne, $CH_3C \equiv CH$, gives a completely different reaction to propene, $CH_3CH = CH_2$, with which one of the following.

   A ammoniacal copper(I) chloride
   B acidified potassium manganate(VII)
   C alkaline potassium manganate(VII)
   D bromine water
   E hydrogen halides

4. Give equations to show how ethyne could be converted into

   A butane-1,4-diol
   B 2-chlorobuta-1,3-diene (chloroprene)
   C ethanal (acetaldehyde)
   D propyne

13 Aromaticity and Benzene

It is convenient to classify organic compounds according to one of two general classes: ALIPHATIC ('fatty') compounds and AROMATIC ('fragrant') compounds. The literal meaning of these terms have little or no significance nowadays, as compounds are categorized much more precisely by consideration of their molecular structure and properties.

Aliphatic compounds are those possessing open chains of carbon atoms or, alternatively, cyclic compounds whose structure and properties resemble such open-chain compounds.

Aromatic compounds are those possessing the ring structure of benzene or other molecular structures that resemble benzene in electronic configuration and chemical behaviour. There are many compounds that, at first appearance, bear little resemblance to benzene, but have a basic similarity in electronic configuration.

However, at this stage, it is convenient to interpret aromatic character in terms of the benzene ring structure, since this definition incorporates most of the commonly encountered aromatic substances.

Historical Development of the Structure of the Benzene Molecule

The tetravalency of carbon was first recognized by Kekulé in 1858, and numerous attempts at formulating the structure of the benzene molecule have since been made. The comparatively large carbon content of aromatic compounds made the structures difficult to formulate, and early attempts produced unacceptable linear structures such as those shown below:

$$CH_3-C\equiv C-C\equiv C-CH_3$$

$$CH_2=CH-C\equiv C-CH=CH_2$$

$$H-C\equiv C-\underset{\underset{H}{|}}{\overset{\overset{H}{|}}{C}}-\underset{\underset{H}{|}}{\overset{\overset{H}{|}}{C}}-C\equiv C-H$$

Such compounds would be expected to readily undergo addition reactions across the unsaturated bonds, whereas benzene shows little tendency to undergo this type of reaction. Furthermore, a linear molecule of this type would be expected to have several isomers, but benzene in fact has no isomers.

The realization that there were no structural isomers of the monosubstituted derivative, C_6H_5Y, implied the possible existence of a cyclic arrangement of carbon atoms, with all atoms being equivalent.

The fact that three structural isomers of disubstituted derivatives of benzene had been detected provided further evidence in favour of a cyclic structure.

In 1865 Kekulé produced the first reasonably acceptable cyclic structure for benzene:

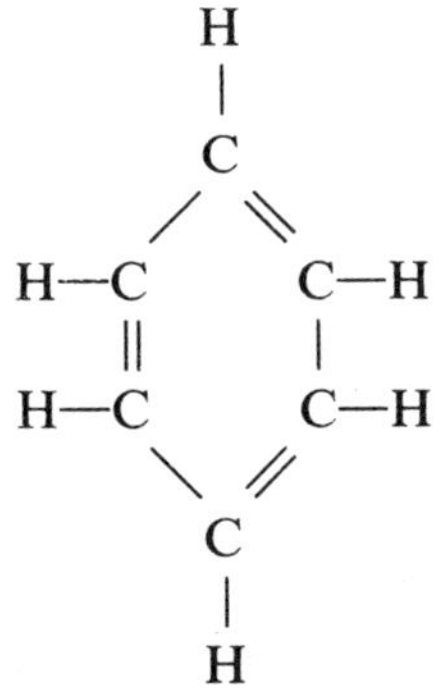

which is more conveniently written as:

Ladenberg immediately pointed out that such a structure would mean that four and not three disubstituted derivatives would exist, since it would be possible for the two Y atoms to be attached to adjacent carbon atoms joined by a single bond (as in I) or, alternatively, to two carbons joined by a double bond (as in II).

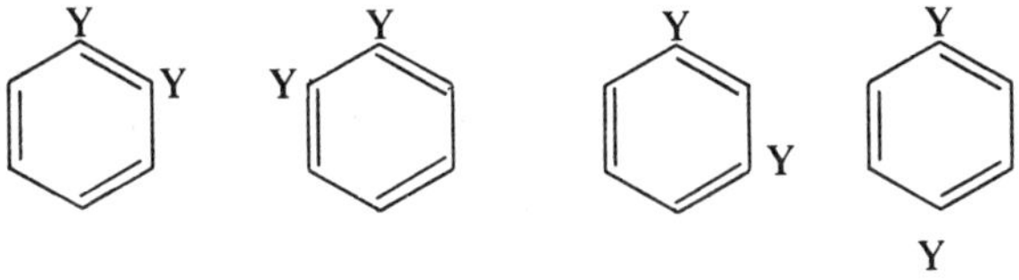

I	II	III	IV

In order to overcome this slight discrepancy, Victor Meyer (1870) suggested that the difference between I and II was only slight and undetectable.

Kekulé supported this, and modified his structure by proposing that benzene rapidly alternated between two structures,

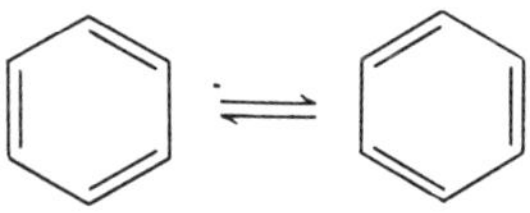

which meant that the disubstituted derivatives, shown in I and II, would be in dynamic equilibrium with each other and hence could not be separated. However, even accepting this reasoning, the theory still failed to account for the fact that benzene does not easily undergo addition reactions, as do the alkenes.

In an attempt to account for the equivalence of the carbon–carbon bonds in benzene, Armstrong (1887) forwarded a theory which disposed of the idea of double bonds altogether, and then Thiele (1889) proposed a '1$\frac{1}{2}$ bond' system between carbon atoms. Unfortunately, neither of these theories was wholly satisfactory, and the Kekulé structures were retained as being generally the most practicable concept. Yet despite its obvious limitations, the Kekulé idea of rapidly alternating structures was still used by chemists as late as 1945. Round about this time the advent of RESONANCE THEORY allowed these simple structures to be utilized in a modified context.

Resonance Theory

One simple structural diagram cannot always adequately represent the distribution of electrons within a molecule. Instead it is necessary to represent the molecule by various alternative structures, with the true structure lying somewhere between the extremes. The true structure is referred to as a RESONANCE HYBRID of all these structures and is not correctly represented by any one of them.

The different molecular structures contributing to the resonance hybrid are referred to as the various CANONICAL FORMS of the molecule, each of which must contain the same number of unpaired electrons.

The relative contribution of each canonical form to each resonance hybrid depends upon its energy content, the more stable forms making the greater contribution.

The resonance hybrid is more stable than any one of the various canonical forms, and the difference in energy between the hybrid and the most stable canonical form is known as the RESONANCE ENERGY.

Generally, the greater the number of canonical forms of about the same energy, the greater is the resonance energy.

Above all else, it is important to realize that the structure of the resonance hybrid is intermediate between the various canonical forms and is not a mixture of them.

Modern physical analysis confirms that the structure of benzene is a resonance hybrid structure of the two Kekulé canonical forms, which are both of equal energy content,

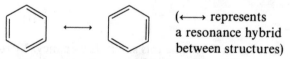

($\longleftrightarrow$ represents a resonance hybrid between structures)

Approximately 80 per cent contribution

together with rather small contributions from the three Dewar structures.

Approximately 20 per cent contribution

Molecular Orbital Image of Benzene

The structure of benzene is probably best considered in terms of molecular orbitals. The molecule is symmetrical with all carbon and hydrogen atoms lying in the same plane. The carbon atoms are arranged in the form of a regular hexagon, with all bond angles in the molecule corresponding to 120°. These bond angles are in accordance with sp^2 hybridization of the carbon atoms and, furthermore, it means that the structure is free from strain.

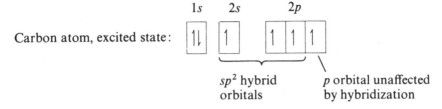

Carbon atom, excited state:

sp^2 hybrid orbitals

p orbital unaffected by hybridization

The carbon atoms are attached to each other and also to the hydrogen atoms by means of σ bonds, with the unbonded p orbitals lying at right angles to the plane of the ring.

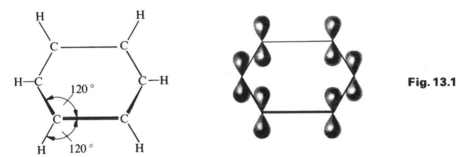

Fig. 13.1

Planar arrangement of carbon and hydrogen atoms

p orbital at right angles to the plane of the molecule

Each p orbital overlaps with the adjacent orbital on either side to give the overall effect of having a cloud of *delocalized* π electrons above and below the plane of the ring. This degree of interaction between the p orbitals is only possible because of the planar nature of the molecule.

Fig. 13.2 Clouds of delocalized π elctrons above and below the plane of the ring

Representation of the Benzene Ring

The molecular orbital structure of benzene is too clumsy to reproduce with reasonable ease in reaction equations, and an alternative mode of representation is sought which is simple but not ambiguous. In many texts a simple Kekulé structure is thought satisfactory, but this has the drawback that it suggests the existence of three double bonds.

Representing the structure simply as a regular hexagon is insufficient as it provides no means of differentiating between benzene and cyclohexane.

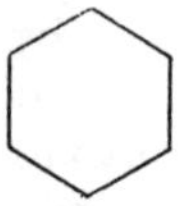

 represents

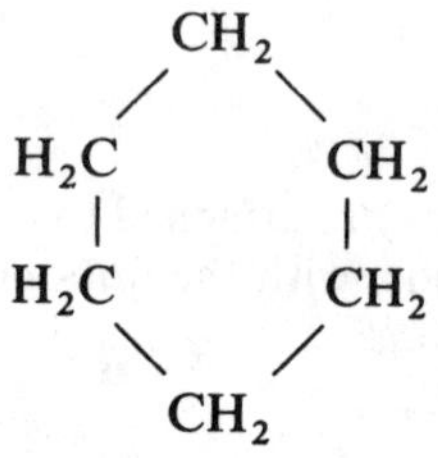

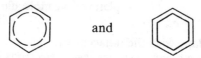

Cyclohexane

One of the simplest and most convenient ways of representing the benzene ring is to insert a circle inside the hexagonal ring in order to illustrate the annular rings of π electrons:

Other popular alternatives include:

and

Naming Substituted Benzene Derivatives

A benzene molecule in which one hydrogen atom has been replaced by an atom or group is referred to as a MONOSUBSTITUTED DERIVATIVE.

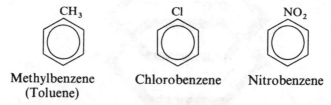

Methylbenzene   Chlorobenzene   Nitrobenzene
(Toluene)

For each DISUBSTITUTED DERIVATIVE there are three different isomers, depending upon the positions of substitution in the ring. When the two substituents are attached to adjacent carbons in the ring, the isomer is referred to as the 1,2- or *ortho*(*o*) derivative; when they are in the next-but-one position, the isomer is referred to as the 1,3- or *meta* (*m*) derivative, and when they are diametrically opposite, it is referred to as the 1,4- or *para* (*p*) derivative. The positions of substitution are indicated by numbering the carbon atoms in the ring and choosing unity so as to give the lowest possible combination of numbers.

For example, consider the three isomers of dibromobenzene.

1,2-Dibromobenzene   1,3-Dibromobenzene   1,4-Dibromobenzene

Three isomers exist for each TRISUBSTITUTED DERIVATIVE of benzene.

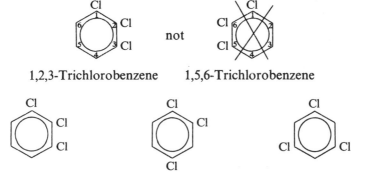

1,2,3-Trichlorobenzene   1,5,6-Trichlorobenzene

1,2,3-Trichlorobenzene   1,2,4-Trichlorobenzene   1,3,5-Trichlorobenzene

If one of the groups present gives rise to a compound with a special name, then only two positions of substitution are mentioned.

2,6-Dinitrobenzenecarboxylic acid   2-Chloro-4-nitrophenol
(2,6-Dinitrobenzoic acid)

The C_6H_5– part of a monosubstituted benzene derivative is called a PHENYL GROUP or RADICAL, which is analogous to the alkyl group in aliphatic systems. For convenience, especially when writing complicated structural formulae, the phenyl group is often abbreviated to '*Ph*'.

Phenyl groups and substituted phenyl groups alike are collectively termed ARYL GROUPS or RADICALS, and may be abbreviated to '*Ar*'.

It is usual to refer to a system as an aryl group when its exact nature, apart from its general aromatic character, is of no specific importance to a particular reaction.

C_6H_5—   Phenyl group or radical

C_6H_5—
C_6H_4Y—   Collectively termed
C_6H_3YZ—   aryl groups or
etc.   radicals

Stability of the Benzene Ring

Resonance Energy of Benzene

A good indication of the extra stability due to delocalization of electrons is given by consideration of benzene's RESONANCE ENERGY, which may alternatively be referred to as its DELOCALIZATION ENERGY. Unfortunately, the latter term, despite probably being more appropriate, is less commonly used.

The resonance energy of benzene may be determined by considering the respective enthalpy changes for the hydrogenation of benzene and cyclohexene.

Cyclohexene contains an alkene carbon–carbon double bond in which the π electrons are localized in the region of the unsaturated carbon atoms.

Each canonical structure for benzene (the Kekulé structure) contains three separate carbon–carbon double bonds and represents a molecule in which no delocalization of π electrons occurs. If this did indeed represent the true structure of benzene, its enthalpy change for the hydrogenation would be expected to have a value exactly three times that determined for cyclohexene.

The enthalpy change for the hydrogenation for cyclohexene is $-121\ kJ\ mol^{-1}$, providing a theoretical value of $-363\ kJ\ mol^{-1}$ ($-121 \times 3\ kJ\ mol^{-1}$) for a hypothetical benzene molecule in which the π electrons are localized in three separate double bonds.

In fact, the enthalpy change determined for the hydrogenation of benzene is only $-209\ kJ\ mol^{-1}$. The resonance energy is therefore $154\ kJ\ mol^{-1}$, indicating the extent to which the delocalization of the π electrons contributes to the overall stability of the molecule.

In general, compounds in which electrons are fairly evenly distributed over the entire bulk of the molecules tend to be more stable and less reactive than those in which electrons are localized. As a result, the polarity of each bond is kept to a minimum and the ease of bond cleavage is therefore inhibited.

Carbon–Carbon Bond Lengths in Benzene

Further support for the equivalence of all carbon–carbon bonds in benzene is revealed by measurement of their length. Each has a length of 0.139 nm, and if a graph of the multiplicity of carbon–carbon bonds, referred to as the BOND ORDER, is plotted against the corresponding bond length, a bond order of 1.5 is obtained for benzene.

Type of bond	Bond length/nm
Single C–C	0.154
Benzene C–C	0.139
Double C–C	0.134
Triple C–C	0.120

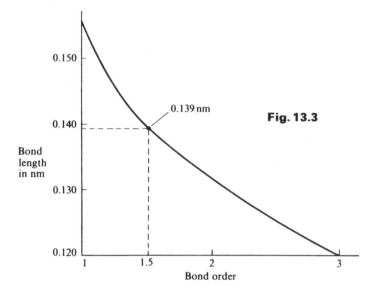

Fig. 13.3

The relationship between bond lengths and bond order is not linear, and this accounts for the fact that the bond lengths in benzene are not exactly midway in value between those for carbon single and double bonds.

Addition versus Substitution in the Benzene Ring

Benzene cannot undergo addition reactions and still retain overall aromatic character. This is exemplified by its hydrogenation to the cycloalkane, cyclo-hexane. Even if it were possible to confine the addition to one pair of adjacent carbons, overall aromaticity would still be destroyed as the remaining π electrons could then only incorporate four of the six carbon atoms in the ring.

Instead, the majority of reactions that benzene undergoes involve substitution in the ring, which takes place with overall retention of aromatic character.

$$\bigcirc + Y_2 \longrightarrow \bigcirc\!-Y + HY$$

Physical Properties

Benzene is a colourless liquid (b.p. 80 °C, m.p. 5.5 °C) with a characteristic 'aromatic' smell. It is immiscible with water, forming the upper of two layers, but is soluble in organic solvents as well as being a useful solvent itself. Like all aromatic compounds, it burns with a smoky and luminous flame, owing to its relatively high carbon content. Benzene is a highly toxic compound and continued inhalation of the vapours is dangerous and can induce anaemia and even leukaemia.

Industrial Source

The two important natural sources of benzene are COAL TAR and PETROLEUM. Petroleum vapour, containing hexane and other hydrocarbons, is passed over a finely divided platinum catalyst at 500 °C and under 10–20 atmospheres pressure. This process is known as 'reforming' or 'platforming', the latter term arising from the type of catalyst employed.

$$C_6H_{14} \xrightarrow[\text{500 °C, 10–20 atm}]{\text{Pt cat.}} C_6H_6 + 4H_2$$
Hexane

Most of the benzene required in the British Isles is obtained from coal tar, but in the United States this source alone is insufficient to meet the demand and large quantities are obtained from petroleum.

Coal Tar

When coal is destructively distilled in a retort by heating at 1000–1300 °C, the products include *coal gas, coal tar, ammoniacal liquor and coke.*

COAL TAR is a black viscous liquid containing more than 200 different compounds, many of which are aromatic, and provides one of the most important natural sources of these compounds. After separation from the other components, the coal tar is fractionally distilled. The main fractions collected are tabulated on page 131.

Treatment of the Fractions

Light Oil (Benzole)

This fraction is shaken with
(1) cold dilute sulphuric acid to remove basic compounds, e.g. pyridine, phenylamine (aniline), ammonia;
(2) water to wash away the excess sulphuric acid;
(3) dilute sodium hydroxide to remove acid compounds, e.g. phenols; and
(4) water to wash away excess alkali.

The oil is dried and then fractionally distilled to separate the various hydrocarbons, e.g. benzene, methylbenzene (toluene), dimethylbenzenes (xylenes). The residue, 'solvent naphtha', is a useful industrial solvent.

Fraction	Distillation temperature range, °C	Main contents of fraction
Light oil (benzole)	90–170	Benzene, C_6H_6 Methylbenzene (Toluene), $C_6H_5CH_3$ Dimethylbenzenes (Xylenes), $C_6H_4(CH_3)_2$ Pyridine, C_5H_5N
Middle oil (carbolic)	170–230	Phenol, C_6H_5OH Methylphenols (Cresols), $CH_3C_6H_4OH$ Naphthalene, $C_{10}H_8$
Heavy oil (creosote)	230–270	Creosote
Green oil (anthracene)	270–400	Anthracene, $C_{14}H_{10}$
Residue	>400	Pitch

Middle Oil (Carbolic)

Naphthalene crystals (m.p. 80 °C) are deposited by allowing the fraction to cool and then separated by centrifuging.

The phenols are separated by treating the remaining oil with warm aqueous sodium hydroxide, forming the sodium salts. The different phenols are regenerated by adding dilute acid and then, after washing, separated by fractional distillation.

Heavy Oil (Creosote)

This fraction, containing mainly a mixture of phenol, methylphenols (cresols), naphthalene and anthracene, is used in the crude form as a wood preservative.

Green Oil (Anthracene)

This fraction consists mainly of anthracene and phenanthrene. Crude anthracene can be separated by shaking with solvent naptha.

Residue

The pitch is removed while still hot and employed in the manufacture of asphalt and in road construction.

Synthetic Preparations

Owing to the great abundance of benzene from industrial sources, it is rarely prepared in the laboratory, and the following reactions tend to be of academic interest only.

Decarboxylation of a Sodium Salt

Sodium benzenecarboxylate (benzoate) is fused with sodalime (calcium oxide slaked with sodium hydroxide).

$$C_6H_5COONa + NaOH \xrightarrow{\text{fuse}} C_6H_6 + Na_2CO_3$$

Sodium benzenecarboxylate
(Sodium benzoate)
(cf. decarboxylation of sodium ethanoate (acetate) to give methane)

From Phenol

Phenol vapour is passed over heated zinc dust.

$$C_6H_5OH + Zn \xrightarrow{\text{heat}} C_6H_6 + ZnO$$

Polymerization of Ethyne

Ethyne, heated to 400 °C under pressure, yields a product which contains a small amount of benzene, but if a complex organo–nickel catalyst is used (Reppe, 1948) at a temperature of 60–70 °C, about an 80 per cent yield of benzene is obtained.

$$3CH\equiv CH \xrightarrow[\text{60–70 °C}]{\text{complex organo–nickel cat.}} C_6H_6$$

Reactions

The availability of π electrons in benzene serves as a source of electrons, i.e. a nucleophilic reagent, and its reactions are characterized by ELECTROPHILIC SUBSTITUTION in the ring.

In these and other ring-substitution reactions, an unstable intermediate is formed in which the entering atom or group and the leaving hydrogen atom are both momentarily bonded to the ring. This causes a disruption in the symmetry of the delocalized π electrons and may be illustrated by an incomplete circle inside the ring. If the attacking species is an electrophile, which is most common, then the reaction intermediate will carry a positive charge which is distributed over the bulk of the molecule.

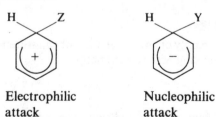

Electrophilic attack   Nucleophilic attack

Similarly, in the case of nucleophilic substitution, a negative charge is distributed over the molecule.

Nitration

A 'nitrating mixture', containing equal molar quantities of concentrated nitric and sulphuric acids carefully mixed together, is added to the benzene. The mixture is then refluxed in a water bath maintained at 55–60 °C.

The weaker nitric acid functions as a base in the highly acidic sulphuric acid medium, releasing the NITRYL (NITRONIUM) CATION, $^+NO_2$, which then undergoes substitution in the ring.

$$HNO_3 + 2H_2SO_4 \underset{\text{slow}}{\rightleftharpoons} {}^+NO_2 + H_3\overset{+}{O} + 2HSO_4$$

This formation of the nitryl (nitronium) cation takes place via two stages:

$$HO - NO_2 + HOSO_2OH \rightleftharpoons {}^-OSO_2OH + H\overset{+}{\overset{|}{O}} - NO_2$$

$$H\overset{+}{\overset{|}{O}} - NO_2 + HOSO_2OH \longrightarrow H_3\overset{+}{O} + {}^-OSO_2OH + \overset{+}{N}O_2$$

Nitrobenzene

Kinetic studies indicate that the overall rate-determining step is the one involving the attack of the nitryl cation on the benzene ring (rate $\alpha[C_6H_6][^+NO_2]$).

Concentrated nitric acid contains very little of the nitryl cation, and hence it has hardly any effect on benzene in the absence of sulphuric acid.

Nitrobenzene is a pale yellow liquid (b.p. 210 °C) with the smell of almonds, but during its preparation small quantities of white crystals of 1,3-dinitrobenzene (m.p. 90 °C) are almost invariably formed.

1,3-DINITROBENZENE can be prepared by refluxing benzene with the nitrating mixture on a water bath maintained at 95 °C or by nitration of nitrobenzene at· 55–60 °C.

1,3-Dinitrobenzene

The reaction products are afterwards added to excess cold water, the 1,3-dinitrobenzene crystallizing out. Traces of the 1,2- and 1,4-isomers are removed during recrystallization from alcohol.

Nitrations are carried out at comparatively low temperatures since at higher ones, quantities of the product are lost because of oxidation by the nitric acid.

1,3,5-Trinitrobenzene (TNB) requires treatment with fuming nitric and sulphuric acids for five days at 110 °C, and then even under these conditions, the yield is only about 40 per cent.

Sulphonation

Sulphonation of benzene to form benzenesulphonic acid is best carried out using fuming sulphuric acid (concentrated sulphuric acid containing an excess of sulphur(VI) oxide (sulphur trioxide)). The reaction takes place on gently warming to 35–50 °C. Alternatively, ordinary concentrated sulphuric acid may be used, but the mixture then requires refluxing for several hours.

The most probable mode of attack seems to be electrophilic substitution by the *electron-deficient sulphur(VI) oxide, SO_3*, although the SO_3H^+ ion, has been considered as a possibility.

$$2H_2SO_4 \rightleftharpoons SO_3 + H_3^+O + HSO_4^-$$

Benzenesulphonic
acid

The overall reaction is reversible with the equilibrium tending towards the left.

Halogenation

Substitution by chlorine or bromine in benzene takes place readily at room temperature in the presence of a 'halogen carrier' catalyst, e.g. Fe, Al, I, but iodine does not easily substitute in this way. The catalyst functions as a Lewis acid, inducing a certain degree of polarity in the halogen molecule.

Although metallic catalysts are commonly used, they are undoubtedly converted into the halide during the reaction and it is in this form that they promote the reaction. Consequently, the catalyst may alternatively be introduced as the appropriate metal halide.

Bromination may be carried out using an iron or iron(III) bromide catalyst, which polarizes the bromine molecule, forming the complex $Br^{\delta+}$ —— $Br^{\delta-}$ ------ $FeBr_3$, which then ionizes to $Br^+[FeBr_4]^-$. It is not possible to state precisely, if at all, to what extent free Br^+ is present.

The reaction may be represented in the following manner:

$$Br\!-\!Br \quad FeBr_3 \rightleftharpoons Br^+[FeBr_4]^-$$

Bromobenzene

Under prolonged conditions and in the presence of a higher proportion of the halogen, the 1,4-dihalide is formed.

In the presence of direct sunlight or ultra-violet radiation benzene reacts with chlorine or bromine at room temperature to form white crystals of the 1,2,3,4,5,6-hexachlorocyclohexane or hexabromocyclohexane respectively.

$$C_6H_6 + 3Br_2 \xrightarrow[\text{room temp}]{h\nu} C_6H_6Br_6$$

1,2,3,4,5,6-hexabromocyclohexane
(Benzene hexabromide)

This is an ADDITION REACTION and proceeds via a FREE-RADICAL

MECHANISM, emphasizing the importance of experimental conditions and mechanism in achieving the desired product.

$$Br_2 \xrightarrow{h\nu} 2Br\cdot \quad \text{Chain initiation}$$

The propagation stages are repeated until $C_6H_6Br_6$ is formed as the major product. The final product has several stereoisomers, and in the case of the hexachloride, one of these is a powerful insecticide.

Friedel–Crafts Alkylation

In the presence of an anhydrous aluminium chloride catalyst, benzene condenses* with a haloalkane to yield the ALKYLBENZENE.

$$R\text{—}Cl \quad AlCl_3 \rightleftharpoons R^+[AlCl_4]^-$$

Alkylbenzene

Unfortunately, the reaction is extremely difficult to stop at this stage since the alkylbenzene is more reactive than benzene itself, and further alkylation of the ring occurs.

Other suitable catalysts include SnF_4, BF_3 and HF. The haloalkanes can be replaced by other compounds, such as alkenes and alcohols.

Friedel–Crafts Acylation

The condensation of benzene with an acyl chloride, RCOCl, or acid anhydride, $(RCO)_2O$, in the presence of an anhydrous aluminium chloride catalyst, gives a good yield of the AROMATIC KETONE. The mixture is refluxed on a water bath at 50 °C.

$$RCO\text{—}Cl \quad AlCl_3 \rightleftharpoons RC^+O + [AlCl_4]^-$$

(or, in the case of the anhydride,

$$(RCO)_2O \quad AlCl_3 \rightleftharpoons RC^+O + [RCOO.AlCl_3]^-)$$

The reaction with the anhydride is generally preferred because the anhydride is more easily obtained in a high state of purity, is more easily handled, and the resulting ketone is more easily separated by distillation.

*A condensation reaction is one in which a new compound is formed from two or more reactants together with the elimination of a simple molecule such as water, ammonia, hydrogen chloride etc.

Synthetic Applications of Aromatic Nitro Compounds

Aromatic NITRO COMPOUNDS are of considerable importance in the manufacture of aryl amines, the most important of which is PHENYLAMINE (aniline); explosives, e.g. methyl-2,4,6-trinitrobenzene (2,4,6-trinitrotoluene, TNT); and DIAZONIUM SALTS, which themselves have numerous synthetic applications, e.g. in the manufacture of azo-dyes and phenols.

PHENYLAMINE (aniline), $C_6H_5NH_2$, is a colourless liquid which is prepared by reducing nitrobenzene with tin or iron and concentrated hydrochloric acid. For large scale industrial preparations, iron filings, being cheaper than tin, and '30 per cent *dilute* hydrochloric acid are used instead (*see* page 207).

It is used in the manufacture of anti-oxidants, as a vulcanizing accelerator for the rubber industry, in synthesizing drugs and in the preparation of diazonium salts. Since phenylamine is slowly oxidized, turning yellow, on exposure to light and air, it is often stored in the form of the more stable crystalline phenylammonium chloride (aniline hydrochloride), $C_6H_5NH_3^+Cl^-$.

DIAZONIUM SALTS are obtained by treating an aromatic primary amine or its salt with nitrous acid (formed during the reaction from sodium nitrite and dilute hydrochloric or sulphuric acid) at 0–5 °C.

$$NaNO_2 + HCl \longrightarrow NaCl + HNO_2$$

$$C_6H_5NH_3Cl + HNO_2 \longrightarrow C_6H_5N_2Cl + 2H_2O$$

Benzenediazonium
chloride

The salt is usually retained in solution and used immediately after preparation, as it can be explosive when dry.

If a solution of the benzenediazonium salt solution is warmed to 50 °C, PHENOL is formed.

$$C_6H_5N_2^+ + 2H_2O \xrightarrow{50°C} C_6H_5OH + N_2 + H_3^+O$$

Benzenediazonium ion   Phenol

The coupling of diazonium salts with phenols yields AZO COMPOUNDS. For example, an alkaline solution of phenol reacts with benzenediazonium chloride to form a *yellow* AZO-DYE.

(4-Hydroxyphenyl)azobenzene
(*p*-Hydroxyazobenzene)
Bright yellow precipitate

Using naphthalen-2-ol (2-naphthol), a *bright red* precipitate of 1-(phenylazo)naphthalen-2-ol is obtained.

These particular dyes are of little practical value owing to their slight solubility in water. However, the solubility of azo-dyes containing a sulphonic acid group,

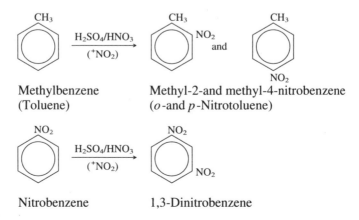

Naphthalen-2-ol   1-(Phenylazo)naphthalen-2-ol
(2-Naphthol)   (Phenylazo-2-naphthol)
                         Bright red precipitate

—SO_3H, is very much greater, and these compounds are of considerable commercial importance in the dyestuffs industry.

Orientation of Substitution in a Monosubstituted Benzene Nucleus

When a second atom or group of atoms is attached to a monosubstituted benzene ring, the position of substitution is determined by the nature of the substituent already attached to the ring and is not dependent upon the attacking atom or group of atoms.

This phenomenon can be exemplified by considering the nitration and bromination of methylbenzene (toluene) and nitrobenzene.

In methylbenzene (toluene), both the nitro group and the bromine atom are directed to the 2- and 4-positions in the ring, whereas in nitrobenzene both of these substituents are directed to the 3-position. Since the same attacking species are directed to different positions in the ring in each case, it is likely that it is the substituent already present, i.e. the methyl group or the nitro group, which actually determines the position of secondary substitution.

Chemical reactions used to provide evidence in this way are referred to as COMPETITIVE REACTIONS.

The position of substitution of the second substituent is governed largely by whether or not the atom or group already present is donating electrons to the ring or withdrawing electrons from it.

Electron-donating substituents enhance the availability of electrons about the ring, which is said to be ACTIVATED. The 2- and 4-positions are the sites predominantly affected by the increase in electron density, rendering them more vulnerable to attack by an electrophilic reagent. Groups inducing this effect are said to ACTIVATE THE RING and DIRECT TO THE 2- and 4-POSITIONS.

NITRATION

Methylbenzene   Methyl-2-and methyl-4-nitrobenzene
(Toluene)   (*o*-and *p*-Nitrotoluene)

Nitrobenzene   1,3-Dinitrobenzene

BROMINATION

Bromo-2- and bromo-4-methylbenzene
(*o*- and *p*-Bromotoluene)

Bromo-3-nitrobenzene
(*m*-Bromonitrobenzene)

Conversely, electron-withdrawing substituents reduce the availability of electrons about the ring, which is said to be DEACTIVATED. Electrons are withdrawn mainly from the 2- and 4-positions rendering the 3-position relatively richer in electrons. Consequently, any subsequent attack by an electrophile takes place preferentially in the 3-position. Groups inducing this effect are said to be DEACTIVATING and are 3-DIRECTING.

However, the halogens prove an exception to these general rules and direct to the 2- and 4-positions despite withdrawing electrons from the ring (*see below*).

Ring activating, directing to 2- and 4-positions	Ring deactivating, directing to 3-position	Ring deactivating, directing to 2- and 4-positions
—R	$-N\overset{O}{\underset{O}{\diagup\diagdown}}$	Halogens
—OH	—C≡N	
—OR	$-\overset{O}{\overset{\|}{C}}\diagdown_H$	
—NH$_2$	$-\overset{O}{\overset{\|}{C}}\diagdown_R$	
—NHR	$-\overset{O}{\overset{\|}{C}}\diagdown_{OH}$	
—NR$_2$	—SO$_3$H	

A useful general guide as to the directing powers of the substituent already present in the benzene ring is given by Vorlander's rule:

(1) saturated groups (containing only single bonds between all atoms) direct predominantly to the 2- and 4-positions; and

(2) unsaturated groups (containing multiple bonds between any atoms) direct predominantly to the 3-position.

It is evident that the halogens, being categorized as a saturated group and consequently directing to the 2- and 4-positions, do not prove to be exceptional to this rule.

It is important to bear in mind that the products of secondary substitution which are usually specified are not the sole products but only those which predominate. For example, when the 2- and 4-derivatives are obtained as the predominant products (not necessarily in equal proportions), there will inevitably be a small proportion of the 3-derivative present.

The distribution of electrons about the ring of a monosubstituted aromatic nucleus is largely influenced by the inductive effects of the substituent and the location of unshared pairs of electrons within this group (mesomeric effects).

If the atom attached to the ring is more electronegative than the carbon to which it is bonded, then electrons will be withdrawn from the ring and *vice versa*.

For example, in methylbenzene (toluene), the benzene carbon, on account of its environment, is more electronegative than the carbon in the methyl group.

Consequently, electrons are attracted towards the ring, which is activated with regard to electrophic attack, especially in the 2- and 4-positions.

If the atom directly attached to the ring contains an unshared pair of electrons, e.g. the nitrogen atom in the $-NH_2$ group, and the oxygen atom in the $-OH$ group, these can interact with the π electrons of the ring and effectively increase the electron density about it.

Phenylamine
(Aniline)

Phenol

In both phenylamine (aniline) and phenol, there is competition between the inductive effects of the nitrogen atom of the amino group and the oxygen atom of the hydroxyl group, which tend to withdraw electrons from the ring, and the interaction of the electron pairs which tend to enhance the availability of electrons about the ring. Unfortunately, there are no simple means of determining which of these two factors will have the greater influence, but by and large, it may be presumed that the electron-releasing powers of the nitrogen and oxygen atoms have a greater impact than the inductive effects, and the overall effect will be to enhance the electron density of the ring.

In the halobenzene molecule, electron pairs on the halogen interact much less readily with the π electrons of the ring than those of nitrogen (as in phenylamine) and oxygen (as in phenol), but as the incoming electrophile closely approaches the ring, the interaction of the halogen lone pairs with the ring is markedly increased, making the 2- and 4-positions more vulnerable to electrophilic substitution.

If the atom attached to the ring is itself attached to a more electronegative atom by means of multiple bonds, then the factors influencing electron availability are reversed.

In the carbonyl group of benzenecarbaldehyde (benzaldehyde), electrons in the π bond are attracted from the carbon atom towards the oxygen and this effect is in turn transmitted to the benzene ring, resulting in a decrease in the availability of electrons. This electron withdrawal from the ring influences primarily the 2- and 4-positions, thus leaving the 3-position relatively denser in electrons and more vulnerable to electrophilic attack.

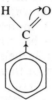

Benzenecarbaldehyde
(Benzaldehyde)

Aromatic Nucleophilic Substitution

As it is the availability of π electrons in benzene that promotes electrophilic attack, it is hardly surprising that NUCLEOPHILIC SUBSTITUTION in the ring is less common. However, if a strong electron-withdrawing substituent is already attached to the ring, then the relative decrease in the availability of π electrons in the 2- and 4-positions may render these sites sufficiently deficient in electrons as to undergo attack by a nucleophile. For example, if nitrobenzene is fused with potassium hydroxide in the presence of air, 2-nitrophenol is formed as the major product.

Major product
2- and 4-Nitrophenol

The electron-withdrawing inductive effect of the nitro group makes the 2-position more deficient in electrons than the more distant 4-, and it is for this reason that the 2-product is formed in greater quantity, despite steric interaction.

The most common mode of nucleophilic attack upon an aromatic nucleus is that in which a substituent other than hydrogen is displaced. For example, the diazo group in diazonium salts and the halogen in aromatic halides can both undergo displacement by a hydroxyl group.

$$ArN_2^+X^- + H_2O \xrightarrow{\text{50 per cent } H_2SO_4} ArOH + N_2 + X^-$$

$$ArCl + NaOH \xrightarrow[\text{high temp and press}]{\text{aq. solution}} ArOH + NaCl$$

QUESTIONS

1. The chemistry of benzene is characterized by which one of the following types of reaction?

    A addition
    B elimination
    C addition followed by immediate elimination
    D substitution
    E polymerization

2. Reactions involving an aromatic nucleus are usually initiated by which one of the following reagents?

    A free radicals
    B unchanged molecules
    C molecules possessing a lone pair of electrons
    D nucleophiles
    E electrophiles

3. Which one of the following substituents deactivates an aromatic nucleus?

    A $-CH_3$
    B $-Br$
    C $-NH_2$
    D $-NR_2$
    E $-OCH_3$

4. What simple reactions could be used to illustrate that benzene does not have a linear structure of the type $CH_2{=}CHC{\equiv}CCH{=}CH_2$?

5. What do you understand by the concept of resonance (delocalization) energy in benzenoid aromatics? Support your answer with reference to the thermochemical evidence available.

6. Arrange the following compounds in decreasing order of reactivity with regard to electrophilic attack.

    A benzene
    B methylbenzene
    C 1,3-dinitrobenzene
    D phenol
    E bromobenzene

7. Explain why the enthalpy of hydrogenation of cyclohexa-1,3-diene is about 21 kJ mol^{-1} less than that of cyclohexa-1,4-diene.

8. Write the mechanisms for each of the following reactions.

    A the light catalysed chlorination of benzene
    B the iron(III) chloride catalysed chlorination of benzene
    C the nitration of benzene
    D the sulphonation of benzene

9. Explain why the bromination of phenylamine (aniline) yields predominantly the 2- and 4-products, whereas the bromination of benzenecarbaldehyde yields the 3-compound as the major product.

10. In what order would you introduce the respective substituents in the benzene ring so as to obtain the following products?

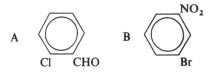

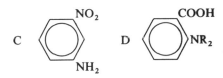

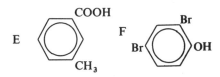

14 Methylbenzene (Toluene)

METHYLBENZENE (toluene) is a higher homologue of benzene, which it resembles in many respects.

Methylbenzene
(Toluene)

It is the simplest member of a family of hydrocarbons known as ARENES, which is a collective name for all hydrocarbons containing a benzene ring.

Physical Properties

Methylbenzene is a colourless liquid which closely resembles benzene, although it has a predictably higher boiling point (111 °C). It is insoluble in water but soluble in organic solvents and is itself a useful solvent. Since the fumes of methylbenzene are considerably less toxic than those of benzene (*see* page 130), it is preferable, whenever possible, to use it instead of benzene, especially with regard to its function as a solvent.

Industrial Source

Enormous quantities of methylbenzene are obtained from COALTAR and PETROLEUM.

Certain sources of petroleum (notably in California) contain large quantities of the cycloalkane, methylcyclohexane. When this is heated under pressure in the presence of molybdenum(III) oxide and aluminium oxide catalysts, dehydrogenation occurs, yielding methylbenzene.

$$
\begin{array}{c}
CH_3 \\
| \\
CH \\
CH_2 \quad\quad CH_2 \\
| \quad\quad\quad | \\
CH_2 \quad\quad CH_2 \\
CH_2
\end{array}
\xrightarrow[\text{560 °C, high press.}]{Mo_2O_3\text{–}Al_2O_3}
\quad CH_3 \text{-ring} \quad + 3H_2
$$

This process, known as HYDROFORMING, was developed during World War II in order to meet the demand for making the explosive TNT (trinitrotoluene or methyl-2,4,6-trinitrobenzene).

Synthetic Preparations

Like benzene, methylbenzene is usually abundantly available from industrial sources and it is seldom found necessary to prepare it in the laboratory.

Friedel–Crafts Alkylation

Chloromethane is bubbled through dry benzene in the presence of an anhydrous aluminium chloride catalyst at a temperature of 40 °C.

$$\text{C}_6\text{H}_6 + \text{CH}_3\text{Cl} \xrightarrow[\text{40 °C}]{\text{AlCl}_3 \text{ cat.}} \text{C}_6\text{H}_5\text{CH}_3 + \text{HCl}$$

A better yield is obtained if the mass of catalyst used is about one-third that of benzene, although further alkylation invariably occurs.

Fittig's Reaction

Sodium is slowly added to a dry ethereal solution of bromobenzene and iodomethane (cf. Wurtz synthesis of alkanes).

$$\text{C}_6\text{H}_5\text{Br} + \text{CH}_3\text{I} + 2\text{Na} \xrightarrow[(\text{C}_2\text{H}_5)_2\text{O}]{\text{dry}} \text{C}_6\text{H}_5\text{CH}_3 + \text{NaBr} + \text{NaI}$$

The methylbenzene is separated by fractional distillation. Ethane, CH_3CH_3, and diphenyl, Ph.Ph, are formed as by-products of the reaction.

Reactions

As might be expected, methylbenzene undergoes two distinctive types of reaction:

(1) SIDE-CHAIN SUBSTITUTION, which proceeds via a free-radical mechanism and is analogous to the substitution of alkanes; and

(2) ELECTROPHILIC SUBSTITUTION OF THE RING.

Substitution of the ring is easier than in benzene since the saturated methyl group, which is electron-donating, activates the ring with regard to electrophilic attack in the 2- and 4-positions.

Halogenation

Substitution of a halogen can take place *in the side chain or in the ring, depending upon the conditions under which the reaction is carried out.*

Side-Chain Substitution

If the chlorine is bubbled through boiling methylbenzene in the presence of ultra-violet light or strong sunlight, substitution occurs in the side chain to yield successively (chloromethyl)benzene, (dichloromethyl)benzene and (trichloromethyl)benzene.

$$CH_3-C_6H_5 + Cl_2 \xrightarrow[\text{boil}]{h\nu} CH_2Cl-C_6H_5 + HCl$$

(Chloromethyl)benzene
(Benzyl chloride)

$$CH_2Cl-C_6H_5 + Cl_2 \longrightarrow CHCl_2-C_6H_5 + HCl$$

(Dichloromethyl)benzene
(Benzal chloride)

$$CHCl_2-C_6H_5 + Cl_2 \longrightarrow CCl_3-C_6H_5 + HCl$$

(Trichloromethyl)benzene
(Benzotrichloride)

Bromination of methylbenzene takes place under similar conditions, forming the corresponding bromine derivatives.

Mechanism

The reaction proceeds via a *free-radical mechanism* in a similar manner as for the halogenation of alkanes.

(1) $\qquad$ $Cl_2 \xrightarrow{h\nu} 2Cl\cdot$ $\qquad$ Chain initiation

(2) $C_6H_5CH_3 + Cl\cdot \longrightarrow C_6H_5CH_2\cdot + HCl$

(3) $C_6H_5CH_2\cdot + Cl_2 \longrightarrow C_6H_5CH_2Cl + Cl\cdot$

$\left.\right\}$ Chain propagation

Steps (2) and (3) are repeated to give the further products, $C_6H_5CHCl_2$ and $C_6H_5CCl_3$.

Oxidation: A Side-chain Reaction

On refluxing methylbenzene with acidified potassium manganate(VII), potassium dichromate(VI) or dilute nitric acid for several hours, benzenecarboxylic (benzoic) acid is formed.

CH$_3$ [O], acid KMnO$_4$ or K$_2$Cr$_2$O$_7$, reflux → CHO [O] → COOH

Benzenecarbaldehyde
(Benzaldehyde)

Benzenecarboxylic acid
(Benzoic acid)

If a milder oxidizing agent is used (e.g. manganese(IV) oxide or chromium(VI) dichloride dioxide (chromyl chloride)) methylbenzene is only oxidized as far as benzenecarbaldehyde (benzaldehyde).

Hydrogenation: Addition in the Ring

When methylbenzene vapour is passed over a finely divided nickel, platinum or palladium catalyst at 200 °C, addition occurs giving methylcyclohexane.

CH$_3$ + 3H$_2$ $\xrightarrow[\text{200 °C}]{\text{Ni, Pt or Pd cat.}}$

CH$_3$ / CH / CH$_2$ CH$_2$ / CH$_2$ CH$_2$ / CH$_2$

Methylcyclohexane

Ring Substitution

If methylbenzene is treated with chlorine or bromine in the presence of a suitable halogen carrier at room temperature and in the absence of sunlight, substitution occurs in the ring, giving a mixture of the 2- and 4-derivatives.

CH$_3$ $\xrightarrow{\text{Cl}_2, \text{FeCl}_3 \text{ cat.}}$ CH$_3$ Cl and CH$_3$ ... Cl

Chloro-2- and chloro-4-methylbenzene
(*o*- and *p*-Chlorotoluene)

Mechanism

The mechanism is analogous to that for the halogenation of benzene.

$$Cl\frown Cl \quad FeCl_3 \longrightarrow Cl^+[FeCl_4]^-$$

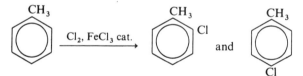

CH$_3$ $\xrightarrow{\text{Cl}^+[\text{FeCl}_4]^-}$ CH$_3$ H Cl $\xrightarrow{[\text{FeCl}_4]^-}$ CH$_3$ Cl + HCl + FeCl$_3$

and CH$_3$ $\xrightarrow{\text{Cl}^+[\text{FeCl}_4]^-}$ CH$_3$ H Cl $\xrightarrow{[\text{FeCl}_4]^-}$ CH$_3$ Cl + HCl + FeCl$_3$

Other Ring Substitution Reactions

NITRATION, SULPHONATION, and FRIEDEL – CRAFTS ALKYLATION and ACYLATION OF THE RING can be brought about in a manner similar to that described for benzene.

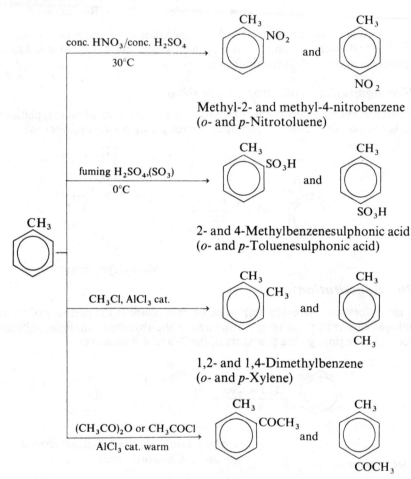

Methyl-2- and methyl-4-nitrobenzene
(*o*- and *p*-Nitrotoluene)

2- and 4-Methylbenzenesulphonic acid
(*o*- and *p*-Toluenesulphonic acid)

1,2- and 1,4-Dimethylbenzene
(*o*- and *p*-Xylene)

2- and 4-Methylphenylethanone
(*o*- and *p*-Methylacetophenone)

In all these reactions, the 4-derivative tends to be yielded in greater quantity, mainly because it is sterically the more favoured product.

If the Friedel–Crafts alkylation is carried out at 80 °C, 1,3-dimethylbenzene is the major product.

Methyl-2,4,6-trinitrobenzene(2,4,6-trinitrotoluene, TNT), like 2,4,6-trinitrobenzene (TNB) and 2,4,6-trinitrophenol (picric acid), is an important high explosive.

QUESTIONS

1. Which one of the following substituents will cause the benzene ring to undergo nitration in the 2- and 4-positions with greater ease than methylbenzene?

   A —CH_2CH_3
   B —Cl
   C —NO_2
   D —CHO
   E —$COOH$

2. Which one of the following reagents does *not* react with methylbenzene?

   A concentrated sulphuric acid
   B chlorine gas
   C bromine water
   D acidified potassium manganate(VII)
   E ethanoic (acetic) anhydride

3. Compare and contrast the mechanism for the chlorination of benzene and methylbenzene (a) in the presence of ultra-violet light and (b) using a 'halogen carrier' catalyst.

4. Methylbenzene is oxidized to benzenecarboxylic acid by the action of dilute nitric acid. Why cannot the more powerful concentrated acid be used instead?

15 *Halohydrocarbons*

HALOALKANES are halogen derivatives of alkanes. Monohalo derivatives (alkyl halides) have a general molecular formula, $C_nH_{2n+1}X$, or simply R—X, where R represents an alkyl group.

e.g. CH_3Cl Chloromethane
                        (Methyl chloride)

CH_3CH_2Br Bromoethane
                        (Ethyl bromide)

CH_3
  \
    CHI   2-Iodopropane
  /   (Isopropyl iodide)
CH_3

They may be classified as *primary* (1°), *secondary* (2°) or *tertiary* (3°), according to the nature of the carbon atom to which the halogen atoms is attached.

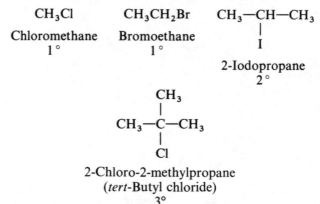

CH_3Cl CH_3CH_2Br CH_3—CH—CH$_3$
                                              |
Chloromethane   Bromoethane   I
    1°   1°
                                      2-Iodopropane
                                           2°

CH_3
 |
CH_3—C—CH$_3$
 |
Cl

2-Chloro-2-methylpropane
(*tert*-Butyl chloride)
3°

ARYL HALIDES are compounds in which the halogen atom is *attached directly* to an aromatic ring. They have a general formula ArX.

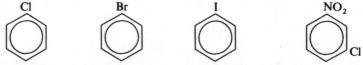

Cl   Br   I   NO$_2$

Chlorobenzene Bromobenzene Iodobenzene 3-Chloronitrobenzene

(Chloromethyl)benzene (benzyl chloride), $C_6H_5CH_2Cl$, and other similar compounds in which the halogen atom is not attached directly to the ring are, strictly speaking, phenyl substituted haloalkanes and not aryl halides, although certain texts classify them as 'side-chain' aryl halides.

HALOETHENES (vinyl halides) are compounds in which the halogen is attached directly to a doubly-bonded carbon, e.g. chloroethene (vinyl chloride), CH_2=CHCl.

Unsaturated halogen compounds of the type, CH_2=CHCH$_2$X, are called ALLYL HALIDES.

If two halogen atoms are attached to adjacent carbons, the compound is referred to as a VICINAL (*VIC*) DIHALIDE, and if both are attached to the same carbon, then it is known as a GEMINAL (*GEM*) DIHALIDE.

Nomenclature

Haloalkanes (Alkyl Halides)

Both common and IUPAC names are in general usage nowadays, although the international system, which considers the compounds as halo-substituted alkanes, is gradually becoming the more popular.

Formula	IUPAC name	Common name
CH_3Cl	Chloromethane	Methyl chloride
CH_3CH_2Br	Bromoethane	Ethyl bromide

CH_3CHCH_3
    |
    I
	2-Iodopropane	Isopropyl iodide

CH$_3$—C—F with CH$_3$ groups	2-Fluoro-2-methylpropane	*tert*-Butyl fluoride
$C_6H_5CH_2Cl$	Chloromethylbenzene	Benzyl chloride

Aryl Halides

These are named in the usual way, using numbers to indicate the position of substituents in the ring.

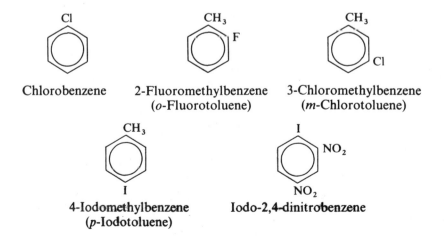

Chlorobenzene

2-Fluoromethylbenzene
(*o*-Fluorotoluene)

3-Chloromethylbenzene
(*m*-Chlorotoluene)

4-Iodomethylbenzene
(*p*-Iodotoluene)

Iodo-2,4-dinitrobenzene

Physical Properties

Because of the polarity of the carbon–halogen bond, which enhances dipole–dipole interaction in the liquid phase, haloalkanes have somewhat higher boiling points than alkanes of comparable relative molecular mass.

Most haloalkanes are liquids, their boiling points depending upon the nature of the alkyl groups and the halogen atom, although the halomethanes (apart from iodomethane), fluoroethane and chloroethane are gases.

Name	Formula	B.p./°C	Density at 20°C/g cm^{-3}
Chloromethane	CH_3Cl	−24	—
Bromomethane	CH_3Br	5	—
Iodomethane	CH_3I	43	2.280
Chloroethane	CH_3CH_2Cl	12.5	—
Bromoethane	CH_3CH_2Br	38	1.440
Iodoethane	CH_3CH_2I	72	1.933
1-Chloropropane	$CH_3(CH_2)_2Cl$	47	
1-Bromopropane	$CH_3(CH_2)_2Br$	71	1.335
1-Iodopropane	$CH_3(CH_2)_2I$	102	1.747

For corresponding halogen atoms, boiling points increase with increasing relative molecular mass. Densities decrease in the same order; this is accounted for in terms of the closer packing of the smaller molecules in the liquid phase.

Bromo- and iodoalkanes are all denser than water.

For corresponding alkyl groups, the boiling points increase in the order fluoro < chloro < bromo < iodo.

The boiling points of aryl halides correspond very closely with those of the corresponding haloalkane of comparable relative molecular mass, but the presence of further substituents in the ring creates large discrepancies, and many of these compounds are solids.

Haloalkanes and aryl halides are both insoluble in water but soluble in organic solvents. The insolubility in water may seem surprising considering the polarity of the carbon–halogen bond, but is probably due to an inability to form hydrogen bonds with the water.

Industrial Source

Cheap and readily available supplies of chlorine make the chlorides the most popular industrial product. Direct halogenation of methane to yield CHLOROMETHANE is carried out at a temperature of 400 °C and proceeds via a free-radical mechanism.

$$CH_4 \xrightarrow[400\,°C]{Cl_2} \text{Mixture of } CH_3Cl, CH_2Cl_2, CHCl_3 \text{ and } CCl_4.$$

The components may be separated by fractional distillation, although many industrial uses of the haloalkanes do not require this.

In the United Kingdom, chloromethane is obtained mainly from methanol and hydrogen chloride, which are passed together over a heated zinc chloride catalyst.

$$CH_3OH + HCl \xrightarrow[\text{heat}]{ZnCl_2 \text{ cat.}} CH_3Cl + H_2O$$

Industrially, chloromethane is an extremely useful raw material, the largest proportion being used to manufacture silicone rubbers (*see* page 315). It is also employed as a solvent for making butyl rubbers, manufacturing tetramethyllead(IV), which, like tetraethyllead(IV), is a useful anti-knock compound, and for preparing methylcelluloses.

BROMOMETHANE is manufactured from methanol, hydrogen bromide and a catalyst. Its highly toxic properties make it a useful rodent controller and fumigating agent.

CHLOROETHANE can be prepared from ethanol and hydrochloric acid using a zinc chloride catalyst, although in the U.K. a large proportion is manufactured from ethane and ethene by a combined process in which ethane is firstly chlorinated at 400 °C and the hydrogen chloride obtained from this stage is used to convert the ethene. The second stage can be performed as a liquid or gas phase reaction.

$$CH_3CH_3 + Cl_2 \xrightarrow{400\,°C} CH_3CH_2Cl + HCl$$

$$CH_2{=}CH_2 + HCl \xrightarrow[\text{AlCl}_3 \text{ cat., } 35-40\,°C]{\text{liquid phase, anhyd.}} CH_3CH_2Cl$$
$$\text{(liquid } CH_3CH_2Cl \text{ solvent)}$$

or $\quad CH_2{=}CH_2 + HCl \xrightarrow[\text{AlCl}_3 \text{ cat., } 130-250\,°C]{\text{vapour phase, anhyd.}} CH_3CH_2Cl$

The principal uses of chloroethane are as a spray for local anaesthetic, and for manufacturing tetraethyl-lead(IV).

Direct fluorination of alkanes is not employed because of the highly exothermic nature of the reaction and the difficulty in handling fluorine and hydrogen fluoride.

Most fluorine compounds are prepared by the replacement of chlorine, using antimony(III) fluoride containing a trace of antimony(V) chloride.

$$3CCl_4 + 2SbF_3 \xrightarrow[\text{SbCl}_5]{\text{trace of}} 3CCl_2F_2 + 2SbCl_3$$
$$\text{Dichloro-}$$
$$\text{difluoromethane}$$

$$2CHClF_2 \xrightarrow{700-900\,°C} CF_2{=}CF_2 + 2HCl$$
$$\text{Tetrafluoroethene}$$

Chlorofluoromethanes are widely used as aerosol propellants and tetrafluoroethene is the monomer from which poly(tetrafluorethene) is manufactured (*see* page 304).

Synthetic Preparation of Haloalkanes

Substitution in Alcohols

The chloroalkane can be prepared by saturating the alcohol with dry hydrogen chloride, which is bubbled through it in the presence of a zinc chloride catalyst, and then refluxing on a water bath. In the case of the more reactive tertiary alcohols, the reaction proceeds in the cold.

$$CH_3CH_2OH + HCl \xrightarrow[\text{reflux}]{ZnCl_2 \text{ cat.}} CH_3CH_2Cl + H_2O$$
$$\text{dry}$$

Chlorination of alcohols can also be brought about by refluxing with sulphur dichloride oxide (thionyl chloride), $SOCl_2$, in the presence of a small amount of pyridine, C_5H_5N, which absorbs the hydrogen chloride as it is formed.

$$CH_3CH_2OH + SOCl_2 \xrightarrow{C_5H_5N} CH_3CH_2Cl + SO_2 + HCl$$

Bromination of tertiary alcohols can be brought about in the cold by treating them with either hydrogen bromide ($NaBr$/conc. H_2SO_4) or red phosphorus and bromine, but primary alcohols are less susceptible and require refluxing.

$$CH_3CH_2OH + HBr \xrightarrow[\text{reflux}]{NaBr/H_2SO_4} CH_3CH_2Br + H_2O$$

The iodoalkane is prepared by adding iodine to a mixture of the alcohol and red phosphorus and then refluxing on a water bath.

$$2P + 3I_2 \longrightarrow 2PI_3$$
$$3CH_3CH_2OH + PI_3 \longrightarrow 3CH_3CH_2I + H_3PO_3$$

An iodide and sulphuric acid cannot be used as the hydrogen iodide produced, being a powerful reducing agent, would be oxidized to iodine by the acid.

Ease of substitution of alcohols:

$$3° \text{ alcohol} > 2° \text{ alcohol} > 1° \text{ alcohol}$$

and is dependent upon the order of stability of the intermediate carbonium ion.

Addition of Hydrogen Halides to Alkenes

$$>C=C< + HBr \longrightarrow \begin{array}{c} | \; | \\ -C-C- \\ | \; | \\ H \;\; Br \end{array}$$

Refer to the reactions of the alkenes.

Halide Exchange Reaction

Refer to the reactions of haloalkanes.

Synthetic Preparations of Aryl Halides

Replacement of a Diazonium Salt: Sandmeyer Reaction

The diazonium salt is obtained by treating a primary aromatic amine, e.g. phenylamine (aniline), with dilute nitrous acid ($NaNO_2$/dil. HCl) at O °C,

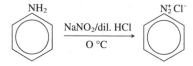

Phenylamine (aniline)   Benzenediazonium chloride

and then heating with the appropriate copper(I) halide (see page 216).

Bromobenzene

Direct Halogenation

Direct halogenation can be brought about by treating benzene (or other aryl compound) with the halogen in the presence of a suitable polarizing catalyst.

The bromine molecule is polarized during the reaction, forming the complex $Br^+[FeBr_4]^-$ (*see* page 134).

The preparation from diazonium salts has a wider application since it can be used for fluorination and iodination, whereas these reactions are difficult to carry out by direct combination.

Whenever possible, chlorobenzene is used for industrial processes as it is considerably less expensive than bromo- and iodobenzene.

Reactions

The haloalkanes are fairly reactive compounds, owing largely to the polarity of the carbon–halogen bond, $R^{\delta+}—X^{\delta-}$. In the vast majority of their reactions, they function as electrophilic reagents, the electron-deficient carbon being susceptible to attack by an electron-rich species. The reactions are therefore characterized by NUCLEOPHILIC SUBSTITUTION of the halogen atom.

In contrast, the aryl halides are comparatively inert and only undergo nucleophilic substitution of the halogen atom with extreme difficulty. However nucleophilic substitution of this type may be promoted by the presence of electron-withdrawing groups, e.g. $—NO_2$, $—CN$ in the ring.

The lack of reactivity of aryl halides with regard to nucleophilic substitution of the halogen *is attributed to the diminished polarity of the carbon–halogen bond.*

The *p* orbitals of the halogen atom interact with those of the ring, causing a drift of electrons towards the carbon atom to which it is attached, and thus reducing the degree of polarity of the bond.

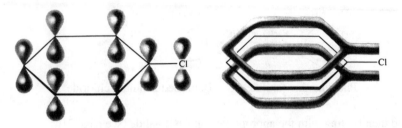

It is for a similar reason that haloethenes (vinyl halides) are relatively unreactive; the *p* orbitals of the halogen this time interacting with the π electrons in the double bond.

In allyl halides, this type of interaction is not possible and their reactivity is more analogous to that of the haloalkanes.

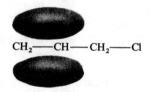

Nucleophilic substitution of haloalkanes provides one of the most important methods of synthetically preparing organic compounds. The substitution of the halogen atom by —OH, —OR, CH_3COO—, —CN and —NH_2 are commonly employed in the preparation of alcohols, ethers, esters, nitriles (cyanides) and amines. Moreover, much of the importance of alcohols in organic chemistry can be attributed to their easy conversion into reactive haloalkanes.

The polar nature of haloalkanes is further illustrated by their readiness to react with inorganic as well as organic reagents.

Alcohol Formation

Haloalkanes provide one of the most useful methods of preparing alcohols.

$$R^{\delta+}\!\!-\!\!X^{\delta-} + {}^-OH \longrightarrow R\!\!-\!\!OH + X^-$$

Primary and secondary haloalkanes undergo alkaline hydrolysis to the alcohol. Water alone acts very slowly at ordinary temperatures, but rapidly hydrolyses tertiary haloalkanes.

$$CH_3\overset{\delta+}{CH_2}\!-\!\overset{\delta-}{Br} + {}^-OH \longrightarrow CH_3CH_2\!-\!OH + Br^-$$

$$\underset{CH_3}{\overset{CH_3}{\diagdown}}\overset{\delta+}{CH}\!-\!\overset{\delta-}{Br} + {}^-OH \longrightarrow \underset{CH_3}{\overset{CH_3}{\diagdown}}CH\!-\!OH + Br^-$$

$$CH_3\!-\!\underset{CH_3}{\overset{CH_3}{\overset{|}{C}}}\!-\!\overset{\delta+\,\delta-}{Br} + H_2O \overset{boil}{\longrightarrow} CH_3\!-\!\underset{CH_3}{\overset{CH_3}{\overset{|}{C}}}\!-\!OH + HBr$$

The reactions (apart from those involving halomethanes) produce a quantity of the alkene as a result of the concurrent elimination reactions (*see* page 160),

$$-\underset{H}{\overset{|}{C}}\!-\!\underset{Br}{\overset{|}{C}}\!- \overset{elimination}{\longrightarrow} {>}C{=}C{<} + HBr$$

but this may be avoided by performing the hydrolysis using a suspension of silver(I) oxide in moist ethoxyethane.

$$2CH_3CH_2Br + Ag_2O + H_2O \overset{(C_2H_5)_2O}{\longrightarrow} 2CH_3CH_2OH + 2AgBr$$

If sodium hydroxide is used instead of water on a tertiary haloalkane, a much larger amount of the elimination product, i.e. the alkene, is obtained.

Aryl halides are not sufficiently reactive to undergo hydrolysis to phenols except under severe conditions. Industrially, phenol can be obtained by heating chlorobenzene with aqueous sodium hydroxide at 360 °C at a high pressure and then hydrolysing the phenoxide (phenate) formed with hydrochloric acid.

Chlorobenzene → (NaOH, 360 °C 150 atm) Sodium phenoxide (Sodium phenate) → (dil. HCl) Phenol

Ether Formation: Williamson's Synthesis

This reaction affords the most important and versatile preparation of ethers since it is suitable for both symmetrical and unsymmetrical ethers as well as alkoxyaromatics (aryl alkyl ethers) and alkoxyalkanes (dialkyl ethers).

Sodium or potassium alkoxide (alkylate), prepared by dissolving the alkali metal in excess of the appropriate alcohol, react with the haloalkane to form the ether.

$$CH_3\overset{\delta+}{CH_2}\!-\!\overset{\delta-}{Br} + CH_3CH_2O^-Na^+ \longrightarrow CH_3CH_2\!-\!O\!-\!CH_2CH_3 + NaBr$$

Sodium ethoxide   Ethoxyethane
(Sodium ethylate)   (Diethyl ether)

$$\begin{array}{c} CH_3 \\ \diagdown \\ \overset{\delta+}{CH}\!-\!\overset{\delta-}{Br} + CH_3CH_2O^-Na^+ \longrightarrow \\ \diagup \\ CH_3 \end{array} \quad \begin{array}{c} CH_3 \\ \diagdown \\ CH\!-\!O\!-\!CH_2CH_3 + NaBr \\ \diagup \\ CH_3 \end{array}$$

2-Ethoxypropane
(Ethyl isopropyl ether)

This reaction may also be performed using the phenoxide (phenate).

$$CH_3\!-\!\overset{\delta+}{CH_2}\!-\!\overset{\delta-}{Br} + \underset{\substack{\text{Sodium phenoxide} \\ \text{(Sodium phenate)}}}{\underset{}{\bigcirc\!\!-\!O^-Na^+}} \longrightarrow \underset{\substack{\text{Ethoxybenzene} \\ \text{(Phenetole)}}}{\underset{}{\bigcirc\!\!-\!OCH_2CH_3}} + NaBr$$

For methoxyaromatics (methyl aryl ethers) it is more usual to use dimethyl sulphate, $(CH_3)_2SO_4$, and a phenol in aqueous sodium hydroxide.

$$\underset{\textbf{Phenol}}{\bigcirc\!\!-\!\textbf{OH}} + (CH_3)_2SO_4 \xrightarrow[\text{heat}]{\text{aq. NaOH}} \underset{\substack{\textbf{Methoxybenzene} \\ \textbf{(Anisole)}}}{\bigcirc\!\!-\!\textbf{OCH}_3} + CH_3NaSO_4$$

Ester Formation

If an alcoholic solution of the silver(I) salt of a carboxylic acid is warmed with an haloalkane, an ester is formed together with the silver(I) halide, which is precipitated.

$$CH_3\overset{\delta+}{CH_2}\!-\!\overset{\delta-}{Br} + CH_3COO^-Ag^+ \xrightarrow{\text{alcohol}} CH_3COOCH_2CH_3 + AgBr$$

Ethyl ethanoate
(Ethyl acetate)

$$\begin{array}{c} CH_3 \\ \diagdown \\ \overset{\delta+}{CH}\!-\!\overset{\delta-}{Br} + CH_3COO^-Ag^+ \xrightarrow{\text{alcohol}} \\ \diagup \\ CH_3 \end{array} \quad \begin{array}{c} CH_3 \\ \diagup \\ CH_3COOCH \quad + AgBr \\ \diagdown \\ CH_3 \end{array}$$

1-Methylethyl ethanoate
(Isopropyl acetate)

Phenyl esters cannot be obtained by the direct interaction of the aryl halide and the carboxylate ion.

Amine Formation

Alkylation of ammonia takes place if an alcoholic solution of ammonia is heated with an haloalkane in a sealed tube. The reaction has the disadvantage that a mixture of different classes of amines results since the alkyl amines are more reactive than the ammonia.

$$NH_3 + CH_3CH_2Br \xrightarrow[\text{sealed tube}]{\text{heat in}} CH_3CH_2NH_2 + HBr$$
in alcohol   1° amine

$$CH_3CH_2NH_2 + CH_3CH_2Br \longrightarrow (CH_3CH_2)_2NH + HBr$$
2° amine

$$(CH_3CH_2)_2NH + CH_3CH_2Br \longrightarrow (CH_3CH_2)_3N + HBr$$
3° amine

$$(CH_3CH_2)_3N + CH_3CH_2Br \longrightarrow (CH_3CH_2)_4N^+Br^-$$
Quaternary ammonium salt
4°

In practice the mixture is difficult to separate, but excess of ammonia enables a better yield of the primary amine to be obtained. Each amine formed exists in equilibrium with its salt (*see* page 207).

The reaction tends to be limited to the aliphatic series, although aryl halides will react if electron-withdrawing substituents are present in the 2- or 4-positions.

Nitrile (Cyanide) Formation

Alkanenitriles are prepared by heating the haloalkane with sodium cyanide in a suitable solvent, generally aqueous alcohol, the water component dissolving the sodium cyanide and the alcohol dissolving the haloalkane.

$$CH_3\overset{\delta+}{CH_2}—\overset{\delta-}{Br} + CN^- \xrightarrow{\text{aq.alcohol}} CH_3CH_2CN + Br^-$$
Propanenitrile
(Ethyl cyanide)

$$\begin{array}{c} CH_3 \\ \diagdown \overset{\delta+}{CH}—\overset{\delta-}{Br} + CN^- \\ \diagup \\ CH_3 \end{array} \xrightarrow{\text{aq.alcohol}} \begin{array}{c} CH_3 \\ \diagdown \\ CHCN + Br^- \\ \diagup \\ CH_3 \end{array}$$
2-Methylpropanenitrile
(Isopropyl cyanide)

Aromatic nitriles are not prepared from the unreactive aryl halides but from diazonium salts (*see* page 216).

Silver(I) cyanide reacts with haloalkanes to form ISOCYANOALKANES (isocyanides), which are readily recognizable by their foul smell.

$$CH_3\overset{\delta+}{C}H_2 \overset{\frown}{-}\overset{\delta-}{Br} + AgCN \longrightarrow CH_3CH_2NC + AgBr$$

Ethyl isocyanide

This is made possible by the covalent structure of the silver(I) cyanide in which the silver atoms are attached to both carbon and nitrogen atoms.

Halide Exchange Reaction

This reaction is suitable for preparing iodoalkanes. The bromoalkane is heated with a solution of sodium iodide in propanone (acetone), the less soluble sodium bromide being precipitated and separated by filtration.

$$CH_3\overset{\delta+}{C}H_2 \overset{\frown}{-}\overset{\delta-}{Br} + Na^+I^- \xrightarrow{propanone} CH_3CH_2I + Na^+Br^-$$

Formation of Methylbenzene (Toluene): Fittig's Reaction

Methylbenzene is formed slowly if sodium is slowly added to a dry ethereal solution of bromobenzene and iodomethane (*see* Wurtz synthesis of alkanes).

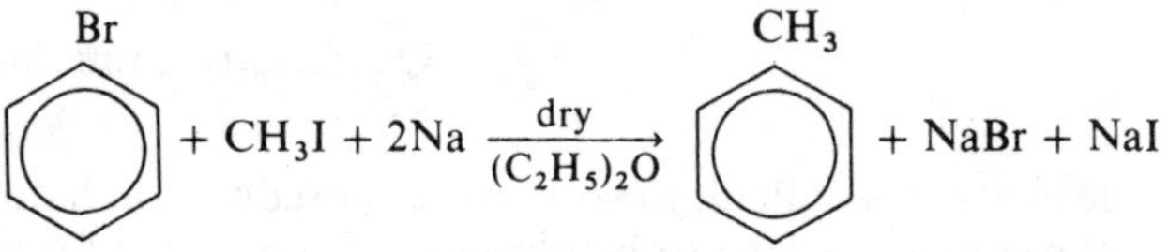

Methylbenzene
(Toluene)

Ethane, CH_3CH_3, and diphenyl, Ph.Ph, are formed as by-products of the reaction.

Mechanism for Nucleophilic Substitution of Haloalkanes

The effect of the structure of the haloalkane has a pronounced effect upon the mechanism of substitution.

Substitution Nucleophilic Unimolecular (S_N1) Reaction

Kinetic studies have shown that the rate of hydrolysis of *tertiary haloalkanes* is dependent only upon the concentration of the haloalkanes.

i.e.   Rate = k[RX]

Consequently, the slow rate-determining step must involve only the haloalkane. The following two-step mechanism, referred to as a SUBSTITUTION NUCLEOPHILIC UNIMOLECULAR (S_N1) REACTION, has been proposed, and involves the formation of a *carbocation* (*carbonium ion*) intermediate.

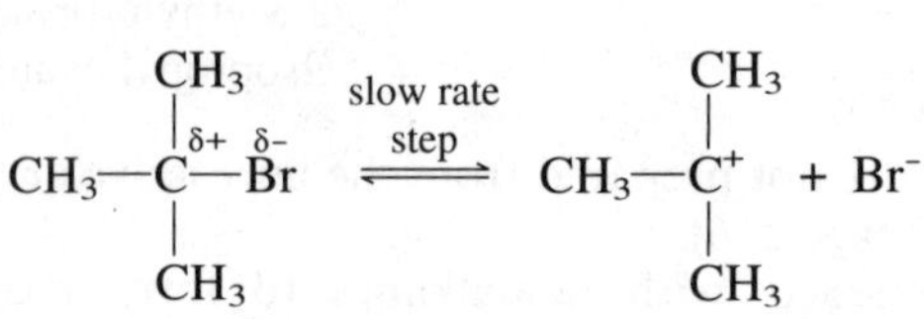

$$(2) \qquad CH_3-\overset{\overset{\displaystyle CH_3}{|}}{\underset{\underset{\displaystyle CH_3}{|}}{C^+}} \quad {}^-OH \xrightarrow{\text{fast}} CH_3-\overset{\overset{\displaystyle CH_3}{|}}{\underset{\underset{\displaystyle CH_3}{|}}{C}}-OH$$

The molecularity of the reaction describes the number of species involved in bond cleavage in the rate-determining step.

The carbocation intermediate is stabilized by the electron-donating alkyl groups, and also by the polar medium.

If the haloalkane is optically active, a racemic product is obtained, since attack by the hydroxyl group can take place from both sides of the carbocation, yielding equal quantities of both the $(+)$ and $(-)$ isomer.

Substitution Nucleophilic Bimolecular (S_N2) Reaction

The alkaline hydrolysis of primary haloalkane exhibits second order kinetics, the rate being dependent upon the concentration of both the haloalkane and the hydroxide ions.

$$\text{i.e.} \quad \text{Rate} = k[RX]\,[^-OH]$$

This means that both reactants must be involved in the rate-determining step. The following one-step mechanism, referred to as a SUBSTITUTION NUCLEOPHILIC BIMOLECULAR (S_N2) REACTION, has been proposed, and involves a transition state in which the entering hydroxide ion and the leaving halide ion are *both partially bonded* to the same carbon.

$$CH_3\overset{\delta+}{C}H_2 \overset{\delta-}{\overbrace{Br}} \,\,^-OH \longrightarrow Br \ldots C \ldots OH \longrightarrow HOCH_2CH_3 + Br^-$$

Haloalkanes containing a chiral centre undergo inversion of configuration.

Secondary haloalkanes show a mixture of both second and first order kinetics, with the former predominating.

Elimination Reactions of Haloalkanes

Elimination of hydrogen and halogen atoms from adjacent carbon atoms of haloalkanes results in the formation of a double bond,

$$-\overset{|}{\underset{|}{C}}-\overset{|}{\underset{|}{C}}- \xrightarrow{\text{elimination}} >C=C< \,+ HX$$
$$H\quad X$$

and affords an important method for preparing alkenes. Although the yield of ethene obtained by refluxing iodoethane with a concentrated alcoholic solution of potassium hydroxide is only low (about 2 per cent), much better yields of alkene can be obtained from the higher haloalkanes, especially secondary and tertiary compounds (*see* page 101).

Concurrent Substitution and Elimination

All reactions involving substitution of haloalkanes are accompanied by concurrent elimination reactions, producing a mixture of products. Careful consideration of the nature of the reactants enables the reaction to be performed under such conditions as to favour the production of the desired product in greater abundance. This usually involves choosing a suitable medium.

Elimination reactions are favoured by a medium of low polarity and a strongly basic nucleophile; hence the use of *alcoholic potassium hydroxide* in the formation of alkenes. Tertiary haloalkanes, which yield a branched and therefore more stable alkene, undergo elimination more easily than primary haloalkanes. It is for these reasons that the hydrolysis of tertiary haloalkanes is carried out in water (which acts as a weak nucleophile) instead of aqueous alkali, which would produce a larger amount of the elimination product.

Rates of nucleophilic substitution:

$$1° \text{ haloalkanes} > 2° \text{ haloalkanes} > 3° \text{ haloalkanes}$$

Rates of elimination reactions:

$$3° \text{ haloalkanes} > 2° \text{ haloalkanes} > 1° \text{ haloalkanes}$$

Mechanism for Elimination

Unimolecular Elimination, E1

For most secondary and tertiary haloalkanes, first order kinetics are observed, i.e. rate = k[RX], and the following mechanism, involving the formation of a *carbocation (carbonium ion) intermediate*, has been proposed (cf. S_N1 mechanism):

$$
\begin{array}{c}
\text{CH}_3 \\
\mid \\
\text{CH}_3-\underset{\mid}{\text{C}}-\text{Br} \\
\text{CH}_3
\end{array}
\xrightleftharpoons[\text{alc.KOH}]{\text{Slow rate step}}
\begin{array}{c}
^-\text{OH} \\
\text{H} \quad \text{CH}_3 \\
\mid \quad \mid \\
\text{CH}_2-\overset{+}{\text{C}} + \text{Br}^- \\
\mid \\
\text{CH}_3
\end{array}
\xrightarrow{\text{fast}}
\begin{array}{c}
\text{CH}_3 \\
\mid \\
\text{CH}_3-\text{C}=\text{CH}_2 + \text{H}_2\text{O} + \text{Br}^-
\end{array}
$$

Bimolecular Elimination, E2

The majority of elimination reactions, especially those involving primary haloalkanes, show second order kinetics, i.e. rate = k[RX][OH], and proceed via an E2 mechanism in which the rate step involves the removal of a proton (H^+) from the 2-carbon of the haloalkane.

$$\text{HO}^- + \text{H}-\overset{2}{\text{CH}_2}-\overset{1}{\text{CH}_2}-\text{Br} \longrightarrow \text{H}_2\text{O} + \text{CH}_2=\text{CH}_2 + \text{Br}^-$$

Reactivity RI > RBr > RCl > RF

Reactions of Aryl Halides involving Substitution in the Ring

The halogens have the unique distinction of directing further substituents to the 2- and 4- positions despite the fact that they are electron-withdrawing from the ring. This is discussed and explained on page 140.

NITRATION, SULPHONATION, HALOGENATION and FRIEDEL–CRAFTS ALKYLATION and ACYLATION can be brought about in a manner similar to that described for benzene.

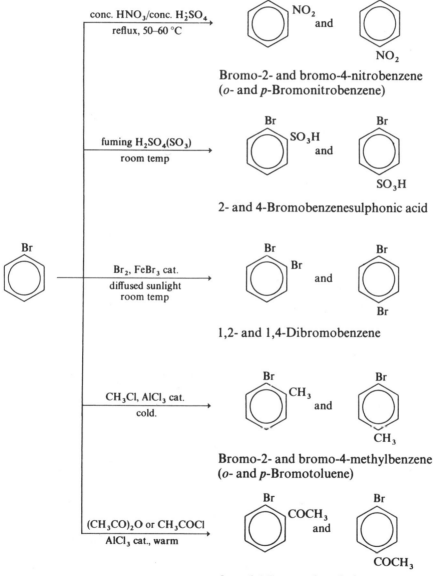

conc. HNO$_3$/conc. H$_2$SO$_4$
reflux, 50–60 °C

Bromo-2- and bromo-4-nitrobenzene
(*o*- and *p*-Bromonitrobenzene)

fuming H$_2$SO$_4$(SO$_3$)
room temp

2- and 4-Bromobenzenesulphonic acid

Br$_2$, FeBr$_3$ cat.
diffused sunlight
room temp

1,2- and 1,4-Dibromobenzene

CH$_3$Cl, AlCl$_3$ cat.
cold.

Bromo-2- and bromo-4-methylbenzene
(*o*- and *p*-Bromotoluene)

(CH$_3$CO)$_2$O or CH$_3$COCl
AlCl$_3$ cat., warm

2- and 4-Bromophenylethanone
(*o*- and *p*-Bromoacetophenone)

In these reactions, steric hindrance in the 2- position favours the formation of the 4- product in greater quantity.

The Grignard Reagent

The GRIGNARD REAGENT, named after its discoverer Victor Grignard (1912), is one of the most important and versatile reagents used in modern syntheses. Turnings or granules of magnesium are treated with a *dry* ethereal solution of a haloalkane and left to stand. The mixture boils of its own accord and the magnesium disappears leaving a cloudy solution.

The structure of the reagent, although not known precisely, is complex and incorporates two ethoxyethane (ether) molecules. However, the latter are usually omitted when writing the formula, which is usually represented as simply the ALKYLMAGNESIUM HALIDE, RMgX.

$$CH_3CH_2Br + Mg \xrightarrow{\text{dry } (C_2H_5)_2O} CH_3CH_2MgBr$$

Ethylmagnesium bromide

The magnesium–carbon bond is largely covalent, but the magnesium–halogen bond is predominantly ionic.

This highly reactive reagent has numerous practical applications, and may be employed for preparing alkanes, alkenes, alkynes, alcohols, aldehydes, ketones and carboxylic acids.

Aromatic Grignard reagents are made in the same way and perform exactly similar reactions.

TETRAHYDROFURAN is often used instead of ordinary ether as a medium for the alkylmagnesium halide and, in fact, has certain advantageous properties (*see* page 195).

Synthetic Applications of Grignard Reagents

Preparation of Alkanes (*see* page 92)

$$RX + Mg \xrightarrow{(C_2H_5)_2O} RMgX$$

$$RMgX + H_2O \xrightarrow{\text{dil. acid}} RH + MgXOH$$

Alkane   Precipitated

Preparation of Alkynes

Only suitable for higher homologues of ethyne (acetylene):

$$CH{\equiv}CH + RMgX \xrightarrow[\substack{CH_2-CH_2 \\ | \qquad \diagdown O \\ CH_2-CH_2}]{\text{tetrahydrofuran}} RH + CH{\equiv}CMgX$$

$$CH{\equiv}CMgX + RX \longrightarrow CH{\equiv}CR + MgBrX$$

Preparation of Alcohols

Suitable for preparing primary, secondary and tertiary alcohols.

Primary Alcohols (*see* page 170)

(1) $RMgX + HCHO \xrightarrow{(C_2H_5)_2O} RCH_2OMgX \xrightarrow[\text{dil. acid}]{H_2O} RCH_2OH + MgXOH$

     Methanal   1 ° alcohol
     (Formaldehyde)   (+C)

$$(2)\ RMgX + \underset{\underset{\begin{array}{c}\text{Epoxyethane}\\\text{(Ethylene oxide)}\end{array}}{O}}{\overset{CH_2-CH_2}{\diagdown\diagup}} \xrightarrow{(C_2H_5)_2O} RCH_2CH_2OMgX$$

$$\xrightarrow[\text{dil. acid}]{H_2O} RCH_2CH_2OH + MgXOH$$

$$(+2C)$$

These reactions provide a means of increasing the length of the carbon chain.

Secondary Alcohols (*see* page 170)

$$RMgX + \underset{\text{(not HCHO)}}{R'CHO} \xrightarrow{(C_2H_5)_2O} \underset{\underset{OMgX}{|}}{RCHR'} \xrightarrow[\text{dil. acid}]{H_2O} \underset{\underset{R'}{\diagup}}{\overset{R}{\diagdown}}CHOH + MgXOH$$

           Aldehyde   2 ° alcohol

Tertiary Alcohols (*see* page 170)

$$RMgX + \underset{\underset{R''}{\diagup}}{\overset{R'}{\diagdown}}C{=}O \xrightarrow{(C_2H_5)_2O} \underset{\underset{OMgX}{|}}{\overset{\overset{R'}{|}}{R-C-R''}} \xrightarrow[\text{aq. NH}_4\text{Cl}]{H_2O} \underset{\underset{OH}{|}}{\overset{\overset{R'}{|}}{R-C-R''}} + MgXOH$$

             Ketone   3 ° alcohol

Aqueous ammonium chloride is used in the hydrolysis to the tertiary alcohol, as the presence of an acid causes dehydration.

Preparation of Aldehydes (*see* page 226)

$$RMgX + \underset{\underset{OCH_2CH_3}{|}}{\overset{\overset{OCH_2CII_3}{|}}{H-C-OCH_2CH_3}} \xrightarrow{(C_2H_5)_2O} \underset{\underset{OCH_2CH_3}{|}}{\overset{\overset{OCH_2CH_3}{|}}{H-C-R}} + MgXOCH_2CH_3$$

        Triethoxymethane
        (Ethyl orthoformate)

$$\xrightarrow[\text{dil. acid}]{2II_2O} \underset{\underset{H}{\diagup}}{\overset{R}{\diagdown}}C{=}O + 2CH_3CH_2OH$$

                          Aldehyde

Preparation of Ketones (*see* page 227)

$$RMgX + R'CN \xrightarrow{(C_2H_5)_2O} R\!-\!\underset{\substack{\|\\ NMgX}}{C}\!-\!R'$$

(not CH_3CN)

Alkanonitrile
(Alkyl cyanide)

$$\xrightarrow[\text{dil. acid}]{2H_2O} \quad \underset{R'}{\overset{R}{\diagdown}}C\!=\!O + MgXOH + NH_3$$

Ketone

Preparation of Carboxylic Acids (*see* page 251)

$$RMgX + CO_2 \xrightarrow{(C_2H_5)_2O} RCOOMgX \xrightarrow[\text{dil. acid}]{H_2O} RCOOH + MgXOH$$

Carboxylic acid

Synthetic Applications of Some Other Organo-metallic Compounds

ORGANO-LITHIUM COMPOUNDS have very similar properties and are polarized in dry ethereal solution, $R^{\delta-}\!-\!Li^{\delta+}$, in the same way as Grignard reagents. For example, PHENYLLITHIUM is produced if either chloro- or bromobenzene in ethoxyethane (ether) is treated with small pieces of freshly cut metallic lithium.

$$C_6H_5Br + 2Li \xrightarrow{(C_2H_5)_2O} C_6H_5Li + LiBr$$

Bromobenzene $\qquad\qquad$ Phenyllithium

Phenyllithium, on treatment with carbon dioxide and water, yields benzenecarboxylic (benzoic) acid.

$$C_6H_5Li \xrightarrow[(C_2H_5)_2O]{CO_2} C_6H_5\overset{O}{\overset{\|}{C}}\!-\!OLi \xrightarrow{H_2O} C_6H_5\overset{O}{\overset{\|}{C}}\!-\!OH \quad + LiOH$$

Benzenecarboxylic acid
(Benzoic acid)

and adds to the carbonyl ($>\!C\!=\!O$) group of aldehydes, ketones and esters.

$$C_6H_5Li \xrightarrow[(C_2H_5)_2O]{RCHO,} \underset{OLi}{RCHC_6H_5} \xrightarrow{H_2O} \underset{OH}{RCHC_6H_5} + LiOH$$

Alcohol

ORGANO-CADMIUM COMPOUNDS, prepared by reacting dry cadmium chloride with a Grignard reagent, react with acyl chlorides to form ketones.

$$2RMgX + CdCl_2 \longrightarrow R_2Cd + 2MgXCl$$

$$R_2Cd + 2R'COCl \longrightarrow 2R\!-\!\underset{\substack{\|\\ O}}{C}\!-\!R' + CdCl_2$$

Ketone

QUESTIONS

1. Without referring to tables, state which of the following haloalkanes has the highest density (measured under the same conditions of temperature and pressure).

   A 1-iodobutane
   B 2-chlorobutane
   C 1-fluoropentane
   D 2-bromopentane
   E 1-iodopentane

2. Bromoethane is best hydrolysed to ethanol by refluxing it with

   A water
   B aqueous sulphuric acid
   C alcoholic potassium hydroxide
   D aqueous potassium hydroxide
   E silver(I) oxide in moist ethoxyethane

3. The experimentally determined rate equation for the alkaline hydrolysis of RBr is given by:

   $$\text{Rate} = k[\text{RBr}]\,[^-\text{OH}]$$

   Which of the following statements is inconsistent with these observations?

   A the reaction is first order with respect to RBr
   B the reaction is second order overall
   C the reaction process is completed by the attack of $^-$OH on R^+
   D the rate-determining step is bimolecular
   E OH^- attacks the bromoalkane before the R^-Br bond is fully cleared

4. Give the names and structures of the major organic products of the reaction (if any) between bromobenzene and the following:

   A Br_2, $FeBr_3$
   B Mg, ethoxyethane
   C conc. HNO_3/conc. H_2SO_4
   D boiling dilute KOH
   E boiling alcoholic KOH
   F CH_3CH_2Cl, $AlCl_3$
   G fuming H_2SO_4

5. By consideration of orbital theory, compare the reactivity of bromoethane, bromoethene (vinyl bromide) and bromobenzene with respect to substitution of the halogen atom.

6. Explain why chloromethane is hydrolysed to methanol by aqueous alkali at $60\,^\circ$C whereas conditions of $360\,^\circ$C and 150 atmospheres are required to convert chlorobenzene to phenol using the same reagent.

7. Suggest the most probable *type* of mechanism for each of the following reactions:

   A $CH_3CH_2CH_2Cl + OH^- \longrightarrow$
      $CH_3CH_2CH_2OH + Cl^-$

   B $(CH_3)_2CClCH(CH_3)_2 \xrightarrow[\text{KOH}]{\text{alcoholic}}$
      $(CH_3)_2C{=}C(CH_3)_2 + HCl$

   C $(CH_3)_3CI + CN^- \xrightarrow{\text{alcohol}}$
      $(CH_3)_3CCN + I^-$

   D $(CH_3)_2CHCH_2CH_2Cl \xrightarrow[\text{KOH}]{\text{alcoholic}}$
      $(CH_3)_2CHCH{=}CH_2 + HCl$

8. Briefly discuss the synthetic application of haloalkanes, choosing as wide a range of products as possible. To what extent has the scope been extended by the use of the Grignard reagent?

16 *Alcohols*

ALIPHATIC MONOHYDRIC ALCOHOLS are monohydroxyl derivatives of alkanes and have a general molecular formula, $C_nH_{2n+1}OH$, or simply ROH, although the definition is sometimes extended to include certain substituted alkyl groups. Compounds containing more than one hydroxyl group are described as POLYHYDRIC ALCOHOLS.

They may be classified as *primary* (1°), *secondary* (2°), *or tertiary* (3°) according to the nature of the carbon atom to which the hydroxyl group is attached.

CH_3OH CH_3CH_2OH

Methanol   Ethanol
(Methyl alcohol)   (Ethyl alcohol)
1°   1°

$$CH_3\!-\!\underset{\underset{OH}{|}}{CH}\!-\!CH_3 \qquad CH_3\!-\!\underset{\underset{OH}{|}}{\overset{\overset{CH_3}{|}}{C}}\!-\!CH_3$$

Propan-2-ol   2-Methylpropan-2-ol
(Isopropyl alcohol) (*tert*-Butyl alcohol)
2°   3°

AROMATIC ALCOHOLS are, in effect, aryl substituents of aliphatic alcohols in which the hydroxyl group is separated from the benzene ring by at least one methylene ($-CH_2-$) group.

CH_2OH CH_2CH_2OH

Phenylmethanol   2-Phenylethanol
(Benzyl alcohol)   (β-Phenylethyl alcohol)

Compounds in which the hydroxyl group is attached directly to the benzene ring are classified as PHENOLS. These compounds have their own characteristic properties and are considered separately in the next chapter.

Alcohols containing two hydroxyl groups are described as DIHYDRIC ALCOHOLS, DIOLS or GLYCOLS, and those containing three hydroxyl groups as TRIHYDRIC ALCOHOLS or TRIOLS.

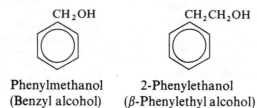

Ethane-1,2-diol   Propane-1,2,3-triol
(Ethylene glycol)   (Glycerol)

The most common of these is ethane-1,2-diol (ethylene glycol), which is a sweet-tasting, poisonous, hygroscopic liquid (b.p. 197 °C), encountered mainly as an anti-freeze additive.

Nomenclature

The IUPAC system is generally adopted for most alcohols, although common names, which are afforded by stating the name of the appropriate alkyl group followed by the word 'alcohol', are still sometimes used for the simpler compounds, e.g. methyl alcohol, isopropyl alcohol, benzyl alcohol etc.

The IUPAC names are afforded by dropping the ending '-ane' of the corresponding alkane and replacing it with the suffix '-ol'. The position of the hydroxyl group in the carbon chain is specified by inserting the appropriate number between the stem of the name and the '-ol'.

Formula	IUPAC name	Common name
CH_3OH	Methanol	Methyl alcohol
CH_3CH_2OH	Ethanol	Ethyl alcohol
$CH_3CH_2CH_2OH$	Propan-1-ol	n-Propyl alcohol
CH_3CHCH_3 $\vert$ OH	Propan-2-ol	Isopropyl alcohol
CH_3 $\vert$ $CH_3{-}C{-}CH_3$ $\vert$ OH	2-Methylpropan-2-ol	*tert*-Butyl alcohol
$C_6H_5CH_2OH$	Phenylmethanol	Benzyl alcohol
$C_6H_5CH_2CH_2OH$	2-Phenylethanol	β-Phenylethyl alcohol

Hydrogen Bonding in Alcohols

Alcohols contain the highly polar—OH group and therefore there exists strong dipole–dipole interactions between the molecules in the liquid phase. However, such interactions do not sufficiently account for the fact that alcohols have considerably higher boiling points than alkanes of comparable relative molecular mass. This discrepancy is explained in terms of *intermolecular hydrogen bonding*, in which the more electronegative oxygen atom attracts the bonding electrons away from the hydrogen atom, thus leaving the hydrogen nucleus partially exposed. This leaves the way open for an oxygen atom of another alcohol molecule to donate a lone pair of electrons and associate in the liquid phase.

$$\overset{\delta+}{H}\!\!-\!\!-\!\!-\!\!\overset{\delta-}{\ddot{O}}\!:\text{---}\overset{\delta+}{H}\!\!-\!\!-\!\!-\!\!\overset{\delta-}{\ddot{O}}\!:$$
$$\vert\vert$$
$$RR$$

Boiling breaks down this association and the molecules exist as monomers in the vapour phase.

Physical Properties

Most simple aliphatic alcohols and the lower aromatic alcohols are liquids at room temperature, the boiling points of which increase with increasing relative molecular mass, although branched isomers tend to be more volatile than their straight-chain and less highly branched counterparts. Aliphatic alcohols containing more than twelve carbons and the higher aromatic ones are waxy solids.

The order of boiling points of isomeric alcohols is 1° alcohols > 2° alcohols > 3° alcohols.

Name	Formula	M.p./°C	B.p./°C	Density at 20°C/ g cm^{-3}
Methanol	CH_3OH	−97	65	0.792
Ethanol	CH_3CH_2OH	−114	78	0.789
Propan-1-ol	$CH_3(CH_2)_2OH$	−126	97	0.804
Propan-2-ol	$(CH_3)_2CHOH$	−88	82	0.786
Butan-1-ol	$CH_3(CH_2)_3OH$	−90	118	0.810
2-Methylpropan-1-ol	$(CH_3)_2CHCH_2OH$	−108	108	0.802
Butan-2-ol	$CH_3CH_2CHOHCH_3$	−114	100	0.808
2-Methylpropan-2-ol	$(CH_3)_3COH$	25	83	0.789
Pentan-1-ol	$CH_3(CH_2)_4OH$	−79	138	0.817
Hexan-1-ol	$CH_3(CH_2)_5OH$	−52	156	0.819
Phenylmethanol	$C_6H_5CH_2OH$	−15	205	1.046
1-Phenylethanol	$C_6H_5CHOHCH_3$	−20	205	1.013
2-Phenylethanol	$C_6H_5CH_2CH_2OH$	−27	221	1.020

The density of the alcohols becomes greater with increasing relative molecular mass, although branching again has the effect of reducing this factor. All aliphatic alcohols are less dense than water, but the aromatic homologues tend to be slightly more dense than water.

Simple alcohols possess many properties characteristic of water, and may be regarded as *monoalkyl derivatives of water*. On the other hand, higher members exhibit properties which are much more analogous to those of the hydrocarbons and are better regarded as *hydroxyl derivatives of alkanes*. For example, methanol, ethanol and propan-1-ol are miscible in water in all proportions, due largely to their ability to form hydrogen bonds with the water molecules, whereas higher members show a marked decrease in solubility. The hydrocarbon nature of hexan-1-ol is indicated by the fact that its solubility at 20 °C is only 0.6 g in 100 g of water.

All alcohols are miscible with most organic solvents, and the simpler ones are themselves useful organic solvents.

Industrial Source

Methanol

Nowadays, methanol is manufactured from methane, obtained from natural gas. The first stage involves a process known as **steam reforming** which involves passing a mixture of methane and steam over a nickel catalyst heated to 900 °C.

$$CH_4 + H_2O \xrightarrow[900°C]{\text{Ni catalyst}} \underbrace{CO + 3H_2}_{\text{synthesis gas}}$$

The resultant mixture, referred to as **synthesis gas**, is passed over a chromium(III) oxide/zinc oxide catalyst at 350–400 °C. The quantity of hydrogen required for this process is in excess of the amount indicated by the equation.

$$2H_2 + CO \xrightleftharpoons[\text{350–400 °C, high press.}]{\text{Cr}_2\text{O}_3/\text{ZnO cat.}} CH_3OH$$

The formation of the product involves a reduction in volume in the system, and a high pressure is required to maintain the equilibrium.

Ethanol

Ethanol is manufactured from ethene (*see* page 109), which is abundantly available as a by-product of the cracking of petroleum, by direct hydrolysis using a phosphoric(V) acid on Celite catalyst. Quantities are still obtained by dissolving ethene in concentrated sulphuric acid followed by hydrolysis, but this technique is gradually becoming obsolete.

The fermentation of sugars (carbohydrates) still provides a useful small source of ethanol. The biological catalysts, enzymes, found in the yeast, break down the sugar molecules into ethanol to give a yield which is in the region of 95 per cent.

Glucose is rarely used in practice as some other suitable and cheaper raw material is usually available, e.g. molasses, potatoes, cereal, rice etc. All of these materials contain starch $(C_6H_{10}O_5)_n$, which on warming with malt to 60 °C for a specific period of time is converted into maltose by the enzyme DIASTASE contained in the malt.

$$2(C_6H_{10}O_5)_n + nH_2O \xrightarrow[60°C]{\text{diastase}} nC_{12}H_{22}O_{11}$$

Starch   Maltose

On the addition of yeast, which contains the enzyme MALTASE, the maltose is broken down into glucose, which at a maintained temperature of 15 °C is then converted into alcohol by the enzyme ZYMASE, also contained in the yeast.

$$C_{12}H_{22}O_{11} + H_2O \xrightarrow[15°C]{\text{maltase}} 2C_6H_{12}O_6$$

$$C_6H_{12}O_6 \xrightarrow[15°C]{\text{zymase}} 2CH_3CH_2OH + 2CO_2$$

Commercial and Absolute Alcohol

Ordinary commercial alcohol is an azeotropic (constant boiling point) mixture of 95.6 per cent ethanol and 4.4 per cent water by mass. Separation by fractional distillation is not possible as the azeotropic mixture boils at only a marginally lower temperature (78.2 °C) than the absolute alcohol (78.3 °C).

Instead, benzene is added to give a mixture that contains 95 per cent ethanol and this is then fractionally distilled, the distillate being collected in three separate parts. The first fraction comes over at 64.8 °C and consists of benzene ethanol water; the second fraction distils over at 68.2 °C and consists of benzene/ethanol, and the final fraction, which distils over at 78.3 °C, is absolute ethanol.

Absolute ethanol is highly hygroscopic and must be stored away from atmospheric moisture if its purity is to be maintained.

Synthetic Preparations of Aliphatic Alcohols

Reduction of Carbonyl Compounds

Grignard Synthesis

This provides the most important and widely applicable method and may be used for preparing primary, secondary and tertiary alcohols. The intermediate alkylmagnesium halide is hydrolysed using dilute acid, or aqueous ammonium chloride in the case of tertiary alcohols.

(1)

$$\underset{H}{\overset{H}{\diagdown}}C{=}O + RMgX \xrightarrow{(C_2H_5)_2O} \underset{R}{\overset{H}{\underset{|}{H{-}C{-}OMgX}}} \xrightarrow[\text{dil. acid}]{H_2O} \underset{R}{\overset{H}{\underset{|}{H{-}C{-}OH}}} + MgXOH$$

Methanal
(Formaldehyde)   1 ° alcohol

Epoxyethane (ethylene oxide) may be used instead of methanal (formaldehyde) (page 163).

(2)

$$\underset{H}{\overset{R'}{\diagdown}}C{=}O + RMgX \xrightarrow{(C_2H_5)_2O} \underset{R}{\overset{H}{\underset{|}{R'{-}C{-}OMgX}}} \xrightarrow[\text{dil. acid}]{H_2O} \underset{H}{\overset{R}{\underset{|}{R'{-}C{-}OH}}} + MgXOH$$

Higher aldehyde   2 ° alcohol
e.g. Ethanal

(3)

$$\underset{R''}{\overset{R'}{\diagdown}}C{=}O + RMgX \xrightarrow{(C_2H_5)_2O} \underset{R}{\overset{R''}{\underset{|}{R'{-}C{-}OMgX}}} \xrightarrow[\text{aq. NH}_4\text{Cl}]{H_2O} \underset{R}{\overset{R''}{\underset{|}{R'{-}C{-}OH}}} + MgXOH$$

Ketone   3 ° alcohol
e.g. Propanone

In the preparation of tertiary alcohols, aqueous ammonium chloride is used for hydrolysis as dilute acid brings about dehydration of the alcohol to yield the alkene, i.e. the elimination product.

Using Lithium Tetrahydridoaluminate(III) in Ethoxyethane

This reagent is suitable for primary and secondary alcohols, the reactions being performed at 0 °C. Lithium tetrahydridoaluminate(III), $LiAlH_4$, reacts violently with water and moisture and, in view of this, its use in elementary practical work is not really desirable.

$$\underset{\substack{| \\ H}}{\overset{\substack{R \\ |}}{C}}=O \quad \xrightarrow[(C_2H_5)_2O]{LiAlH_4} \quad RCH_2OH$$

Aldehyde   1 °alcohol

$$\underset{\substack{| \\ R}}{\overset{\substack{R \\ |}}{C}}=O \quad \xrightarrow[(C_2H_5)_2O]{LiAlH_4} \quad \underset{\substack{| \\ R}}{\overset{\substack{R \\ |}}{C}}HOH$$

Ketone   2 °alcohol

The power of lithium tetrahydridoaluminate(III) as a reducing agent is illustrated by the fact that it is capable of reducing carboxylic acids, which are normally resistant to such changes, to alcohols. However, in this context, it is generally preferable to use the appropriate ester.

Lithium tetrahydridoborate(III), $LiBH_4$, in ethoxyethane or tetrahydrofuran, is rather milder in action than lithium tetrahydridoaluminate(III) and is sometimes used as an alternative reagent. Another reagent that is sometimes used for reducing aldehydes and ketones is sodium tetrahydridoborate(III), $NaBH_4$, which is used in a medium of water or methanol, as it is insoluble in ethoxyethane.

Hydrolysis of Haloalkanes

This reaction is suitable for preparing primary, secondary and tertiary alcohols, and is discussed in more detail in the previous chapter.

$$RX + {}^-OH \longrightarrow ROH + X^-$$

Esters can also be hydrolysed to alcohols to refluxing with aqueous alkali (*see* page 266).

Synthetic Preparations of Aromatic Alcohols

The Cannizzaro Reaction

Aromatic aldehydes, e.g. benzenecarbaldehyde (benzaldehyde), when shaken with a concentrated solution of potassium hydroxide, undergo simultaneous oxidation and reduction (disproportionation) yielding the potassium salt of the corresponding carboxylic acid together with the alcohol.

$$2C_6H_5CHO + KOH \longrightarrow C_6H_5CH_2OH + C_6H_5COOK$$

Benzene-   Phenylmethanol   Potassium
carbaldehyde   (Benzyl alcohol)   benzenecarboxylate
(Benzaldehyde)   (Potassium benzoate)

The potassium salt is dissolved in water and the alcohol extracted with ethoxyethane.

This reaction provides what is probably the best preparation of phenyl-methanol.

Hydrolysis of (Chloromethyl)benzene (Benzyl Chloride)

(Chloromethyl)benzene (benzyl chloride) is readily hydrolysed on boiling with aqueous alkali to phenylmethanol.

$$C_6H_5CH_2Cl + KOH \longrightarrow C_6H_5CH_2OH + KCl$$

The hydrolysis of benzyl esters to the alcohol may be accomplished in a similar manner.

Reduction of Benzenecarboxylates (Benzoates)

Benzenecarboxylic (benzoic) acid, or preferably an ester of the acid, can be reduced to the alcohol by lithium tetrahydridoaluminate(III) in dry ethoxyethane.

$$C_6H_5COOC_2H_5 + 2[H] \xrightarrow[(C_2H_5)_2O]{LiAlH_4} C_6H_5CH_2OH + CH_3CH_2OH$$

Reactions

The chemistry of the alcohols is characterized by the reactions of their functional group, i.e. the hydroxyl group. The reactions can be divided into two categories; those in which *alkyl–hydroxy (R—OH) fission* occurs and those in which *alkoxy–hydrogen (RO—H) fission occurs*, either of which may yield the substitution or elimination product, and usually a mixture of both. The type of cleavage that occurs is largely governed by the nature of the alkyl group to which the hydroxyl group is attached.

Complete fission of the hydroxyl group is favoured by the greater electron-donating effects of tertiary alkyl groups which contribute towards stabilizing the intermediate CARBOCATION (CARBONIUM ION), R^+, whereas the lesser effects of primary groups favour the formation of the ALKOXIDE (ALKYLATE) ION, RO^-.

Preferred positions of cleavage for 1°, 2° and 3° alcohols:

$$R—CH_2—O{+}H \qquad \overset{R}{\underset{R}{\diagup}}CH{+}O{+}H \qquad \overset{R}{\underset{R}{\diagup}}R—C{+}O—H$$

or

This in many ways resembles the amphoteric nature of water. In the presence of an acid, HA, the alcohol may function as a base, with the *oxygen atom donating a lone pair of electrons to a proton*. The resulting ROH_2^+ ion then loses a water molecule to form a carbocation.

$$\left.\begin{array}{l} HA + H_2O \rightleftharpoons H_3O^+ + A^- \\ HA + ROH \rightleftharpoons ROH_2^+ + A^- \end{array}\right\} \quad \begin{array}{l}\text{Water and alcohol}\\\text{acting as a base}\end{array}$$

$$\Big\Updownarrow$$

$$R^+ + H_2O$$

Since a carbocation is stabilized by tertiary alkyl groups, it follows that these same groups will enhance the basic character of an alcohol.

Basic strength of alcohols:

$$3° \text{ alcohol} > 2° \text{ alcohol} > 1° \text{ alcohol}$$

Conversely, in the presence of a base, B, alcohols may function as an acidic reagent.

$$\left. \begin{array}{l} B + H_2O \rightleftharpoons HB^+ + {}^-OH \\ B + ROH \rightleftharpoons HB^+ + RO^- \end{array} \right| \begin{array}{l} \text{Water and alcohol} \\ \text{acting as an acid} \end{array}$$

Acidic strength of alcohols:

$$1° \text{ alcohols} > 2° \text{ alcohols} > 3° \text{ alcohols}$$

Aromatic alcohols, e.g. $C_6H_5CH_2OH$, are similar in their reactivity to tertiary aliphatic alcohols owing to the electron-donating properties of the benzene ring, although reactions taking place in aqueous solution tend to be much slower owing to their lower solubility in water.

Electrophilic reagents, undergoing substitution in the ring, are directed to the 2- and 4-positions by the saturated, electron-donating side-chain substituent.

Acidic Strength of Alcohols

As well as exhibiting acidic properties in basic media, alcohols can also function as very weak acids in their own right. This is illustrated by their ability to liberate hydrogen with the alkali metals, although it must be readily appreciated that their *acidic strengths are much weaker than even that of water*.

It has already been stated that alkoxy–hydrogen fission is most prevalent in primary alcohols, and it is therefore these compounds that are most likely to release a proton and function as an acid. The degree of polarity is dependent upon the electron-releasing or withdrawing powers of the group to which it is attached. Electron-releasing groups inhibit the withdrawal of electrons away from the hydrogen atom of the hydroxyl group and impair its facility to release a proton. Since all alkyl groups are electron-releasing, it is therefore the least active of these, namely the primary groups, which promote acidic strength.

Name	Formula	pK_a
Water	H_2O	14
Methanol (1°)	CH_3OH	15.5
Ethanol (1°)	CH_3CH_2OH	16
2-Methylpropan-2-ol (3°) (*tert*-Butyl alcohol)	$(CH_3)_3COH$	18

Reactions Involving R–OH Fission

Rates of reaction:

$$3° \text{ alcohol} > 2° \text{ alcohol} > 1° \text{ alcohol}$$

Halogenation

Using Hydrogen Halides

Chlorination is best brought about by bubbling dry hydrogen chloride (alternatively, concentrated hydrochloric acid may be used) through absolute alcohol in the presence of an anhydrous zinc chloride catalyst until the solution is saturated, and then refluxing on a water bath.

$$CH_3CH_2OH + HCl \xrightarrow[\text{reflux}]{ZnCl_2 \text{ cat.}} CH_3CH_2Cl + H_2O$$

Primary alcohols undergo bromination on refluxing with hydrogen bromide, which is generated from sodium bromide and concentrated sulphuric acid. The acid serves as both a catalyst and a dehydrating agent, removing water as it is formed. Alternatively, bromination may be carried out by treating the alcohol with red phosphorus and bromine.

$$CH_3CH_2OH + HBr \xrightarrow[\text{reflux}]{NaBr/conc. H_2SO_4} CH_3CH_2Br + H_2O$$

An iodide and sulphuric acid cannot be used to bring about iodination as the hydrogen iodide produced, being a powerful reducing agent, is oxidized to iodine by the acid. Instead, the alcohol is treated with red phosphorus and iodine.

Tertiary and aromatic alcohols are predictably more readily halogenated by the hydrogen halides, the reactions taking place fairly rapidly on shaking in the cold.

Mechanism

The reaction proceeds via three basic stages.

(1) Donation of a lone pair of electrons from the oxygen atom of the alcohol (a Lewis base) to a proton released from the acid.

(2) Loss of a water molecule from the protonated alcohol to form a carbocation (carbonium ion).

(3) Nucleophilic attack by a halide ion upon the carbocation to form the haloalkane.

$$CH_3CH_2-\overset{..}{\underset{..}{O}}H \quad H^+X^- \rightleftharpoons CH_3CH_2-\overset{+}{O}H_2 + :X^-$$

$$CH_3CH_2-\overset{+}{O}H_2 \rightleftharpoons CH_3\overset{+}{C}H_2 + H_2O$$

$$CH_3\overset{+}{C}H_2 \quad :X^- \longrightarrow CH_3CH_2-X$$

Using Phosphorus Halides

Bromine or iodine is added to a mixture of the alcohol and red phosphorus and then refluxed on a water bath.

$$2P + 3Br_2 \longrightarrow 2PBr_3$$

$$3CH_3CH_2OH + PBr_3 \longrightarrow 3CH_3CH_2Br + H_3PO_3$$

Phosphorus pentachloride reacts in the cold with anhydrous ethanol forming chloroethane.

$$CH_3CH_2OH + PCl_5 \longrightarrow CH_3CH_2Cl + POCl_3 + HCl$$

Phosphorus trichloride reacts similarly, although slightly less readily, to yield the haloalkane and phosphonic (phosphorous) acid

$$3CH_3CH_2OH + PCl_3 \longrightarrow 3CH_3CH_2Cl + H_3PO_3$$

Using Sulphur Dichloride Oxide (Thionyl Chloride)

The alcohol is refluxed with sulphur dichloride oxide (thionyl chloride) in the presence of a small quantity of pyridine, C_5H_5N, which serves to absorb the hydrogen chloride as it is formed.

$$CH_3CH_2OH + SOCl_2 \xrightarrow{C_5H_5N} CH_3CH_2Cl + SO_2 + HCl$$

Bubbling chlorine through ethanol yields a colourless oily liquid known as trichloroethanal (chloral), CCl_3CHO (refer to the chlorination of ethanal (acetaldehyde), page 238).

Dehydration to Alkenes

Dehydration of ethanol can be brought about by passing the vapour over an aluminium oxide catalyst heated to 350 °C, or by heating to 170 °C with excess concentrated sulphuric acid.

$$CH_3CH_2OH \xrightarrow[\text{or Al}_2O_3,\, 350\,°C]{\text{excess conc. H}_2SO_4,\, 170\,°C} CH_2{=}CH_2 + H_2O$$

Mechanism

The first two stages are similar in principle to those described for the halogenation of alcohols using a hydrogen halide, and involve protonation of the alcohol followed by the loss of a water molecule to form a carbocation (carbonium ion). The process is terminated by the removal of a proton from the carbocation by a hydrogensulphate ion.

$$CH{=}CH_2 + H_2SO_4$$

Dehydration of secondary and tertiary alcohols containing four or more carbon atoms yields a mixture of two alkene products.

$$CH_3CH_2CH{=}CH_2$$

But-1-ene

$$CH_3CH_2\underset{\underset{OH}{|}}{C}HCH_3 \xrightarrow{\text{conc.}\ H_2SO_4}$$

Butan-2-ol

$$CH_3CH{=}CHCH_3$$

But-2-ene

The alkene produced in greater abundance is indicated by SAYTZEFF'S RULE, which states that *the alkene formed preferentially is the one containing the higher number of alkyl groups*. Therefore, in the above example, but-2-ene is yielded as the predominant product. This is endorsed by the results of combustion experiments, which show that the alkene containing the greater number of alkyl groups is energetically the more stable. Furthermore, the *trans* isomer is more stable than the *cis*. (*See* page 109).

Compound	Enthalpy of combustion/ kJ mol^{-1}
But-1-ene	2715
But-2-ene (*cis*)	2708
But-2-ene (*trans*)	2704

The same theory and principles can also be applied to the elimination reactions of haloalkanes.

The rate of the acid-catalysed dehydration of 1-phenylethanol to yield phenylethene (styrene) is comparable with the rates for tertiary alcohols, owing to the electron-donating properties of the benzene ring.

Ether Formation

Partial dehydration of ethanol only as far as ethoxyethane ('ether') can be brought about by performing the reaction under carefully controlled conditions. An excess of alcohol is maintained by adding it gradually to the reaction mixture, controlled to a temperature of 140 °C.

$$2CH_3CH_2OH \xrightleftharpoons{\text{conc. } H_2SO_4, \, 140 \,°C} CH_3CH_2OCH_2CH_3 + H_2O$$
Ethoxyethane
('Ether')

Mechanism

Reactions Involving RO—H Fission

Rates of reaction:

$$1° \text{ alcohols} > 2° \text{ alcohols} > 3° \text{ alcohols}$$

With Metals

Alcohols, being much weaker acids than water, react much less vigorously with sodium and potassium to liberate hydrogen and form the alkoxide (alkylate).

$$2CH_3CH_2OH + 2Na \longrightarrow 2CH_3CH_2ONa + H_2$$

Sodium ethoxide
(Sodium ethylate)

Alkoxides are hygroscopic, crystalline solids which are readily hydrolysed in water to the alkali and alcohol.

The reaction of alkoxide and phenoxide $(C_6H_5O^-)$ ions with haloalkanes is important in the preparation of ethers (Williamson's synthesis, page 197), the halogen undergoing nucleophilic displacement.

$$CH_3CH_2O^- + CH_3\overset{\delta+}{CH_2}-\overset{\delta-}{Cl} \xrightarrow[\text{solvent}]{CH_3CH_2OH} CH_3CH_2OCH_2CH_3 + Cl^-$$

Ethoxyethane
(Diethyl ether 'Ether')

The acidic strength of alcohols is insufficient to form alkoxides (alkylates) with sodium or potassium hydroxide.

Esterification

The process whereby an alcohol reacts reversibly with an acid to form an ester is known as esterification. In the majority of cases this involves the replacement of a hydroxyl group of an acid by an alkyl group of an alcohol. For example, ethanol reacts with concentrated sulphuric and nitric acids in the cold to form ethyl hydrogensulphate and ethyl nitrate respectively. (Dangerous reaction!).

$$CH_3CH_2OH + HONO_2 \rightleftharpoons CH_3CH_2ONO_2 + H_2O$$

Ethyl nitrate

Nitrate esters are especially important in manufacturing explosives. Nitration of propane-1,2,3-triol (glycerol), $CH_2OHCHOHCH_2OH$, yields propane-1,2,3-triyl trinitrate ('nitroglycerine'), $CH_2NO_3CHNO_3CH_2NO_3$, which when mixed with finely divided silicon(IV) oxide (kieselguhr) in the correct proportions, is used in manufacturing dynamite.

Probably the most important class of esters is that formed between alcohols and carboxylic acids.

The alcohol and the carboxylic acid are boiled under reflux in the presence of 5 per cent of concentrated sulphuric acid or by bubbling gaseous hydrogen chloride through the reaction mixture. (The use of a mineral acid catalyst is known as the Fischer–Speier method.)

$$CH_3COOH + H^{18}OCH_2CH_3 \xrightleftharpoons[\text{reflux}]{H^+ \text{ cat.}} CH_3CO^{18}OCH_2CH_3 + H_2O$$

Ethyl ethanoate
(Ethyl acetate)

Isotopic labelling of the oxygen atom of the alcohol using ^{18}O shows that primary and some secondary alcohols undergo alkoxy–hydrogen fission. Mass spectrometry detects the radioactive oxygen only in the fragments produced from the ester and not from the water. However, tertiary and other secondary alcohols undergo alkyl–hydroxy fission, leading to a poorer yield of the ester.

As the overall process is reversible, the same catalyst can be used to hydrolyse the ester into the alcohol and carboxylic acid. (The mechanism of this reaction is discussed under the reactions of carboxylic acids.)

Esterification may also be accomplished using an acyl or benzenecarbonyl (benzoyl) chloride.

$$CH_3COCl \quad + \quad CH_3CH_2OH \longrightarrow CH_3COOCH_2CH_3 \quad + \quad HCl$$

Ethanoyl chloride
(Acetyl chloride)

Oxidation

Many suitable oxidizing agents are available, but of those commonly employed, potassium manganate(VII) (permanganate) and potassium dichromate(VI) are probably the most popular. The manganate(VII) can be used in a neutral, alkaline or acidic medium, whereas the dichromate(VI) functions only in a medium of sulphuric acid. The product of oxidation is governed largely by the type of alcohol and partly by the power of the oxidizing agent. *Oxidation of alcohols can be employed diagnostically to provide a means of distinguishing between the different classes.*

Primary alcohols are readily oxidized on heating to aldehydes, but in the presence of excess of the oxidizing agent, the reaction proceeds further, yielding the carboxylic acid.

$$CH_3CH_2OH \xrightarrow[\substack{KMnO_4 \text{ or} \\ K_2Cr_2O_7}]{[O]} CH_3CHO \xrightarrow{[O]} CH_3COOH$$

Ethanal   Ethanoic acid
(Acetaldehyde)   (Acetic acid)

For the reaction with acidified dichromate(VI) solution, these two stages of oxidation may be represented as follows:

$$3CH_3CH_2OH + Cr_2O_7^{2-} + 8H^+ \longrightarrow 3CH_3CHO + 2Cr^{3+} + 7H_2O$$
$$3CH_3CHO + Cr_2O_7^{2-} + 8H^+ \longrightarrow 3CH_3COOH + 2Cr^{3+} + 4H_2O$$

The employment of a milder oxidation process, e.g. warming with manganese(IV) oxide in 60 per cent sulphuric acid or passing the vaporized alcohol through a tube packed copper turnings heated to 200–300 °C, enables the aldehyde to be more easily isolated and prevents further oxidation.

Secondary alcohols are oxidized to the corresponding ketone, and only under severe conditions are they oxidized to a carboxylic acid as this process would involve breaking a carbon–carbon linkage.

$$\begin{array}{c} CH_3 \\ \diagdown \\ \quad\quad CHOH \xrightarrow{[O]} \\ \diagup \\ CH_3 \end{array} \quad \begin{array}{c} CH_3 \\ \diagdown \\ \quad\quad C{=}O + H_2O \\ \diagup \\ CH_3 \end{array}$$

Propanone (Acetone)

Tertiary alcohols are comparatively stable to oxidation and are not oxidized at all in neutral or alkaline media, whereas under the same conditions primary and secondary alcohols retain the same carbon skeleton in undergoing oxidation to the aldehyde, acid or ketone.

In an acidic medium, tertiary alcohols undergo dehydration to the alkene which is then readily oxidized to the diol. Further oxidation causes carbon–carbon fission, yielding the oxidation products of monohydric alcohols.

$$RCH\text{---}CHR' \xrightarrow{[O]} RCHO + R'CHO$$
$$\underset{OH}{|} \quad \underset{OH}{|} \qquad \qquad \downarrow [O] \quad \downarrow [O]$$
$$\text{Diol} \qquad \qquad RCOOH \quad R'COOH$$

Mechanism for Oxidation

$$CH_3\text{---}\underset{H}{\overset{H}{C}}\text{---}OH \xrightarrow{[O]} CH_3\text{---}\underset{H}{\overset{OH}{C}}\text{---}O\,H \xrightarrow{-H_2O} CH_3\text{---}\underset{H}{C}=O \xrightarrow{[O]} CH_3COOH$$

QUESTIONS

1. A certain compound is a viscous, high boiling point liquid, miscible with water. The compound is most likely to be

 A CH_3CH_2OH
 B $CH_3CH_2CH_2OH$
 C $CH_3CHOHCH_3$
 D $CH_3CH_2CH_2CH_2OH$
 E $CH_2OHCHOHCH_2OH$

2. Which of the following alcohols is most likely to yield the carboxylic acid, $CH_3CHCOOH$, on oxidation?
 $\qquad\quad |$
 $\qquad\;\; CH_3$

 A propan-2-ol
 B butan-1-ol
 C 2-methylpropan-1-ol
 D 2-methylpropan-2-ol
 E 2-methylbutan-1-ol

3. A compound corresponding to a molecular formula $C_4H_{10}O$ gives no reaction with cold aqueous potassium manganate(VIII) but reacts with phosphorus pentachloride evolving hydrogen chloride. The most likely structural formula of the compound is

 A $CH_3OCH_2CH_2CH_3$

 B CH_3CHOCH_3
 $\quad\;\; |$
 $\quad\;\; CH_3$

 C $CH_3CHOHCH_2CH_2CH_3$

 D $CH_3\text{---}\underset{OH}{\overset{CH_3}{\underset{|}{\overset{|}{C}}}}\text{---}CH_3$

 E CH_3CH_2CHOH
 $\qquad\qquad |$
 $\qquad\qquad CH_3$

4. Give the formula and IUPAC name of the alcohol which on undergoing dehydration yields each of the following alkenes as the major product.

 A $CH_3CH_2CH_2CH_2CH{=}CH_2$
 B $(CH_3)_2C{=}CHCH_3$
 C $(CH_3)_2C{=}C(CH_3)_2$

 D

5. Outline simple chemical reactions which would serve to distinguish between the following pairs of compounds. Give equations.

A   butan-1-ol and octane
B   butan-1-ol and oct-1-ene
C   butan-1-ol and butan-2-ol
D   2-methylbutan-2-ol and pentan-2-ol

6. In what way do the reactions of ethanol with hydrogen halides and concentrated sulphuric acid (dehydration) reflect its basic properties? Illustrate your answer with reference to the mechanism for each process.

7. The ease with which an alcohol esterifies with a carboxylic acid decreases in the order, primary > secondary > tertiary, whereas the order is reversed for the reactions with hydrogen halides. Comment on the reasons for these observations.

8. Compare the acidic and basic strengths of primary, secondary and tertiary monohydric alcohols. How are these properties affected by the nature of the medium?

9. Briefly discuss the factors affecting the different modes of fission that occur in alcohols. Illustrate your answer with reference to propan-1-ol and 2-methylpropan-2-ol.

Phenols

Phenols are compounds containing a hydroxyl group *attached directly* to an aromatic nucleus and have a general formula ArOH. Like alcohols they may be monohydric or polyhydric according to the number of hydroxyl groups that they contain.

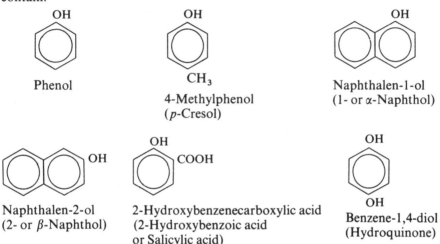

Phenol

4-Methylphenol
(*p*-Cresol)

Naphthalen-1-ol
(1- or α-Naphthol)

Naphthalen-2-ol
(2- or β-Naphthol)

2-Hydroxybenzenecarboxylic acid
(2-Hydroxybenzoic acid
or Salicylic acid)

Benzene-1,4-diol
(Hydroquinone)

The simplest and most important member of this family of compounds is phenol itself.

Physical Properties

Most pure phenols are colourless solids or liquids, although they are often found to contain a red tint owing to the presence of oxidation products. All phenols having a sufficiently high vapour pressure have a characteristic 'carbolic' odour, which in the case of phenol itself is highly toxic.

Phenol is a colourless, hygroscopic, crystalline solid (m.p. 42 °C) although the presence of water impurity causes an appreciable lowering of the melting point. The liquid form of phenol containing about 5 per cent water is known as 'carbolic acid'. Below 65.8 °C phenol is only partially miscible with water, but above this temperature it is miscible in all proportions.

The boiling points of phenols are higher than aliphatic analogues of comparable relatively molecular mass, due largely to the more pronounced effects of intermolecular hydrogen bonding.

Compound	B.p./°C
Phenol	181
Cyclohexanol	162
Hexan-1-ol	157

The introduction of a hydroxyl group into an already substituted aromatic ring, especially in the 4- position to a methyl, halogen or nitro group, produces a marked increase in the boiling point. This is illustrated by the table below, showing the effect in the nitrophenols. Most 2-, 3- and 4-substituted isomers usually boil within a 10 °C range of each other.

Compound	M.p./°C	B.p./°C
Phenol	42	181
Nitrobenzene	5.5	210
2-Nitrophenol	45	217
3-Nitrophenol	96	
4-Nitrophenol	114	245

The greater volatility of 2-nitrophenol is attributed to INTRAMOLECULAR HYDROGEN BONDING, whereas the higher boiling points of the 3- and 4-isomers are a direct result of INTERMOLECULAR HYDROGEN BONDING.

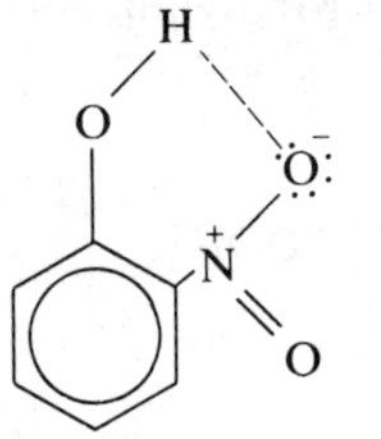

Fig. 17.1

Intramolecular hydrogen bonding in 2-nitrophenol

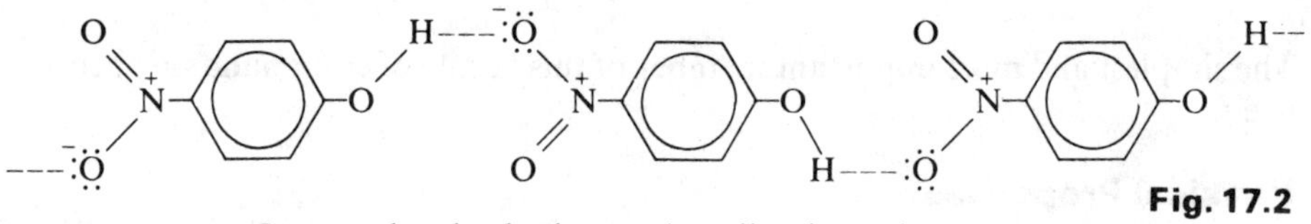

Fig. 17.2

Intermolecular hydrogen bonding in 4-nitrophenol

As a result of their ability to associate with themselves and also with water molecules, 3- and 4-nitrophenol are appreciably more soluble in water than 2-nitrophenol, which cannot form intermolecular hydrogen bonds.

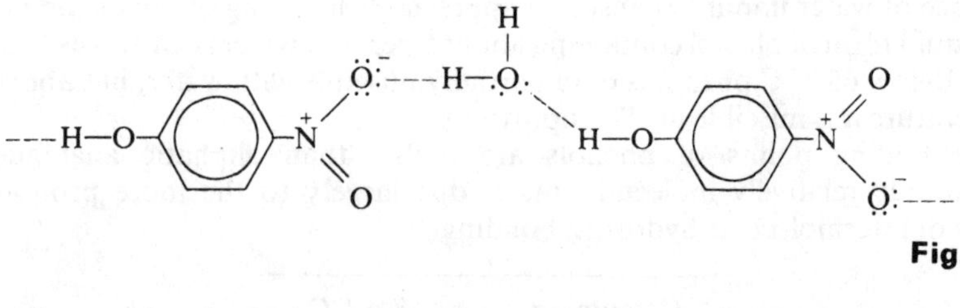

Fig. 17.3

Intermolecular hydrogen bonds between water and 4-nitrophenol

The low miscibility and higher volatility of 2-nitrophenol enables it to be easily separated from the other isomers by steam distillation.

Industrial Source and Synthetic Preparations

A great proportion of the total supply of phenol is obtained from synthetic methods of preparation, many of which can be modified and adopted in the laboratory.

Alkali Fusion with Sodium Benzenesulphonate

One of the earlier synthetic methods which is still widely used involves the fusion of sodium benzenesulphonate, produced by the sulphonation of benzene, with sodium hydroxide at 300–350 °C.

$$C_6H_5SO_3Na + 2NaOH \xrightarrow{300-350\,°C} C_6H_5ONa + Na_2SO_3 + H_2O$$

In the laboratory preparation, the reactants are heated in a nickel crucible at a somewhat lower temperature of about 250 °C. The phenol is generated as an oily liquid by dissolving the sodium phenoxide in water and acidifying.

$$C_6H_5ONa + HCl \longrightarrow C_6H_5OH + NaCl$$

Hydrolysis of Chlorobenzene

This process was first introduced by the Dow Chemical Company (1928), and involves the hydrolysis of chlorobenzene by aqueous sodium hydroxide at 360 °C and 150 atmospheres pressure.

$$C_6H_5Cl \xrightarrow[360\,°C,\ 150\ atm]{aq.\ NaOH} C_6H_5ONa \xrightarrow{dil.\ HCl} C_6H_5OH$$

From Benzene (Raschig Process)

Benzene is chlorinated by passing the vapour, together with hydrogen chloride and air, over a heated copper(II) chloride catalyst at 230 °C.

$$2C_6H_6 + 2HCl + O_2 \xrightarrow[230\,°C]{CuCl_2\ cat.} 2C_6H_5Cl + 2H_2O$$

The chlorobenzene is then catalytically hydrolysed by passing it with steam over a silicon catalyst at 425 °C.

$$C_6H_5Cl + H_2O \xrightarrow[425\,°C]{Si\ cat.} C_6H_5OH + HCl$$

From Petroleum Products

A later innovation (1954), which is gradually becoming the *main source of phenol*, consists of compressing propene and benzene, which are both derived cheaply from petroleum by cracking, to 30 atmospheres and passing them over a phosphoric(V) acid catalyst at 250 °C to form (1-methylethyl)benzene (cumene).

$$C_6H_6 + CH_3CH{=}CH_2 \xrightarrow[250\,°C,\ 30\ atm]{H_3PO_4\ cat.} C_6H_5CH(CH_3)_2$$

(1-Methylethyl)benzene
(Cumene)

The (1-methylethyl)benzene is then oxidized by air to (1-methylethyl)benzene hydroperoxide, which on treating with aqueous sulphuric acid is converted into phenol and propanone (acetone).

(1-Methylethyl)benzene hydroperoxide   Phenol   Propanone
(Cumene   (Acetone)
hydroperoxide)

From Coal Tar

Coal tar provides a natural source of phenol and benzenediols (cresols), but nowadays provides less than 10 per cent of the total supply. After crystallization of the naphthalene from the middle oil fraction, the phenols are extracted with dilute sodium hydroxide and then regenerated by saturating the solution with carbon dioxide.

$$C_6H_5OH + NaOH \longrightarrow C_6H_5ONa + H_2O$$

$$2C_6H_5ONa + H_2O + CO_2 \longrightarrow 2C_6H_5OH + Na_2CO_3$$

Hydrolysis of Diazonium Salts

This reaction can be performed easily in the laboratory and simply requires warming a solution of benzenediazonium salt, prepared from phenylamine (aniline), sodium nitrite, and sulphuric acid, on a water bath at 50 °C.

$$C_6H_5N_2^+ + 2H_2O \xrightarrow{50\,°C} C_6H_5OH + N_2 + H_3O^+$$

The phenol is recovered by steam distillation and extracted with ethoxyethane.

Large scale production of phenol was developed during World War I in order to meet the amount required for the manufacture of 2,4,6-trinitrophenol (picric acid) (*see* page 188) which is employed in the manufacture of explosives. Nowadays, large quantities are used in manufacturing phenol-methanal (phenol-formaldehyde) resins, e.g. Bakelite.

Reactions

Phenol undergoes two distinctive types of reaction: (1) SIDE-CHAIN SUBSTITUTION, which generally involves replacement of the acidic proton; and (2) ELECTROPHILIC SUBSTITUTION IN THE RING.

Reactions of the Hydroxyl Group

Reactions involving the hydroxyl group resemble those of the alcohols to a certain extent, but differ in as much as phenol exhibits much stronger acidic characteristics, i.e. the dissociation of phenol in water lies much further towards the right-hand side of the equation.

$$C_6H_5OH \rightleftharpoons C_6H_5O^- + H^+$$

$$\big\Vert\ ^-OH$$

$$H_2O$$

The greater acidity of phenol is illustrated by its solubility in aqueous sodium hydroxide, with which it forms a solution of sodium phenoxide (phenate), from which white crystals can be crystallized. However, its inability to liberate carbon dioxide from sodium hydrogencarbonate enables phenol to be distinguished from carboxylic acids.

Its solubility in aqueous alkali plays a very significant part in the chemistry of phenol. The interaction between the hydroxide ions, furnished by the alkali, and the phenolic protons to form water promotes the formation of phenoxide (phenate) ions. These ions have a greater electron density than the phenol molecules and therefore are able to function much more readily as a nucleophilic reagent.

Unlike the alkoxide (alkylate) ion, the phenoxide (phenate) ion is stabilized by resonance, the structures II, III and IV making a small but significant contribution towards the acid strength of phenol.

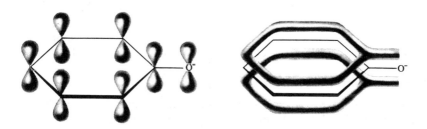

In the case of the undissociated molecule and the phenoxide (phenate) ion, I, only one of each of the two possible Kekulé structures is represented.

In terms of the molecular orbital structure, the lone pair of electrons from oxygen is considered to interact with, and form part of, the delocalized π electrons of the ring, thus increasing the effective electron density about it.

Name	Formula	pK_a
Phenol	C_6H_5OH	10.00
3-Methylphenol	$3\text{-}CH_3C_6H_4OH$	10.08
4-Methylphenol	$4\text{-}CH_3C_6H_4OH$	10.26
Benzene-1,2-diol (Catechol)	$2\text{-}HOC_6H_4OH$	9.85
Benzene-1,3-diol (Resorcinol)	$3\text{-}HOC_6H_4OH$	9.81
Benzene-1,4-diol (Hydroquinone)	$4\text{-}HOC_6H_4OH$	10.35
2-Chlorophenol	$2\text{-}ClC_6H_4OH$	8.48
3-Chlorophenol	$3\text{-}ClC_6H_4OH$	9.02
4-Chlorophenol	$4\text{-}ClC_6H_4OH$	9.38
2,4,6-Trichlorophenol	$2,4,6\text{-}Cl_3C_6H_2OH$	7.6
2-Nitrophenol	$2\text{-}NO_2C_6H_4OH$	7.21
3-Nitrophenol	$3\text{-}NO_2C_6H_4OH$	8.35
4-Nitrophenol	$4\text{-}NO_2C_6H_4OH$	7.15
2,4,6-Trinitrophenol	$2,4,6\text{-}(NO_2)_3C_6H_2OH$	0.42

Substitution of electron-withdrawing groups in the ring, especially in the 2- and 4- positions, enables the ring in turn to withdraw more electrons from the oxygen atom, thus stabilizing the phenoxide ion still further and promoting the ionization process.

The cumulative effect of the substitution of three $-NO_2$ groups is illustrated by the near mineral acid strength of 2,4,6-trinitrophenol (picric acid) $2,4,6\text{-}(NO_2)_3C_6H_2OH$, the pK_a value of which is as little as 0.42.

Conversely, substitution of electron-releasing groups, e.g. $-CH_3$, in the ring generally, but not invariably, has the effect of reducing the acidic strengths of phenols. This is reflected in the pK_a values of the methylphenols (cresols), which are all weaker acids than phenol itself.

Esterification

Phenol does not esterify with ethanoic (acetic) acid, but in alkaline solution the nucleophilic phenoxide ion readily attacks the electrophilic acyl, RCO—, and aroyl, ArO—, centres of ethanoyl (acetyl) chloride, CH_3COCl, and benzenecarbonyl (benzoyl) chloride, C_6H_5COCl.

Phenyl ethanoate
(Phenyl acetate)

Ether Formation: Williamson's Synthesis

On treatment of haloalkane with phenol in alkaline solution, the halogen undergoes nucleophilic substitution by the phenoxide (phenate) anion.

$$\text{(phenoxide)} + CH_3CH_2^{\delta+}\!\!-\!Cl^{\delta-} \xrightarrow{\text{aq. NaOH}} \text{(ethoxybenzene)} + Cl^-$$

Ethoxybenzene
(Phenetole)

Owing to the high activation of the ring of the phenoxide ion, alkylation in the ring sometimes occurs.

In practice, dimethyl sulphate, $(CH_3)_2SO_4$, is preferred to the halomethane for preparing methoxyaromatics (aryl methyl ethers).

Displacement of the Hydroxyl Group

Reactions involving the replacement of the hydroxyl group are predictably inefficient. Phenols do not undergo any reaction with hydrogen halides and react only very slowly with phosphorus pentahalides to give a poor yield of the aryl halide.

$$\text{(phenol, OH)} + PCl_5 \longrightarrow \text{(chlorobenzene, Cl)} + POCl_3 + HCl$$

Poor yield

Complex Formation with Iron(III) Chloride

In solution, phenol reacts with iron(III) chloride to form a violet coloured complex, the exact nature of which is uncertain, although it seems likely that the iron exhibits a covalency of six.

Ring Substitution

In addition to exhibiting acidic properties phenol is characterized by electrophilic substitution in the 2- and 4-positions of the aromatic ring.

In the phenol molecule, there is competition between the electron-withdrawing inductive effect of the hydroxyl group and the more powerful electron-releasing effect of the electron pairs on the oxygen atom, resulting in the overall activation of the ring with regard to electrophilic substitution. However, in the case of the phenoxide (phenate) ion, the inductive effect is reversed as a result of the negative charge on the oxygen atom and reinforces the ring-activating effect of the electron pairs.

Electrophilic substitution in the ring is therefore enhanced by an alkaline medium which promotes the formation of the phenoxide ion.

The greater activity of the ring in phenol compared with the benzene molecule itself is reflected by the milder conditions under which electrophilic substitution is carried out. Furthermore, other substitutions, which are not possible in benzene, are possible owing to this greater activity.

These properties show a marked contrast to the chemistry of the alcohols, in which the alkyl group is not appreciably affected by the hydroxyl group.

Nitration

The nitration of phenol is carried out at room temperature using dilute nitric acid, forming a mixture of 2- (major product) and 4-nitrophenol.

(Major product)
2- and 4-Nitrophenol

The two isomers can be separated by steam distillation.

A greater yield of the 4-isomer is obtained if a mixture of sodium nitrate and dilute sulphuric acid is used as the nitrating agent.

The use of concentrated nitric acid yields the 2,4,6-trinitro product (picric acid), as the major product together with an excessive amount of oxidation products.

2,4,6-Trinitrophenol
(Picric acid)

In order to avoid such a degree of oxidation, 2,4,6-trinotrophenol is generally prepared indirectly by nitration of the 2- and 4-hydroxybenzenzenesulphonic acids.

2- and 4-Hydroxybenzenesulphonic acid

Mechanism for the Formation of 4-Nitrophenol

Since the concentration of nitryl (nitronium) cations, NO_2^+, present in dilute nitric acid is extremely small, it is unlikely that this species plays any significant part in the nitration process. The evidence indicates that the electrophilic species is in fact the NITROSYL (NITROSONIUM) CATION, NO^+, generated by the *nitrous acid* present in the system.

$$HNO_2 + 2HNO_3 \rightleftharpoons H_3^+O + 2NO_3^- + {}^+NO$$

4-Nitrosophenol

The nitrosophenol formed is oxidized rapidly by the nitric acid to nitrophenol.

As nitrous acid is formed as one of the products, the rate of reaction becomes progressively more rapid as the concentration of this acid, and hence that of the electrophilic nitrosyl cation, increases.

The use of nitrous acid ($NaNO_2$/dil. H_2SO_4) alone at 5–8 °C, yields 4 nitrosophenol exclusively.

Oxidizing 4-nitrosophenol with nitric acid provides a means of preparing 4-nitrophenol without any contamination by the 2- isomer.

Nitrophenols are colourless or pale yellow crystalline solids.

Sulphonation

Sulphonation of phenol takes place readily at room temperature using ordinary concentrated sulphuric acid, yielding mainly 2-hydroxybenzenesulphonic acid. If a temperature of 100 °C is used, the 4- derivative is then produced as the major product.

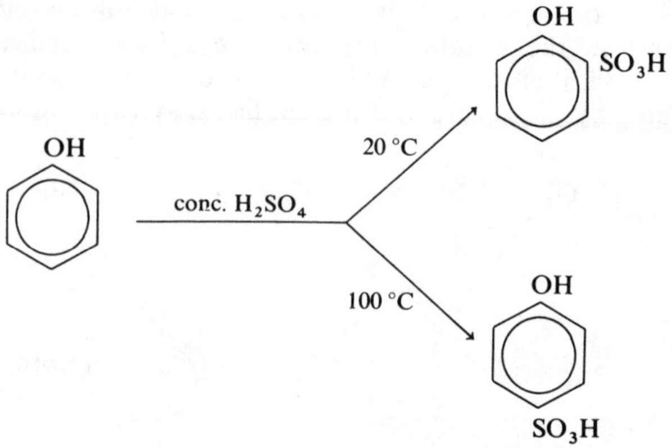

2- and 4-Hydroxybenzenesulphonic acid

Halogenation

Halogenation of the ring occurs at room temperature and without the use of a halogen carrier catalyst. In order to facilitate the formation of the monosubstituted derivatives, bromination is carried out in a solvent of low polarity, e.g. anhydrous carbon disulphide or tetrachloromethane (carbon tetrachloride).

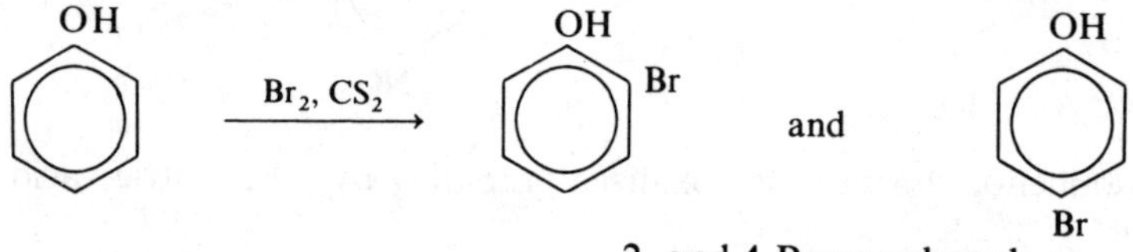

2- and 4-Bromophenol

(Major product)

In aqueous solution, bromine forms an immediate white precipitate of 2,4,6-tribromophenol, which is sometimes used as an antiseptic.

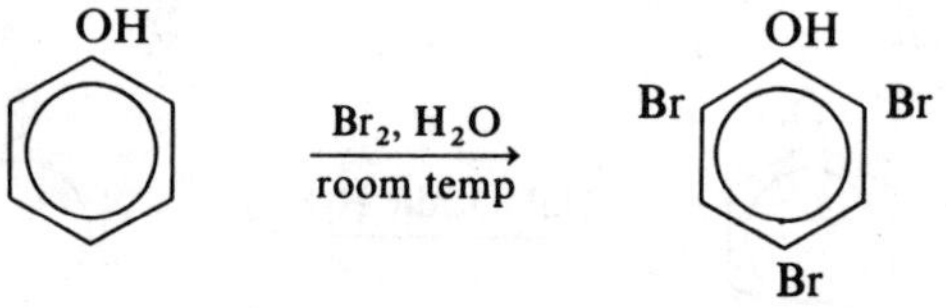

2,4,6-Tribromophenol

A similar reaction takes place with chlorine water yielding 2,4,6-trichlorophenol.

Chlorination of phenol without the use of a solvent at temperatures between 40 °C and 150 °C yields a mixture of 2- and 4-chlorophenol (major product).

Alkylation

Ring alkylation takes place on gently warming the phenol with an alcohol or alkene in the presence of a sulphuric acid catalyst.

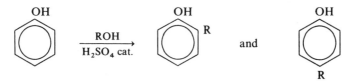

2- and 4-Alkylphenol

The reaction involves the conversion of the parent alcohol molecule into a carbonium ion, and the reaction is therefore favoured by the use of secondary and tertiary alcohols.

Friedel–Crafts alkylation produces a low yield of the alkylphenol.

Acylation

Phenolic ketones are generally prepared by means of the FRIES REARRANGEMENT REACTION.

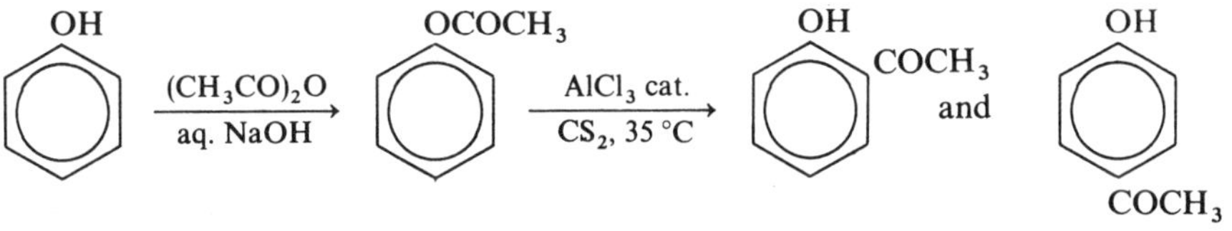

2- and 4-Hydroxyphenylethanone
(*o*- and *p*-Hydroxyphenyl ethyl ketone)

Acylation may be brought about by the Friedel–Crafts reaction, but this has the disadvantage that it requires a large excess of aluminium chloride.

Carbonation: Kolbé–Schmitt Reaction

Sodium phenoxide (phenate) is heated with carbon dioxide at 130 °C and under a pressure of 5–7 atmospheres. Acid hydrolysis of the resulting sodium 2-hydroxybenzenecarboxylate (salicylate) yields 2-hydroxybenzenecarboxylic (salicylic) acid.

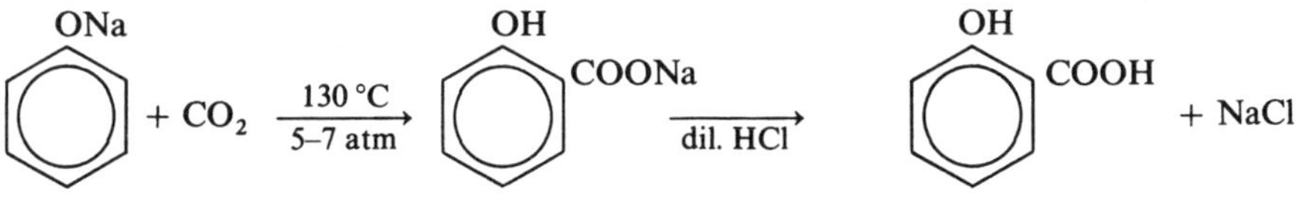

Sodium
2-hydroxybenzenecarboxylate
(Sodium salicylate)

2-Hydroxybenzenecarboxylic acid
(Salicylic acid)

Aldehyde Formation: Reimer–Tiemann Reaction

Phenol is boiled with trichloromethane (chloroform) in 40 per cent aqueous sodium hydroxide solution and then acidified with dilute acid.

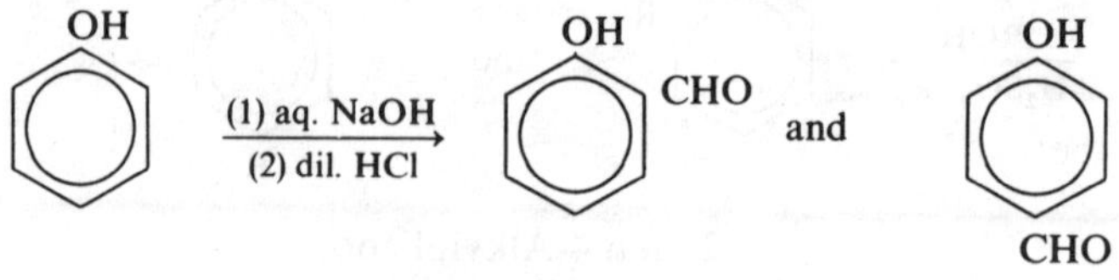

OH
$\xrightarrow[\text{(2) dil. HCl}]{\text{(1) aq. NaOH}}$
OH CHO
and
OH

CHO

2-Hydroxybenzenecarbaldehyde   4-Hydroxybenzenecarbaldehyde
(Salicylaldehyde)
Major product

Using tetrachloromethane (carbon tetrachloride) instead of trichloromethane yields the hydroxy acid.

The main uses of 2-hydroxybenzenecarboxylic acid is in its conversion into *aspirin* (2-ethanoyloxybenzenecarboxylic acid or acetylsalicylic acid) by heating with ethanoic (acetic) anhydride.

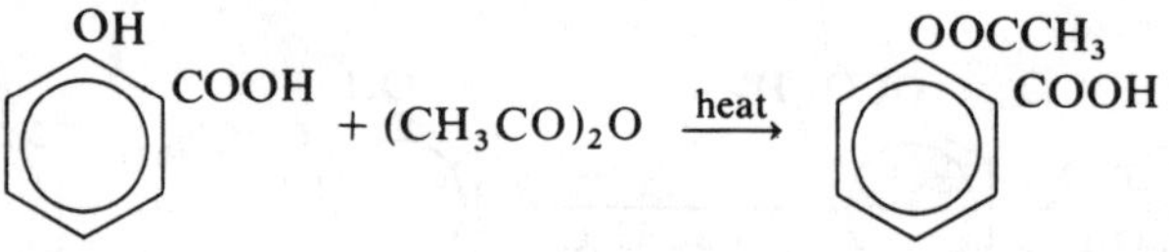

OH
COOH
$+ (CH_3CO)_2O$ $\xrightarrow{\text{heat}}$
OOCCH$_3$
COOH

2-Ethanoyloxybenzenecarboxylic
acid
(Acetylsalicylic acid, Aspirin)

The methyl ester of 2-hydroxybenzenecarboxylic acid, $2\text{-HOC}_6H_4COOCH_3$, is the principal component of *oil of wintergreen*.

Coupling with Diazonium Cations

Refer to page 216.

Phenol-Methanal (Phenol-Formaldehyde) Resins

If phenol is treated with either an acidic or preferably an alkaline solution of methanal (formaldehyde), HCHO, and allowed to stand at room temperature, it forms 4-hydroxymethylphenol as the major product. The yield of this isomer is enhanced by the use of the alkali catalyst.

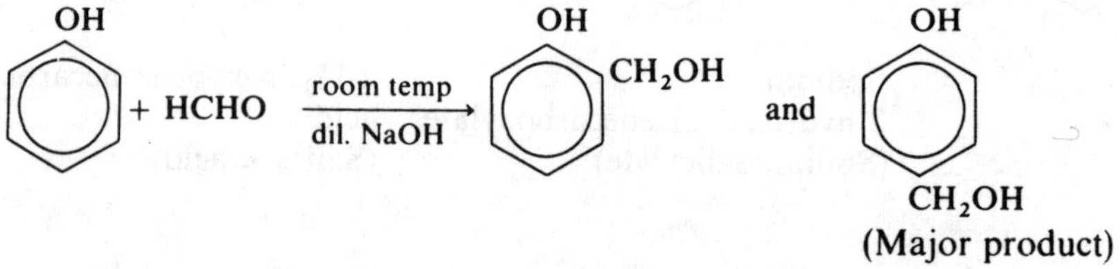

OH
$+ \text{HCHO}$ $\xrightarrow[\text{dil. NaOH}]{\text{room temp}}$
OH CH$_2$OH
and
OH

CH$_2$OH
(Major product)

2- and 4-Hydroxymethylphenol
(*o*- and *p*-Hydroxybenzyl alcohol)

Heating with a larger quantity of methanal in an acidic medium produces rigid, three-dimensional, cross-linked polymers, e.g. Bakelite.

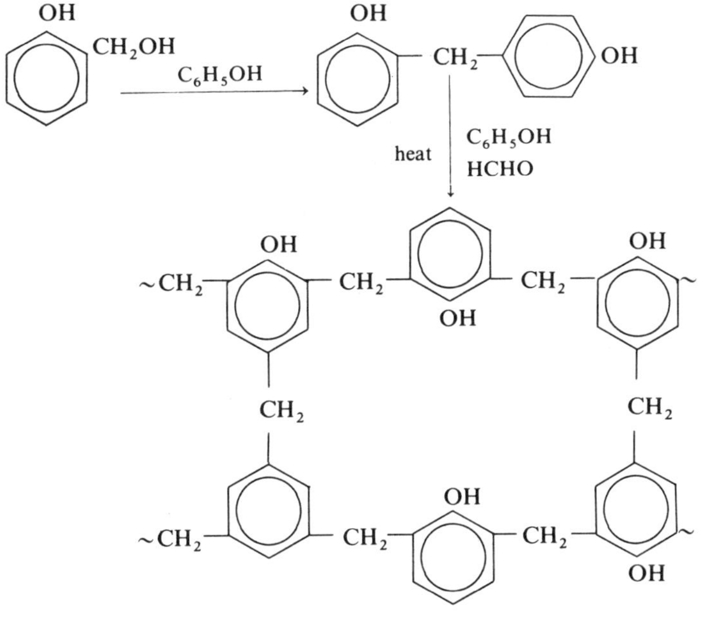

Bakelite

Variations in technique enable different resins and plastics to be manufactured.

QUESTIONS

1. The greater volatility of 2-nitrophenol compared with the 4-isomer is attributed to

   A its ability to form intermolecular hydrogen bonds
   B its ability to form intramolecular hydrogen bonds
   C its ability to dissociate on warming
   D weak dipole–dipole interactions between molecules
   E van der Waals' forces

2. Without referring to tables, indicate which of the following groups, when introduced in the aromatic nucleus in the positions stated, will promote the acidic properties of phenol to the greatest extent.

   A NO_2 in the 4-position
   B NO_2 in the 2-position
   C Cl in the 2-position
   D Cl in the 4-position
   E CH_3 in the 2-position

3. Treatment of phenol with bromine in a non-polar solvent in the cold gives as the major product

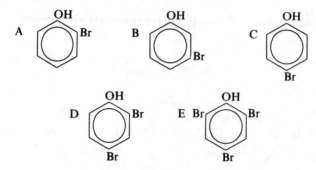

4. Why is phenol much more acidic than ethanol? Comment on how the introduction of a nitro group in the 2- and 4-positions of phenol affects its acidic strength.

5. Compare the ease with which phenol and chlorobenzene undergo the following reactions, naming the major products in each case.

A nitration
B sulphonation
C bromination
D acylation

18 Ethers

Saturated aliphatic ethers form a homologous series and correspond to a general molecular formula, $C_nH_{2n+2}O$, being isomeric with aliphatic monohydric alcohols ($C_nH_{2n+1}OH$). They possess the structure,

$$R—O—R'$$

where R and R' may be aliphatic or aromatic.

CH_3OCH_3

Methoxymethane
(Dimethyl ether)

$CH_3CH_2OCH_2CH_3$

Ethoxyethane
(Diethyl ether—'Ether')

Methoxybenzene
(Anisole)

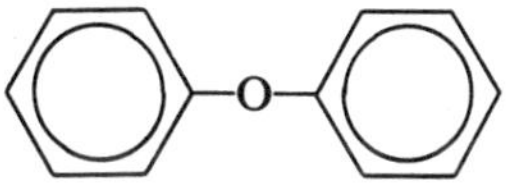

Phenoxybenzene
(Diphenyl ether)

Compounds in which R and R' are identical are described as SYMMETRICAL or SIMPLE ethers, and where R and R' are different, as UNSYMMETRICAL or MIXED ethers.

Ethoxybenzene, commonly referred to as just 'ether', is by far the most important of these compounds, and is used extensively as a solvent and at one time as an anaesthetic.

A number of CYCLIC ETHERS, notably tetrahydrofuran and epoxyethane (ethylene oxide), are also of considerable importance.

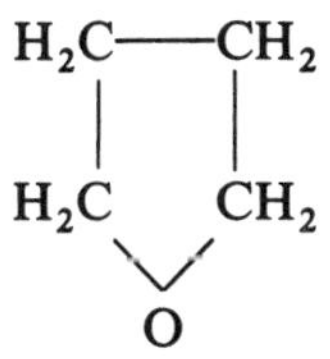

Tetrahydrofuran

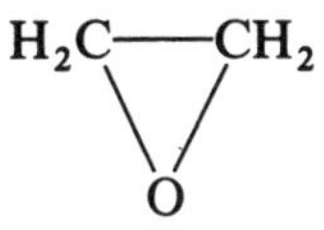

Epoxyethane
(Ethylene oxide)

TETRAHYDROFURAN is better able to donate electron pairs than ether, and is therefore slightly more basic and capable of forming more stable complexes with, say, Grignard reagents. (Compare pK_a values, page 198). Moreover, its reduced volatility makes it safer and easier to handle. One of the major reasons why tetrahydrofuran is not generally stated as a medium for Grignard reagents, and, for other reactions for which it is suitable, is that it is only comparatively recently that it has become widely available in commercial quantities.

Cyclic ethers containing three-membered rings are collectively known as EPOXIDES, the simplest and most important of these being epoxyethane (ethylene oxide) (b.p. 11 °C). The synthetic adaptability of this compound has already been discussed on page 111.

Nomenclature

The common system specifies the alkyl and/or aryl groups attached to the oxygen atom followed by the word 'ether'. Certain alkyl aryl ethers are afforded names which give no indication as to the structure, e.g. anisole (methoxybenzene) and phenetole (ethoxybenzene).

The IUPAC system regards them as alkoxy derivatives of alkanes or of the aryl nucleus,

$$\text{e.g.} \quad CH_3CH_2CHCH_3$$
$$\mid$$
$$OCH_3$$

2-Methoxybutane

Formula	IUPAC name	Common name
CH_3OCH_3	Methoxymethane	Dimethyl ether
$CH_3OCH_2CH_3$	Methoxyethane	Ethyl methyl ether
$CH_3CH_2OCH_2CH_3$	Ethoxyethane	Diethyl ether—'ether'
$C_6H_5OCH_3$	Methoxybenzene	Methyl phenyl ether or anisole
$C_6H_5OCH_2CH_3$	Ethoxybenzene	Ethyl phenyl ether or phenetole
$C_6H_5OC_6H_5$	Phenoxybenzene	Diphenyl ether

Physical Properties

The lower aliphatic ethers are highly flammable gases or volatile liquids, and possess a distinctive and characteristic odour. Phenoxybenzene (diphenyl ether) is a solid (m.p. 28 °C) at room temperature.

Although the oxygen atom contains unshared pairs of electrons, the molecules are not associated in the liquid phase as there are no suitably available hydrogens. The compounds therefore have normal boiling points, comparable with those of alkanes of corresponding relative molecular mass and of course much lower than those of analogous alcohols.

Name	Formula	M.p./°C	B.p./°C	Density at 20°C/ g cm^{-3}
Methoxymethane	CH_3OCH_3	−142	−25	0.661
Methoxyethane	$CH_3OCH_2CH_3$	−116	7	0.069
Ethoxyethane	$(CH_3CH_2)_2O$	−116	35	0.714
Tetrahydrofuran	$CH_2CH_2\begin{smallmatrix}\\ \diagdown \\ O \\ \diagup \\\end{smallmatrix}CH_2CH_2$	−108	65	0.888
Methoxybenzene	$C_6H_5OCH_3$	−38	154	0.994
Ethoxybenzene	$C_6H_5OCH_2CH_3$	−30	172	0.974
Phenoxybenzene	$(C_6H_5)_2O$	28	258	1.072

In as much as aliphatic alcohols may be regarded as monalkyl derivatives of water, ethers may be regarded as DIALKYL DERIVATIVES. This is reflected in their solubility in water. Methoxymethane and methoxyethane are fairly soluble since the molecules are able to form hydrogen bonds with the water molecules, but as the hydrocarbon content of the molecules increases, there is a rapid decline in solubility. Ethers are much less soluble in water than are alcohols, but are themselves extremely important solvents.

Most of the simple ethers are considerably less dense than water, although the density increases with increasing relative molecular mass and some of the aromatics are in fact denser than water.

Industrial Source

ETHOXYETHANE (DIETHYL ETHER) is manufactured by passing ethanol *vapour* into a heated mixture of alcohol (in excess) and concentrated sulphuric acid at a carefully maintained temperature of 140 °C. This process is known as CONTINUOUS ETHERIFICATION.

$$2CH_3CH_2OH \underset{140\,°C}{\overset{conc.\ H_2SO_4}{\rightleftharpoons}} CH_3CH_2OCH_2CH_3 + H_2O$$

If the alcohol is not present in excess or if a higher temperature of 170–180 °C is reached, further dehydration to yield ethene occurs. (*See* pages 101 and 175.)

Ethoxyethane is also obtained as a by-product in the manufacture of ethanol from ethene.

Synthetic Preparations

Williamson's Synthesis

This provides probably the most important and flexible method of preparation, being suitable for both symmetrical and unsymmetrical compounds. The process involves the displacement of a halogen from an haloalkane by an alkoxide (alkylate) or phenoxide (phenate) ion.

$$RX + R'O^-Na^+ \xrightarrow{reflux} ROR' + NaX$$

Methoxyaromatics are more efficiently prepared from the dimethyl sulphate and the appropriate phenol.

Methoxybenzene
(Anisole)

Refer to pages 155 and 186.

Partial Dehydration of Alcohols

The essential difference between the laboratory and the industrial preparation is that in the former the alcohol is employed solely in the *liquid phase*.

$$2ROH \xrightleftharpoons[140\,°C]{\text{conc. } H_2SO_4} ROR + H_2O$$

This method is limited only to symmetrical ethers.
Refer to page 176.

From Haloalkanes and Dry Silver(I) Oxide

$$2RX + Ag_2O \xrightarrow{\text{warm}} ROR + 2AgX$$

This preparation is for symmetrical ethers only.

From Aliphatic Primary Amines

Refer to page 213.

Reactions

Unlike alcohols, ethers do not contain a replaceable proton and are generally unreactive compounds, not reacting with metals, strong bases or phosphorus pentahalides, and not easily undergoing substitution with ionic species. This general lack of pronounced chemical affinity shows a certain similarity to the alkanes.

However, the oxygen atom is sufficiently basic to undergo protonation in an acidic medium by the donation of a lone pair of electrons, i.e. it functions as a Lewis base.

$$R-\ddot{\underset{..}{O}}-R' \overset{H^+}{\rightleftharpoons} R-\overset{+}{\underset{H}{\ddot{O}}}-R'$$

The protonated species is then susceptible to subsequent attack by a nucleophile.

It is as a result of this phenomenon that ethers, unlike alkanes, dissolve hydrogen chloride gas and concentrated sulphuric acid to form salts, e.g. $CH_3CH_2O^+CH_2CH_3HSO_4^-$. This property may be utilized for separating $\underset{H}{}$ ethers from other organic compounds such as alkanes and haloalkanes.

Compound	pK_a
Ethoxyethane	−2.1
Tetrahydrofuran	−3.6

In AROMATIC ETHERS the alkoxy group is mildly ring-activating and directs to the 2- and 4-positions.

Cleavage Reactions Involving HX

Fission of an oxygen-carbon single bond in ethers occurs only under vigorous conditions.

In the case of the hydrogen halides, hydrogen iodide is the strongest acid and the iodide ion functions as the best nucleophile. The ether is refluxed with an *excess* of the hydrogen halide.

$$R-\overset{..}{\underset{..}{O}}-R' \,\,H^+ \xrightarrow[\text{reflux}]{\text{HI}} R-\overset{+}{\underset{\underset{H}{|}}{\overset{..}{O}}}-R' \longrightarrow R^+ + R'-\overset{..}{\underset{..}{O}}H$$

$$\downarrow I^-$$

$$R-I$$

An alcohol is formed as one of the initial products but then reacts with more hydrogen iodide to yield the iodoalkane.

$$R'-\overset{..}{\underset{..}{O}}H \,\,H^+I^- \xrightarrow{\text{reflux}} R'-\overset{+}{\underset{..}{O}}H_2 + I^-$$

$$R'-\overset{+}{\underset{..}{O}}H_2 \longrightarrow \overset{+}{R'} + H_2O$$

$$\overset{+}{R'} \,\, I^- \longrightarrow R'I$$

The alcohol may be isolated by employing milder conditions.

Alkylaromatics yield a phenol and a haloalkane.

$$\xrightarrow[\text{120--130 °C}]{\text{HI}}$$

Reactivity: HI > HBr > HCl

The principle of this reaction is utilized in the ZEISEL METHOD for the quantitative determination of methoxy or ethoxy groups.

A weighed sample of the alkoxy compound is refluxed with excess hydrogen iodine. The resulting volatile iodoalkane is distilled into an alcoholic silver(I) nitrate solution and the mass of the precipitated silver(I) iodide determined.

Autoxidation

On exposure to sunlight ethers slowly absorb oxygen, forming peroxides, which are unstable and explode violently if heated.

$$RCH_2-O-CH_2R' + O_2 \xrightarrow{h\nu} RCH_2-O-\underset{\underset{OOH}{|}}{C}HR'$$

A peroxide

Oxidation of this type can be avoided by storing ethers, usually ordinary ethoxyethane, in dark, well-sealed bottles in the presence of a little alcohol.

ABSOLUTE ETHOXYETHANE, free from traces of water and alcohol, can be obtained by distilling ordinary ethoxyethane from concentrated sulphuric acid, which has the effect of removing both water and any peroxide present, and then storing over sodium.

Grignard Reagents: Complex Formation

Absolute ethoxyethane functions as a suitable solvent for Grignard reagents by donating electrons to the magnesium atom.

$$2(CH_3CH_2)_2O + RMgX \rightleftharpoons \begin{array}{c} CH_3CH_2-\overset{..}{\underset{..}{O}}-CH_2CH_3 \\ R-Mg-X \\ CH_3CH_2-\overset{..}{\underset{..}{O}}-CH_2CH_3 \end{array}$$

Many of the higher ethers are unsuitable as solvents for this reagent since they form complexes which are insoluble in the excess solvent.

Note the use and advantages of tetrahydrofuran as an alternative solvent.

Refer to pages 162 and 195.

QUESTIONS

1. Ethoxyethane (b.p. 35 °C) is more volatile than ethanol (b.p. 78 °C) largely because of

   A the greater relative molecular mass of the ether

   B the strength of the C—O bonds in the ether

   C the highly polar —OH group in ethanol

   D the different shapes of the molecules

   E intramolecular hydrogen bonding between the ether molecules

2. Compare and contrast the physical properties of alcohols and ethers, paying particular regard to their volatility and solubility in water.

3. Give the structural formulae and IUPAC names of all compounds corresponding to $C_4H_{10}O$, and outline reactions which would enable you to distinguish between them.

4. 'Simple monohydric aliphatic alcohols may be considered as monoalkyl derivatives of water and simple aliphatic ethers as dialkyl derivatives.' Suggest evidence to justify this statement.

5. In what way does the structure of the Grignard reagent reflect the basic nature of ethoxyethane? Write the structure of the Grignard reagent in the presence of a tetrahydrofuran medium.

19 Amines and their Derivatives

Amines are alkyl or aryl derivatives of ammonia, and may be classified as primary, secondary or tertiary according to the number of alkyl and/or aryl groups attached to the nitrogen atom.

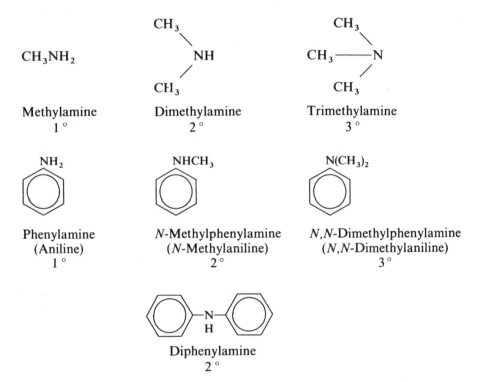

CH_3NH_2

Methylamine
1 °

Dimethylamine
2 °

Trimethylamine
3 °

Phenylamine
(Aniline)
1 °

N-Methylphenylamine
(N-Methylaniline)
2 °

N,N-Dimethylphenylamine
(N,N-Dimethylaniline)
3 °

Diphenylamine
2 °

Compounds containing two amine groups are known as DIAMINES.

AROMATIC AMINES are compounds in which the nitrogen atom is attached directly to the aromatic ring. This means that (phenylmethyl)amine (benzylamine), and other such compounds in which the aromatic ring is separated from the amino group by at least one methylene ($—CH_2—$) group are, strictly speaking, phenyl-substituted alkylamines, although certain texts do classify them as 'side-chain' arylamines.

Structure of Amines

As in ammonia, the nitrogen atom of aliphatic amines is sp^3 hybridized with one orbital containing a lone pair of electrons.

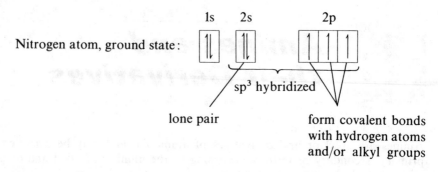

The basic tetrahedral orientation of the hybrid orbitals is distorted by the strong repulsive forces between the lone pair and the bond pairs of the amine molecule, resulting in the formation of a trigonal pyramid arrangement.

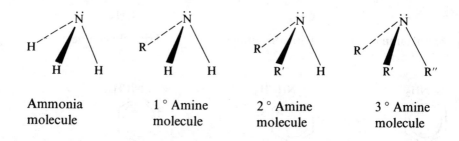

The symmetry of the trigonal pyramid is dependent upon the number of alkyl groups attached to the nitrogen and also upon their electronic and steric nature.

The structure of phenylamine (aniline) has not yet been fully ascertained. It was thought for a long time that phenylamine was a planar molecule but modern physical analysis suggests that the nitrogen atom is possibly sp^3 hybridized with the orbital containing the electron pair interacting separately with each of the π electron clouds of the aromatic nucleus.

Nomenclature

Aliphatic Amines

These are named by specifying the alkyl groups attached to the nitrogen atom followed by the ending '-amine'.

Formula	Name
CH_3NH_2	Methylamine
$CH_3CH_2NH_2$	Ethylamine
$(CH_3)_2NH$	Dimethylamine
$CH_3CH_2CH_2NH_2$	Propylamine

Formula	Name
CH_3 　　$\diagdown$ 　　　$CH—NH_2$ 　　$\diagup$ CH_3	1-Methylethylamine (Isopropylamine)
$CH_3CH_2NHCH_3$	Ethylmethylamine
$(CH_3)_3N$	Trimethylamine
$(CH_3)_3CNH_2$	1,1-Dimethylethylamine (*tert*-Butylamine)

More complex tertiary amines with different alkyl groups are named as derivatives of the longest chain, and an italic capital N is inserted before the name of each substituent.

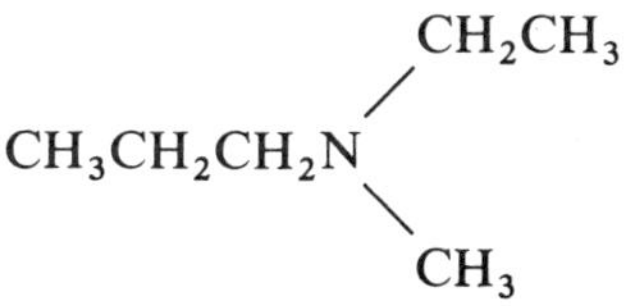

$$CH_3CH_2CH_2N\begin{array}{l} \diagup CH_2CH_3 \\ \diagdown CH_3 \end{array}$$

N-Ethyl-*N*-methylpropylamine

Compounds containing a tetravalent nitrogen are called QUATERNARY AMMONIUM COMPOUNDS and are named by changing the ending '-mine' to '-mmonium'.

$$(CH_3)_4N^+I^- \qquad \text{Tetramethylammonium iodide}$$

Aromatic Amines

The simplest of these is phenylamine (aniline), and most other simple compounds are named as derivatives of phenylamine.

Methylphenylamines are collectively called TOLUIDINES.

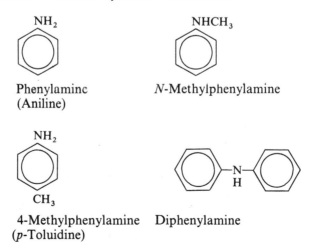

Phenylamine
(Aniline)

N-Methylphenylamine

4-Methylphenylamine　　Diphenylamine
(*p*-Toluidine)

Both aliphatic and aromatic amines can be named by inserting the ending '-amine' as a suffix to the name of the alkane or other appropriate hydrocarbon.

This method is rarely used for simple amines, but is widely adopted for compounds such as, hexane-1,6-diamine, $NH_2(CH_2)_6NH_2$, and benzenes-1,3-diamine, $1,3\text{-}(NH_2)_2C_6H_4$.

Physical Properties

The simple aliphatic amines are gases and possess a characteristic 'ammonia' smell. Most of the higher homologues are liquids, which have a distinctive 'fishy' odour, and some of the very high relative molecular mass compounds are solids.

They are polar compounds and their molecules, with the exception of tertiary amines, form intermolecular hydrogen bonds with each other, thus increasing their boiling points above those of less polar compounds of comparable relative molecular mass.

$$
\begin{array}{ccc}
H & R & H \\
| & | & | \\
--H-N\!:---H-N\!:---H-N\!:-- \\
| & | & | \\
R & H & R
\end{array}
$$

For isomeric amines, the boiling points decrease in the order:

$$1° \text{ amines} > 2° \text{amines} > 3° \text{ amines},$$

due to the progressive decrease in intermolecular hydrogen bonding. Volatility is enhanced by branching in the carbon chain.

	Isomer	B.p./°C
four isomers of $C_4H_9NH_2$	$CH_3CH_2CH_2CH_2NH_2$	78

	$CH_3CHCH_2NH_2$
	    $\mid$
	    CH_3
		68

	$CH_3CH_2CHNH_2$
	       $\mid$
	       CH_3
		63

	CH_3
	    $\mid$
	 CH_3-C-NH_2
	    $\mid$
	    CH_3
		56

All three classes of aliphatic amines are capable of forming hydrogen bonds with water and, as a result, all simple compounds are fairly soluble. However, as the hydrocarbon content increases there is a general decline in solubility, this being especially significant for those compounds containing more than six carbons. Amines are also soluble in many of the usual non-polar organic solvents.

Phenylamine (aniline) is a highly toxic liquid (b.p. 184 °C), and provides the additional hazard of being all too easily absorbed through the skin. The physical state of other aromatic amines is greatly affected by the presence and nature of further substituents in the ring.

Although amines are either only slightly soluble in water (e.g. phenylamine: 3.7 g/100 g water) or virtually insoluble, they dissolve readily in suitable organic solvents.

Industrial Source

METHYLAMINES are manufactured by passing methanol and ammonia over an aluminium oxide catalyst on an inert support at 400–450 °C and under a high pressure.

$$NH_3 \xrightarrow[\text{high press., 400–450 °C}]{\text{CH}_3\text{OH, Al}_2\text{O}_3 \text{ cat.}} CH_3NH_2 \xrightarrow{\text{CH}_3\text{OH}} (CH_3)_2NH \xrightarrow{\text{CH}_3\text{OH}} (CH_3)_3N$$

Of the methylamines, DIMETHYLAMINE is presently in greatest demand, since it is used for the manufacture of synthetic fibre solvents, unsymmetrical dimethylhydrazones, which are used for jet and rocket fuels, and many other industrially important compounds.

ETHYLAMINES are manufactured by passing ethanol, ammonia and hydrogen, under pressure, over a metallic hydrogenation catalyst at 150–240 °C.

Higher alkylamines can be prepared from the more expensive haloalkanes, and also by the reductive amination of aldehydes and ketones. Both of these processes are outlined under the section on synthetic laboratory preparations.

PHENYLAMINE (ANILINE) is manufactured from nitrobenzene, which is itself prepared from the abundantly available benzene. The principle is basically similar to the laboratory preparation, but the technique has to be modified somewhat.

Benzene is nitrated at 50–55 °C using a nitrating mixture of concentrated nitric acid and sulphuric acid, which is added gradually to the reaction vessel and mechanically stirred. The system is cooled by passing water through lead cooling coils inside the vessel.

The nitrobenzene is reduced to phenylamine using iron turnings and 30 per cent *dilute* hydrochloric acid in an iron vessel lined with brickware. The mixture is stirred under reflux.

Phenylammonium chloride
(Anilinium chloride)

The mixture is neutralized by the addition of lime and the phenylamine separated by steam distilling under reduced pressure.

Aromatic amines are sometimes obtained by treating chlorobenzene with ammonia at a high temperature and high pressure in the presence of a copper(I) oxide catalyst.

This reaction involves nucleophilic aromatic substitution of the halogen. This is difficult to carry out, especially under laboratory conditions, unless the ring contains activating substituents.

In the United States, phenylamine is also obtained by the catalytic hydrogenation of nitrobenzene.

Phenylamine is utilized in the rubber industry for preparing anti-oxidants and accelerators for vulcanizing. Fairly large quantities are employed for manufacturing dyestuffs and small amounts for synthesizing drugs.

Synthetic Preparations

Hofmann Degradation of Amides

This reaction gives a good yield of the primary amine uncontaminated with secondary and tertiary amines.

The amide is warmed with bromine and a concentrated aqueous solution of alkali.

$$CH_3CONH_2 + Br_2 + 4NaOH \rightarrow CH_3NH_2 + 2NaBr + Na_2CO_3 + 2H_2O$$

Ethanamide
(Acetamide)

The mechanism for this process is outlined on page 270.

Reduction of Nitriles

This is accomplished by treating an alkanenitrile with sodium and absolute alcohol or with lithium tetrahydridoaluminate(III) in ethoxyethane.

$$RCN + 4[H] \xrightarrow[\text{(C}_2\text{H}_5)_2\text{O}]{\text{LiAlH}_4,} RCH_2NH_2$$

Methylamine can be obtained by the reduction of hydrogen cyanide.

$$HCN + 4[H] \xrightarrow[\text{(C}_2\text{H}_5)_2\text{O}]{\text{LiAlH}_4,} CH_3NH_2$$

The nature of the medium eliminates any opportunity for concurrent hydrolysis of the nitrile.

A further application of the same principle is the reduction of oximes.

$$RCH{=}NOH + 4[H] \xrightarrow[\text{(C}_2\text{H}_5)_2\text{O}]{\text{LiAlH}_4,} RCH_2NH_2 + H_2O$$

From Haloalkanes

Higher alkylamines can be prepared by heating the haloalkane with an excess of alcoholic ammonia under pressure in a sealed tube, although in certain instances the reaction is performed by allowing the reactants to stand together at room temperature for a long period of time.

$$RX + \text{alc. } NH_3 \xrightarrow[\text{heat}]{\text{sealed tube}} RNH_2 + HX$$

$$RNH_2 + RX \longrightarrow R_2NH + HX$$

$$R_2NH + RX \longrightarrow R_3N + HX$$

$$R_3N + RX \longrightarrow R_4N^+X^-$$

Since the alkylamines are more reactive than ammonia, the reaction rate becomes progressively quicker and this reaction is not generally convenient for preparing individual amines, which in the system exist in equilibrium with their salts.

$$RNH_2 + HX \rightleftharpoons RNH_3^+X^-$$

On an industrial scale, adequate separation can be obtained by adding alkali to liberate the free amines and fractionally distilling. Chemical means of separation are also employed.

Improved yields of secondary and tertiary amines can be obtained using a haloalkane and a primary amine as starting reagents and heating in alcoholic solution.

Reductive Amination of Aldehydes and Ketones

This reaction involves passing the carboxyl compound together with hydrogen and ammonia over a nickel–chromium catalyst at a high temperature.

Aldehyde   1° amine

Ketone   1° amine

Aromatic aldehydes can also be employed successfully.

Benzenecarbaldehyde
(Benzaldehyde)

Synthetic Preparation of Phenylamine (Aniline)

PHENYLAMINE (ANILINE) is usually prepared in the laboratory by reducing nitrobenzene using tin and *concentrated* hydrochloric acid, the latter being added a little at a time during reflux.

Tin(II) chloride, formed during the reaction, is the principal reducing agent, being itself oxidized to the tin(IV) salt.

$$C_6H_5NO_2 + 3Sn^{2+} + 6H^+ \longrightarrow C_6H_5NH_2 + 3Sn^{4+} + 2H_2O$$

The tin(IV) chloride forms a complex acid with hydrochloric acid and combines with the phenylamine produced in the reaction.

$$SnCl_4 + 2HCl \longrightarrow H_2[SnCl_6]$$

$$2C_6H_5NH_2 + H_2[SnCl_6] \longrightarrow 2(C_6H_5NH_3)[SnCl_6]$$

The phenylamine is liberated from the double salt by treating it with excess concentrated sodium hydroxide. A relatively large quantity of sodium hydroxide is required as tin(IV) hydroxide is formed. The hydroxide precipitates out, but then dissolves as hexahydroxostannate(IV) ions when the solution is strongly alkaline. The phenylamine is then extracted by steam distillation.

The phenylamine is 'salted out' from the distillate and then extracted with ethoxyethane.

For large scale preparations it is more economical to use iron turnings instead of the more expensive tin.

Reactions

The majority of compounds so far studied in each series serve as very weak Lewis bases (nucleophiles) as a result of having electron-rich functional groups. Aliphatic amines function as much stronger Lewis bases owing to their ability to donate the electron pair on the nitrogen to a proton, and are indeed stronger bases than ammonia.

$$RNH_2 + H_2O \rightleftharpoons RNH_3^+ + {}^-OH$$

$$(cf. NH_3 + H_2O \rightleftharpoons NH_4^+ + {}^-OH)$$

The basic strength of amines in water depends upon two factors: (1) the availability of electron pairs to donate to a proton; and (2) the ease with which the protonated amine can undergo solvation with the water molecules and so become stabilized.

The release of electron pairs for donation is favoured by electron-donating inductive effects, and on these grounds alone the basic strength would be expected to decrease in the order:

$$3° \text{ amine} > 2° \text{ amine} > 1° \text{ amine} > NH_3$$

However, solvation is facilitated by hydrogen bonding between the hydrogen atoms attached to the nitrogen of the amine and the oxygen atom of the water. Therefore, ease of solvation of protonated amines decreases in the order:

$$NH_3 > 1° \text{ amine} > 2° \text{ amine} > 3° \text{ amine}$$

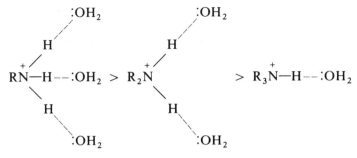

The rationalized effect of the electron pair releasing power and the ease with which amines solvate results in the basic strength increasing in the order:

$$2° \text{ amine} > 1° \text{ amine} > 3° \text{ amine} > NH_3$$

The basic strength may be modified as a result of the different electron-releasing inductive powers of the various alkyl groups, although the steric hindrance afforded by some of the more bulky groups may have the effect of impairing reactivity despite favourable electronic effects.

Name	Formula	pK_b
Ammonia	NH_3	4.75
Methylamine	CH_3NH_2	3.36
Ethylamine	$CH_3CH_2NH_2$	3.27
Dimethylamine	$(CH_3)_2NH$	3.28
Propylamine	$CH_3(CH_2)_2NH_2$	3.16
Trimethylamine	$(CH_3)_3N$	3.36
Phenylamine	$C_6H_5NH_2$	9.38
2-Methylphenylamine	$o\text{-}CH_3C_6H_4NH_2$	9.62

Name	Formula	pK_b
3-Methylphenylamine	$3\text{-}CH_3C_6H_4NH_2$	9.33
4-Methylphenylamine	$4\text{-}CH_3C_6H_4NH_2$	9.00
2-Hydroxyphenylamine	$2\text{-}HOC_6H_4NH_2$	9.28
3-Hydroxyphenylamine	$3\text{-}HOC_6H_4NH_2$	9.83
4-Hydroxyphenylamine	$4\text{-}HOC_6H_4NH_2$	8.53
2-Methoxyphenylamine	$2\text{-}CH_3OC_6H_4NH_2$	9.15
3-Methoxyphenylamine	$3\text{-}CH_3OC_6H_4NH_2$	9.80
4-Methoxyphenylamine	$4\text{-}CH_3OC_6H_4NH_2$	8.71
2-Chlorophenylamine	$2\text{-}ClC_6H_4NH_2$	11.44
3-Chlorophenylamine	$3\text{-}ClC_6H_4NH_2$	10.54
4-Chlorophenylamine	$4\text{-}ClC_6H_4NH_2$	10.07
2-Nitrophenylamine	$2\text{-}NO_2C_6H_4NH_2$	14.28
3-Nitrophenylamine	$3\text{-}NO_2C_6H_4NH_2$	11.55
4-Nitrophenylamine	$4\text{-}NO_2C_6H_4NH_2$	13.02

In contrast to the aliphatic amines, which are stronger bases than ammonia, phenylamine is a much weaker base. This is attributable to the positive charge, acquired on protonation, being widely distributed about the alkyl group(s) of the aliphatic amines, whereas in the case of the PHENYLAMMONIUM (anilinium) ION, $C_6H_5NH_3^+$, the charge is localized in the region of the nitrogen atom as it

NH₂ + H⁺ ⇌ NH₃⁺

Phenylammonium ion
(Anilinium ion)

cannot be distributed about the ring in the same way as the negative charge possessed by the phenoxide anion.

The basic character of phenylamine can be increased by introducing nucleophilic substituents, e.g. CH_3O— and —OH, on to the ring, especially in the 4-position, so causing an increase in electron density about the ring. This effect is transmitted to the amino group, making the nitrogen atom richer in electrons and correspondingly more basic.

Protonation of the amino group of phenylamine also has a significant effect on its directing powers. In the phenylamine molecule, there is competition between the electron-withdrawing inductive effect of the amino group and the more powerful electron-releasing mesomeric effect of the lone pair on the nitrogen atom, resulting in overall activation of the ring with regard to electrophilic substitution. (Compare with the effect of the hydroxyl group on the ring in phenol.)

However, donation of the lone pair to a proton, especially in a strongly acid medium, leaves only the inductive effect operating, and for electrophilic substitution, the cation directs predominantly to the 3- position, owing to the deactivation of the ring.

Salt Formation

Both aliphatic amines and phenylamine, despite the latter being a much weaker base, form stable crystalline salts with mineral acids, e.g. $CH_3NH_3^+Cl^-$, $CH_3NH_3^+HSO_4^-$, $C_6H_5NH_3^+Cl^-$.

In fact, because of the fairly rapid deterioration of phenylamine on exposure to light, owing to oxidation, it is often stored in the form of the phenylammonium chloride (m.p. 198 °C), the free phenylamine being regenerated by treating the salt with excess aqueous sodium hydroxide.

$$C_6H_5NH_3^+Cl^- + NaOH \longrightarrow C_6H_5NH_2 + NaCl + H_2O$$

Amines, like ammonia, form water-insoluble salts with chloroplatinic acid, e.g. $(RNH_3)_2PtCl_6$, and this acid can be used for the analytical determination of an amine. Analysis of this type is performed by igniting a weighed, dry sample of the chloroplatinate and weighing the residue of platinum.

Acylation: Amide Formation

Both aliphatic and aromatic primary and secondary amines are readily acylated in the cold by acyl halides and acid anhydrides to yield the corresponding amide.

$$RNH_2 + R'COX \longrightarrow RNHCOR' + HX$$

Amide

$$RNH_2 + (R'CO)_2O \longrightarrow RNHCOR' + R'COOH$$

N-Phenylalkanamide
(Anilide)

Since the nitrogen atom of tertiary amines does not contain a replaceable hydrogen atom they are incapable of forming amides.

BENZENECARBONYLATION (benzoylation) of primary and secondary amines can be carried out using a benzenecarbonyl (benzoyl) halide in the presence of excess aqueous alkali.

$$RNH_2 + C_6H_5COCl \xrightarrow[\text{aq. NaOH}]{\text{excess}} RNHCOC_6H_5 + HCl$$

Isocyanide (Carbylamine) Test for Primary Amines

When a primary amine, either aliphatic or aromatic, is warmed with tri-chloromethane (chloroform) and a few drops of alcoholic alkali, an ISOCYANIDE (isonitrile or carbylamine) is formed, the latter being immediately recognizable by its foul smell.

$$RNH_2 + CHCl_3 + 3KOH \longrightarrow RNC + 3KCl + 3H_2O$$

Alkylisocyanide

This test provides a means of easily distinguishing primary amines from the other two classes and, as the sensitivity depends upon the volatility of the isocyanide formed, simple primary amines are very easily detected. It is generally preferable to use the test in conjunction with one of the other distinguishing reactions, e.g. with nitrous acid.

Quaternary Ammonium Salts

The ammonolysis of haloalkanes (discussed earlier in this chapter as a means of preparing amines) gives rise to a mixture of primary, secondary and tertiary amines, their salts and the QUATERNARY AMMONIUM SALT.

Whereas the use of excess of ammonia enables a better yield of the primary amine to be obtained (*see* page 157) the presence of excess haloalkane produces a higher yield of the quaternary ammonium salt. The reaction involves the progressive substitution of hydrogens attached to the nitrogen atom of the amine by an alkyl group, usually a methyl, of the haloalkane. This process is sometimes referred to as *exhaustive methylation*. The reaction applies to all classes of amines including aromatic amines.

A more specific method of synthesizing quaternary ammonium salts involves heating a tertiary amine with excess of the appropriate haloalkane.

$$(CH_3)_3N + CH_3I \xrightarrow{\text{heat}} (CH_3)_4N^+I^-$$

Tetramethylammonium
iodide

Despite the strong nucleophilic properties of the tertiary amine, heat is required to overcome steric crowding around the nitrogen.

Structure and Physical Properties

The four alkyl groups are tetrahedrally covalently bonded to the nitrogen forming a singly charged cation which forms an ionic bond with the anion.

$$\begin{bmatrix} CH_3 & & CH_3 \\ & N & \\ CH_3 & & CH_3 \end{bmatrix}^+ \quad I^-$$

The salts are odourless and colourless crystalline solids which are soluble in water.

Reactions

Whereas the addition of aqueous alkali to the salts of amines liberates the free amine, it has no effect on the quaternary ammonium salt since the latter has no proton to which the hydroxyl group can donate a lone pair.

On warming with an aqueous solution of silver(I) oxide, the salts are converted into QUATERNARY AMMONIUM HYDROXIDES, which dissociate completely into ions and are alkalis comparable in strength to the caustic alkalis.

$$(CH_3)_4N^+I^- \xrightarrow{Ag_2O/H_2O} (CH_3)_4NOH \longrightarrow (CH_3)_4N^+ + {}^-OH$$

Quaternary ammonium hydroxides, on heating to temperatures above $120\,°C$, decompose to form an amine, water and an alkene.

$$\underset{\underset{H}{|}}{RCHCH_2}N^+(CH_3)_3{}^-OH \xrightarrow{\text{heat}} RCH{=}CH_2 + (CH_3)_3N + H_2O$$

In this case, the alkene formed preferentially is the one containing the fewer alkyl groups (Hofmann elimination as opposed to the Saytzeff type of elimination discussed on page 176).

Reactions of this type can be used to determine the structures of amines, especially heterocyclic and tertiary ones.

With Nitrous Acid

Owing to the instability of nitrous acid it is always generated during a reaction, usually by the action of dilute sulphuric or hydrochloric acid on sodium nitrite. The products resulting from its action depend upon the type of amine employed and the conditions under which the reaction is carried out.

ALIPHATIC PRIMARY AMINES always evolve nitrogen with nitrous acid, owing to the decomposition of the ALKYLDIAZONIUM ION which is formed as an unstable intermediate.

$$RNH_2 + HONO \xrightarrow{H^+} R-N^+{\equiv}N{:} + 2H_2O$$

Alkyldiazonium
ion

$$R^+ + N_2$$

The subsequent reactions of the carbocation (carbonium ion) can produce a whole variety of products with only a small variation in the acid concentration. The methyl carbocation interacts with water to form methanol.

$$\overset{+}{C}H_3 + H_2\ddot{O}{:} \longrightarrow CH_3OH_2^+ \xrightarrow{-H^+} CH_3OH$$

Interaction between the methanol formed and the other methyl carbocations usually produces a large proportion of methoxymethane (dimethyl ether).

$$\overset{+}{C}H_3 + CH_3\ddot{O}H \longrightarrow CH_3-\overset{H^+}{O}CH_3 \xrightarrow{-H^+} CH_3OCH_3$$

With ethylamine and higher primary alkylamines the amount of ether obtained is comparatively small, and it is usually formed together with a certain amount of alkene resulting from the loss of a proton from a carbocation.

$$R\overset{+}{C}H-CH_3 \xrightarrow{-H^+} RCH{=}CH_2$$

In addition to the alcohols, ethers and alkenes, some nitroalkane is also formed from the direct interaction between the carbocation and the nitrite ions in solution.

$$R^+ + {:}NO_2^- \longrightarrow RNO_2$$

Nitroalkane

The quantity of nitroalkane obtained increases as the yield of alcohol falls. If a halogen acid is used, small quantities of haloalkane are also formed.

$$R^+ + Cl^- \longrightarrow RCl$$

Aromatic primary amines react with nitrous acid to form diazonium cations which are somewhat more stable than their aliphatic counterparts, and these are discussed in more detail at a later stage in this chapter.

SECONDARY AMINES, both aliphatic and aromatic, react with nitrous acid to yield *N*-NITROSOAMINES (amides of nitrous acid) which can be easily recognized as yellow oils.

$$R_2NH + HONO \longrightarrow R_2N-N=O + H_2O$$

N-Nitroso-*N*, *N*-dialkylamine

NHCH$_3$ CH$_3$—N—N=O

+ HONO $\longrightarrow$ + H$_2$O

N-Methylphenylamine   *N*-Nitroso-*N*-methylphenylamine
(*N*-Methylaniline)   (*N*-Nitroso-*N*-methylaniline)

ALIPHATIC TERTIARY AMINES cannot undergo diazotization or nitrosation since they do not possess any replaceable hydrogens on the nitrogen, and generally remain in solution in the form of their salts.

$$R_3N + HONO \longrightarrow R_3\overset{+}{N}H + NO_2^-$$

The free amine can be regenerated by treating with dilute alkali. Sometimes a rather complex reaction occurs in which the chief products are aldehydes and the nitroso derivatives of secondary amines.

The high reactivity of the ring enables TERTIARY AROMATIC AMINES to undergo nitrosation in the 4- position (cf. phenol).

N(CH$_3$)$_2$ N(CH$_3$)$_2$

+ HONO $\xrightarrow[\text{0–10 °C}]{\text{NO}^+}$ + H$_2$O

NO

N,*N*-Dimethylphenylamine   4-Nitroso-*N*,*N*-dimethylphenylamine
(*N*,*N*-Dimethylaniline)   (*p*-Nitroso-*N*,*N*-dimethylaniline)

The nitrites of all classes of amines may be formed by bubbling carbon dioxide into a suspension of finely divided sodium nitrite in a methanolic solution of the amine.

$$RNH_2 + HONO \xrightarrow[\text{CH}_3\text{OH}]{\text{NaNO}_2/\text{CO}_2} RNH_3^+ NO_2^-$$

Amine nitrite

Summary

1° *Amines*

Aliphatic: $RNH_2 \xrightarrow{\text{HONO}} N_2 + ROH +$ Mixture of ethers, alkenes, nitroalkanes, haloalkanes

(Methylamine usually forms methoxymethane as the predominant product.)

Phenylamine $C_6H_5NH_2 + HONO + H^+ \xrightarrow{\text{0–5 °C}} C_6H_5-N^+\equiv N + 2H_2O$
(aniline):
                          Benzenediazonium salt

$2°$ *Amines (Aliphatic and Aromatic)*

$$R_2NH \xrightarrow{\text{HONO}} R_2N-N=O + H_2O$$

Nitrosoamine
Yellow oils

$3°$ *Amines*

Aliphatic:

$$R_3N \xrightarrow{\text{HONO}} R_3N\overset{+}{H} + NO_2^-$$

Remain in solution

Aromatic:

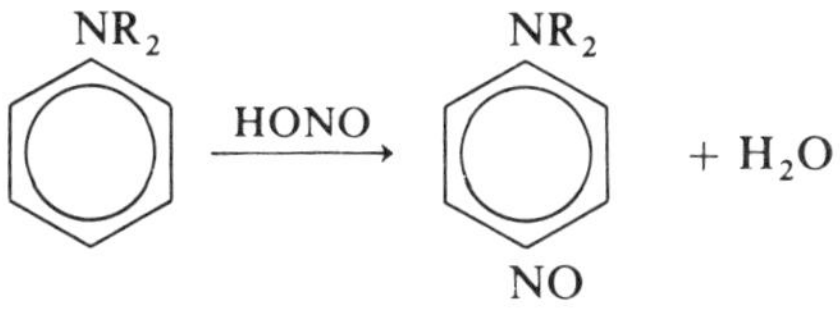

+ H_2O

4-Nitroso derivative

Benzenediazonium Salts

Phenylamine and other aromatic primary amines react with nitrous acid at 0–5 C to yield diazonium salts which are fairly stable in comparison with their aliphatic counterparts.

$$C_6H_5NH_2 + HONO + H^+ \xrightarrow{0-5\,°C} C_6H_5 - \overset{+}{N} \equiv N: + 2H_2O$$

Benzenediazonium ion

Although benzenediazonium salts can be isolated in the crystalline form, they are usually retained in solution and used immediately after preparation as they undergo decomposition on standing, even in the cold. In the solid state, the salts tend to be explosive and can be easily detonated by the application of a slight shock or on mild warming.

The greater stability of the benzenediazonium cation is attributed to the way in which the positive charge can be distributed about the ring.

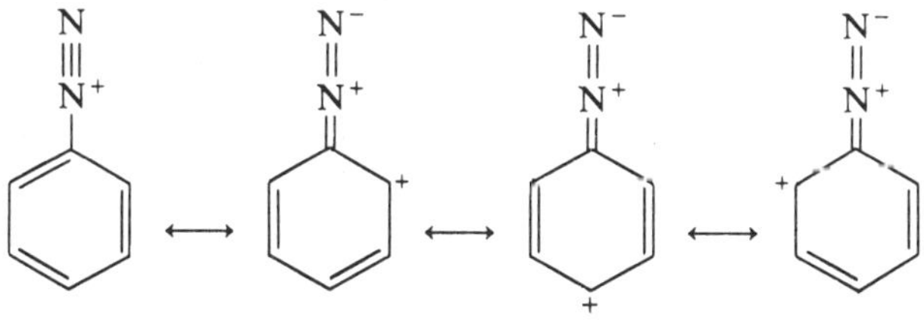

Reactions of Benzenediazonium Salts

These fall into two main categories:

(1) NUCLEOPHILIC SUBSTITUTION REACTIONS, in which the diazonium group is liberated as nitrogen to form a *carbocation* (*carbonium ion*) prior to attack by the nucleophile.

(2) COUPLING REACTIONS in which the benzenediazonium cation functions as an electrophile and as such attacks nucleophilic centres, notably the 4-position of the phenoxide ion.

Nucleophilic Substitution Reactions

On warming in aqueous solution, the diazonium ion loses the nitrogen to form a carbocation, which readily undergoes nucleophilic attack by water molecules to produce the phenol.

$$C_6H_5N_2^+ \xrightarrow[\substack{\text{slow, rate step} \\ \text{xss. dil. } H_2SO_4}]{\text{warm, } -N_2} C_6H_5^+ \xrightarrow{H_2O} C_6H_5OH + H^+$$

The presence of excess, dilute sulphuric acid prevents coupling (see below) occurring.

CHLOROBENZENE and BROMOBENZENE respectively are obtained when copper(I) chloride or when copper(I) bromide, dissolved in the appropriate concentrated hydrohalic acid, are warmed with a solution of the diazonium cation (Sandmeyer reactions).

$$C_6H_5N_2^+ + Cl^- \xrightarrow[\text{conc. HCl, warm}]{\text{CuCl catalyst,}} C_6H_5Cl + N_2$$

$$C_6H_5N_2^+ + Br^- \xrightarrow[\text{conc. HBr, warm}]{\text{CuBr catalyst,}} C_6H_5Br + N_2$$

IODOBENZENE is formed when the diazonium cation is warmed with an aqueous solution of potassium iodide.

$$C_6H_5N_2^+ + I^- \xrightarrow[\text{warm}]{\text{aqueous KI,}} C_6H_5I + N_2$$

BENZENECARBONITRILE (BENZONITRILE) is obtained by treating the diazonium cation with copper(I) cyanide and aqueous potassium cyanide. To prevent the liberation of hydrogen cyanide, the diazonium compound is first neutralized with aqueous sodium carbonate.

$$C_6H_5N_2^+ + CN^- \xrightarrow[\text{aq. KCN, warm}]{\text{CuCN catalyst}} C_6H_5CN + N_2$$

All these reactions follow first order kinetics and proceed via an S_N1 mechanism.

Coupling Reactions

The coupling of a diazonium cation with a phenoxide or similar anion is of immense importance, especially in the synthesis of AZODYES. The importance of these in the dyestuffs industry is outlined on pages 136–37.

In practice, the benzenediazonium salt solution is added to an alkaline solution of the phenol.

Mechanism

(4-Hydroxyphenyl)azobenzene
Bright yellow precipitate

With naphthalen-2-ol (2-naphthol), benzenediazonium salts form bright red crystalline dyes, and this reaction is often used to characterize aromatic primary amines (via the formation of the diazonium salt).

Ring Substitution

Nitration

Phenylamine (aniline) reacts vigorously with a nitrating mixture of concentrated nitric and sulphuric acids to form a mixture of the nitro derivatives and the oxidation products, which are formed simultaneously.

Oxidation can be avoided and the reaction more easily controlled by acylating the amino group, using ethanoic (acetic) anhydride, prior to treating with the nitrating mixture. Since the ethanamido (acetamido) group, $-NHCOCH_3$, does not activate the ring to the same extent as the more powerful amino group, the process is made much more manageable.

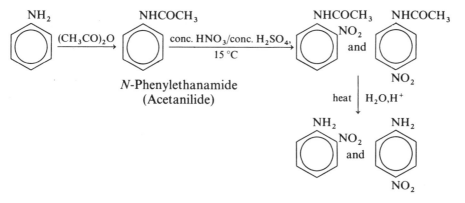

N-Phenylethanamide
(Acetanilide)

2- and 4-Nitrophenylamine
(*o*- and *p*-Nitroaniline)

The 2- and 4-nitrophenylamines are liberated by hydrolysing with 70 per cent sulphuric acid.

Sulphonation

Phenylamine can be sulphonated at room temperature using fuming sulphuric acid to form a mixture of 2-, 3- and 4-aminobenzenesulphonic acids, which are sometimes referred to as orthanilic, metanilic and sulphanilic acids respectively. The amino group being protonated in the acidic medium causes the 3- isomer to be formed as the major product.

4-Aminobenzenesulphonic acid can be obtained as the sole product by heating the phenylamine with ordinary concentrated sulphuric acid at 180 °C for several hours ('baking process').

$$\text{NH}_2 \xrightarrow[\text{180 °C, several hours}]{\text{conc. H}_2\text{SO}_4} \left[\begin{array}{c} \text{NH}_2 \\ \text{SO}_3\text{H} \end{array} \rightleftharpoons \begin{array}{c} \overset{+}{\text{N}}\text{H}_3 \\ \text{SO}_3^- \end{array} \right]$$

4-Aminobenzenesulphonic acid
(Sulphanilic acid)

Evidence indicates that the reaction involves the intermediate formation of phenylammonium hydrogensulphate, $C_6H_5NH_3^+HSO_4^-$, the side-chain of which directs electrophilic reagents to the 2- and 4- positions.

4-Aminobenzenesulphonic acid is widely used in manufacturing drugs and as a source of dyes.

Halogenation

When phenylamine is treated with chlorine water or bromine water in the cold, a white precipitate of 2,4,6-trichloro- or 2,4,6-tribromophenylamine is formed instantaneously.

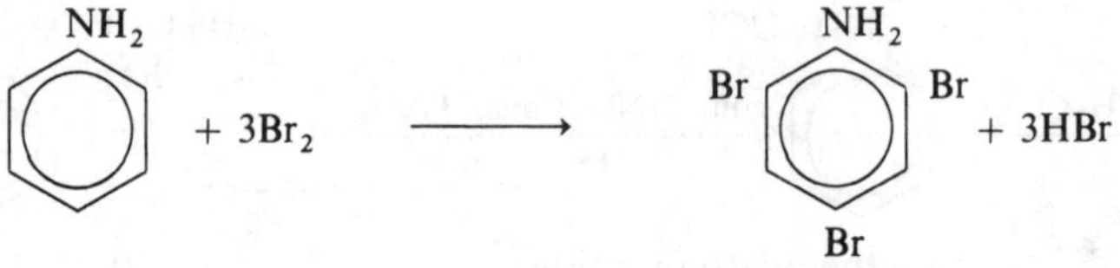

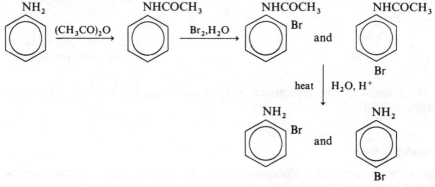

2,4,6-Tribromophenylamine
(2,4,6-Tribromoaniline)

However, if the activity of the ring is reduced by first acylating the amino group, the 2- and 4- monosubstituted derivatives of phenylamine are obtained.

2- and 4-Bromophenylamine
(*o*- and *p*-Bromoaniline)

Acid hydrolysis yields the monohalogenated phenylamine derivatives.

QUESTIONS

1. Which one of the following compounds yields a yellow oil when treated with nitrous acid?

A $CH_3CH_2CH_2CH_2NH_2$
B $CH_3CH_2CH(NH_2)CH_3$
C $CH_3CH_2N(CH_3)_2$
D $(CH_3)_2CHNHCH_3$
E $(CH_3)_3CNH_2$

2. Ethylamine reacts with ethanoyl (acetyl) chloride to yield

A ethanamide
B ethylmethylamine
C *N*-ethylethanamide
D *N,N*-diethylethanamide
E methoxyethane

3. Discuss the factors governing the basic properties of amines in an aqueous medium. Illustrate your answer with reference to both aliphatic and aromatic primary, secondary and tertiary amines.

4. Comment on how the introduction of a nitro group in the 2- and 4- positions of phenylamine (aniline) reduces its basic strength.

5. Compare and contrast the reactions of aromatic primary amines and phenols.

6. Suggest a process by which ethene may be obtained from the quaternary ammonium compound,

$$CH_3CH_2N^+(CH_3)_3I^-.$$

7. Explain why phenylamine (aniline) forms comparatively stable diazonium compounds in solution whereas aliphatic amines do not.

8. Compare and contrast the reactions of primary, secondary and tertiary aliphatic amines with nitrous acid.

9. Explain how each of the following groups affects electrophilic substitution in an aromatic nucleus to which it is attached.

A —NH_2 B —NH_3
C —$N(CH_3)_2$ D —$N(CH_3)_3^+$
E —$NHCOCH_3$

10. Discuss the importance of nitro compounds in the synthesis of aromatic amines and thence diazonium salts and phenols.

20 *Aldehydes and Ketones*

Aldehydes and ketones are referred to as *carbonyl compounds* as they both contain the carbonyl, $>C=O$, functional group.

Both saturated aliphatic series are homologous and correspond to a general molecular formula, $C_nH_{2n}O$.

The two families differ in as much as aldehydes all possess a single hydrogen attached to the carbonyl carbon (the —CHO is therefore known as the ALDEHYDE group) whereas ketones always contain two hydrocarbon groups.

$$\begin{array}{cc} \overset{\displaystyle R}{\underset{\displaystyle H}{\diagdown\diagup}}C=O & \overset{\displaystyle R}{\underset{\displaystyle R'}{\diagdown\diagup}}C=O \\ \text{Aldehyde} & \text{Ketone} \end{array}$$

R and R' may be aliphatic or aromatic.

The simplest aldehyde is methanal (formaldehyde), HCHO, and is exceptional in that it does not contain a hydrocarbon substituent.

There are also a number of cyclic ketones, the most common one being cyclohexanone, $C_6H_{10}O$, which are of considerable chemical importance, and these correspond to a general molecular formula, $C_nH_{2n-2}O$.

Cyclohexanone

Differences in chemical behaviour between aldehydes and ketones are governed primarily by their fundamental difference in basic structure, although the size and electronic character of the hydrocarbon substituent(s) may play a significant part.

Aldehydes are generally more reactive, being more easily oxidized and also more susceptible to nucleophilic addition.

The carbonyl carbon atom is sp^2 hybridized, forming a coplanar arrangement of σ bonds with the oxygen atom and with the hydrogen and/or hydrocarbon groups. The p orbital unaffected by the hybridization overlaps with a p orbital of the oxygen atom to form a π bond (cf. alkenes).

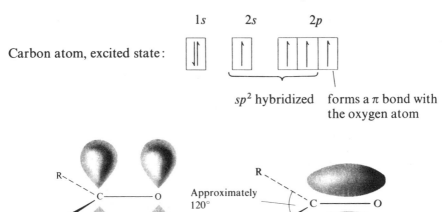

Carbon atom, excited state:

1s   2s   2p

sp^2 hybridized   forms a π bond with the oxygen atom

Approximately 120°

The regular sp^2 hybrid bond angles vary slightly from the normal 120° according to the size and structure of the hydrocarbon groups.

Polarity of the Carbonyl Group

The polarizing mesomeric effect (*see* page 47) operative in the carbonyl group causes the effective electron density to be much greater in the region of the more electronegative oxygen atom. For simplicity, this is probably best represented as $>C^{\delta+}=O^{\delta-}$.

The molecular orbital structure and the two resonance contributions are illustrated on page 47.

Nomenclature

Aldehydes

The name ALDEHYDE originates from the fact that the compounds are obtainable by dehydrogenating alcohols (*al*cohols *dehyd*rogenated).

Common names are derived by replacing the ending '-ic' of the corresponding carboxylic acid with the suffix '-aldehyde'.

IUPAC names are obtained by dropping the ending '-e' of the corresponding alkane and replacing it with suffix '-al'.

Since the carbonyl group can carry only one alkyl group, it is by necessity always at the end of the carbon chain.

Formula	*IUPAC name*	*Common name*
HCHO	Methanal	Formaldehyde
CH_3CHO	Ethanal	Acetaldehyde
CH_3CH_2CHO	Propanal	Propionaldehyde
$CH_3(CH_2)_2CHO$	Butanal	*n*-Butyraldehyde
$C_6H_5CH_2CHO$	Phenylethanal	Phenylacetaldehyde

The simplest of the aromatic aldehydes is BENZENECARBALDEHYDE (benzaldehyde), C_6H_5CHO.

Ketones

Common names are designated by specifying each of the hydrocarbon groups attached to the carbonyl group followed by the word 'ketone'.

IUPAC names are derived by taking the stem of the name of the corresponding alkane and replacing the ending '-e' with the suffix 'one'. The position of the carbonyl group is specified in the usual way, the carbonyl carbon being included in the numbering of the straight chain.

Formula	IUPAC name	Common name
CH_3COCH_3	Propanone	Acetone (Dimethyl ketone)
$CH_3COCH_2CH_3$	Butanone	Methyl ethyl ketone
$CH_3CO(CH_2)_2CH_3$	Pentan-2-one	Methyl propyl ketone
$CH_3CH_2COCH_2CH_3$	Pentan-3-one	Diethyl ketone

Ketones in which the carbonyl group is attached directly to a benzene ring are named as phenyl derivatives of the appropriate aliphatic carbonyl compound. These compounds were formerly referred to collectively as phenones.

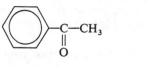
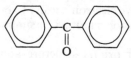

Phenylethanone	Diphenylmethanone
(Acetophenone)	(Benzophenone)

Physical Properties

Simple aliphatic aldehydes and ketones, with the exception of methanal (formaldehyde), are all colourless liquids at 20 °C. The lower aldehydes possess rather unpleasant, pungent smells, whereas the ketones, and also benzenecarbaldehyde, have pleasant, sweet odours.

Aldehydes

Name	Formula	M.p./°C	B.p./°C	Density at 20°C/ g cm^{-3}
Methanal	HCHO	−92	−21	0.815
Ethanal	CH_3CHO	−124	21	0.783
Propanal	CH_3CH_2CHO	−81	49	0.807
Butanal	$CH_3(CH_2)_2CHO$	−99	76	0.817
Benzenecarbaldehyde	C_6H_5CHO	−26	179	1.046

Ketones

Name	Formula	M.p./°C	B.p./°C	Density at 20°C/ $g\ cm^{-3}$
Propanone	CH_3COCH_3	−95	56	0.791
Butanone	$CH_3COCH_2CH_3$	−87	80	0.806
Pentan-2-one	$CH_3CO(CH_2)_2CH_3$	−78	102	0.811
Pentan-3-one	$CH_3CH_2COCH_2CH_3$	−40	102	0.814
Phenylethanone	$C_6H_5COCH_3$	20	202	1.028
Diphenylmethanone	$C_6H_5COC_6H_5$	48	306	1.083

Intermolecular attractions between both these series of polar compounds cause them to have higher boiling points than alkanes and other non-polar compounds of comparable relative molecular mass, but, since the molecules are unable to form hydrogen bonds with each other (the carbonyl carbon–hydrogen bond is insufficiently polar to allow an oxygen atom any scope for donating a lone pair), they are considerably more volatile than the corresponding alcohol and carboxylic acid.

The lower aliphatic aldehydes and ketones are appreciably soluble in water, due largely to their ability to form hydrogen bonds with the water molecules.

$$\begin{array}{c} R \\ \diagdown {\scriptstyle \delta+ \quad \delta-} \qquad {\scriptstyle \delta+ \quad 2\delta-} \\ C{=}\overset{..}{O}: {-}{-}{-}H{-}\overset{..}{O}: \\ \diagup \qquad\qquad\quad | \\ R' \qquad\qquad\quad H^{\delta+} \end{array}$$

Higher members containing more than five carbons, and the aromatic compounds, are virtually insoluble in water.

All the carbonyl compounds in these series are miscible with most of the usual oxygen-containing organic solvents and the simpler ones, notably propanone (acetone), are themselves useful solvents.

The density of the aliphatic compounds of both series is less than that of water, and follows the usual general pattern of increasing in value with increasing relative molecular mass. Compounds containing an aromatic nucleus have a density slightly greater than unity.

Industrial Source

METHANAL (FORMALDEHYDE) is manufactured by the *air-oxidation of methanol* which is passed in the vapour state over a granulated silver (platinum and copper are occasionally used instead) catalyst, electrically heated to about 450 °C.

$$2CH_3OH + O_2 \xrightarrow[560-650\,°C]{Ag\ cat.} 2HCHO + 2H_2O \qquad \text{Exothermic}$$

$$CH_3OH \xrightarrow{Ag\ cat.} HCHO + H_2 \qquad\qquad \text{Endothermic}$$

The oxidation process is self-supporting and the optimum temperature of 560–650 °C inside the catalyst chamber is maintained by controlling the flow of air.

In the U.S.A., a process involving no dehydrogenation is sometimes employed and requires a catalyst composed of a mixture of metallic oxides.

The air-oxidation of propane–butane mixtures, obtained from natural gas or petroleum, provides another source of methanal, but again it is a technique that is more widely adopted in the United States.

Being a gas, methanal is usually stored as a 40 per cent aqueous solution known as FORMALIN, or in the form of one of its polymers (*see* page 232).

The tremendous development in recent years in the manufacturing of plastics and resins, e.g. Bakelite (*see* page 193), has provided a major outlet for large quantities of methanal.

Large quantities of ETHANAL (ACETALDEHYDE) are obtained by the air-oxidation of ethanol,

$$2CH_3CH_2OH + O_2 \xrightarrow[\text{high temp.}]{\text{Ag cat.}} 2CH_3CHO + 2H_2O \quad \text{Exothermic}$$

$$CH_3CH_2OH \xrightarrow{\text{Ag cat.}} CH_3CHO + H_2 \quad \text{Endothermic}$$

and also by direct dehydrogenation.

$$CH_3CH_2OH \xrightarrow[300\,°C]{\text{finely divided Cu cat.}} CH_3CHO + H_2$$

It can also be prepared by the acid hydrolysis of ethyne, although nowadays this method is obsolescent.

$$CH{\equiv}CH + H_2O \xrightarrow{H_2SO_4,\ HgSO_4} CH_3CHO$$

Ethanal is an important starting reagent for manufacturing numerous other compounds, e.g. ethanoic (acetic) acid and anhydride, trichloroethanal (chloral), buta-1,3-diene (used in rubbers) and dyes.

PROPANONE (ACETONE) is obtained by dehydrogenating propan-2-ol over a copper, brass or zinc oxide catalyst at 350–380 °C.

$$(CH_3)_2CHOH \xrightarrow[\text{cat., 350–380 °C}]{\text{Cu, brass or ZnO}} (CH_3)_2CO + H_2$$

It is an extremely important solvent and used in manufacturing haloforms and 'Perspex'.

Wacker Process

A more recent innovation, suitable for preparing a number of carbonyl compounds, is the Wacker process, developed in Germany.

Ethanal (Acetaldehyde)

Ethene and oxygen under moderate pressure are passed into an acidified solution containing palladium(II) chloride and copper(II) chloride at 20–60 °C.

$$CH_2{=}CH_2 + PdCl_2 + H_2O \longrightarrow CH_3CHO + Pd + 2HCl$$

$$2Pd + 4HCl + O_2 \longrightarrow 2PdCl_2 + 2H_2O$$

The copper(II) chloride promotes the second reaction, enhancing the reconversion of the palladium back into the chloride.

$$Pd + 2CuCl_2 \longrightarrow 2CuCl + PdCl_2$$

Propanone (Acetone)

Propanone is prepared similarly, but from propene.

$$CH_3CH{=}CH_2 + PdCl_2 + H_2O \xrightarrow{CuCl_2} CH_3COCH_3 + Pd + 2HCl$$

Butanone (Methyl Ethyl Ketone)

Butanone is prepared similarly, but from but-1-ene.

$$CH_3CH_2CH{=}CH_2 + PdCl_2 + H_2O \xrightarrow{CuCl_2} CH_3CH_2COCH_3 + Pd + 2HCl$$

The processes for the preparation of ethanal from calcium ethanoate (acetate) and calcium methanoate (formate), and propanone by fermentation of carbohydrates and also from calcium enthanoate (acetate), are obsolete.

BENZENECARBALDEHYDE (BENZALDEHYDE) is manufactured by chlorinating the side chain of methylbenzene (toluene) to (dichloromethyl)benzene (benzal chloride) and then hydrolysing.

$$C_6H_5CH_3 \xrightarrow[heat]{Cl_2} C_6H_5CHCl_2 \xrightarrow[100\,°C]{H_2O} C_6H_5CHO$$

Another technique is to pass methylbenzene vapour and air over a vanadium(V) oxide catalyst heated to 350 °C.

$$C_6H_5CH_3 + O_2 \xrightarrow[350\,°C]{V_2O_5\ cat} C_6H_5CHO + H_2O$$

Uses of benzenecarbaldehyde include scenting soaps, flavouring food (almonds), and manufacturing dyes and antibiotics.

Synthetic Preparations

Oxidation of Alcohols

Aldehydes and ketones may be prepared by the controlled oxidation of primary and secondary alcohols using an acidified solution of potassium dichromate(VI) or manganate(VII) (permanganate). Refer to page 178.

$$CH_3CH_2OH \xrightarrow[warm]{[O],\ acid\ K_2Cr_2O_7} CH_3CHO + H_2O$$

Ethanol   Ethanal
(1 ° alcohol)   (Acetaldehyde)

$$(CH_3)_2CHOH \xrightarrow[warm]{[O],\ acid\ K_2Cr_2O_7} (CH_3)_2CO + H_2O$$

Propan-2-ol   Propanone
(2 ° alcohol)   (Acetone)

The alcohol is added dropwise to the oxidizing solution and the reaction mixture is maintained at a temperature below the boiling point of the alcohol and above that of the carbonyl compound.

In order to avoid further oxidation to the carboxylic acid, the aldehyde or ketone is distilled from the reaction mixture as it is formed. Owing to the relative volatility of the carbonyl compound (no hydrogen bonding) a good separation is easily obtained, especially with ketones since they are less readily oxidized to the acid.

$$CH_3CH_2OH \xrightarrow{[O]} CH_3CHO \xrightarrow{[O]} CH_3COOH$$

B.p.: 78 °C   21 °C   118 °C

$$(CH_3)_2CHOH \xrightarrow{[O]} (CH_3)_2CO \xrightarrow{[O]} CH_3COOH$$

B.p.: 82 °C   56 °C   118 °C

In order to reduce secondary oxidation, it is preferable to use a dichromate(VI) solution rather than a manganate(VII) as the former is somewhat milder in its action.

Alternatively, oxidation may be accomplished by dehydrogenation of the alcohol, the vapour of which is passed over a copper catalyst heated to about 300 °C.

$$CH_3CH_2OH \xrightarrow{Cu\ cat.,\ 300\ °C} CH_3CHO + H_2$$

$$(CH_3)_2CHOH \xrightarrow{Cu\ cat.,\ 300\ °C} (CH_3)_2CO + H_2$$

Oppenauer Oxidation Reaction

Higher homologues of propanone can be obtained from the appropriate secondary alcohol by using an 1,1-dimethylethoxy-aluminium (aluminium tertiary-butoxide) catalyst:

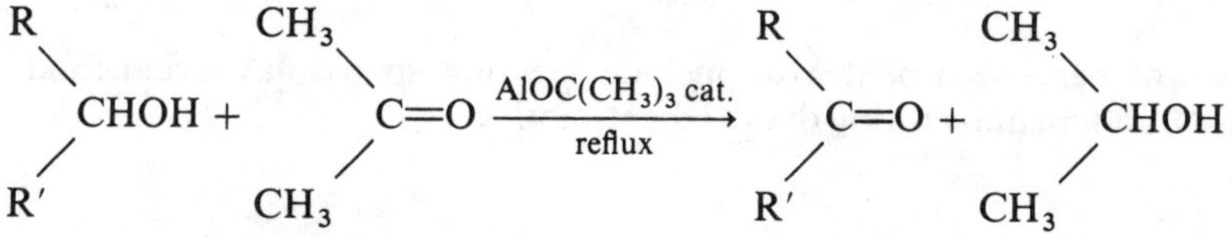

2° alcohol   Large excess

From Grignard Reagents

This reagent can be employed in a number of different ways.

Using a 1,1,1-Triethoxyalkane (Ethyl Esters of Ortho Carboxylic Acids)

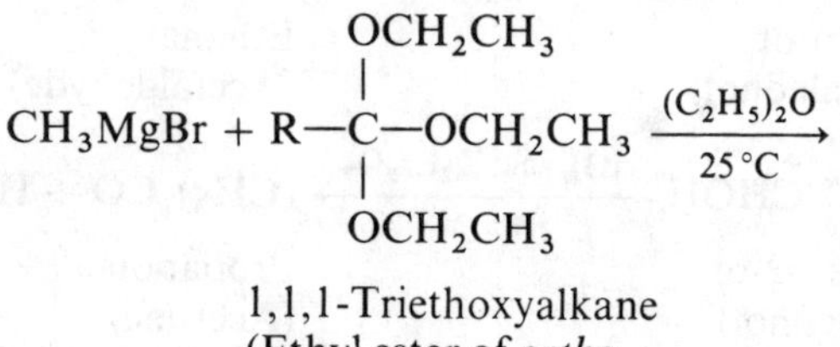

$$CH_3MgBr + R\!-\!\underset{\underset{OCH_2CH_3}{|}}{\overset{\overset{OCH_2CH_3}{|}}{C}}\!-\!OCH_2CH_3 \xrightarrow[25\ °C]{(C_2H_5)_2O}$$

1,1,1-Triethoxyalkane
(Ethyl ester of *ortho*
carboxylic acid)

$$OCH_2CH_3$$
$$|$$
$$R-C-CH_3 + MgBrOCH_2CH_3$$
$$|$$
$$OCH_2CH_3$$

A 1,1-diethoxyalkane
(An acetal)

$\downarrow$ H_2O dil. acid

$$\overset{CH_3}{\underset{R}{\diagdown}}C{=}O + 2CH_3CH_2OH$$

In the above reaction, if the R group is a hydrogen atom the product is ethanal, and if the R group is CH_3, propanone is yielded.

From Alkyl and Aryl Nitriles

$$RMgBr + R'C{\equiv}N \xrightarrow[0\,°C]{(C_2H_5)_2O} R-\underset{\underset{NMgBr}{\|}}{C}-R'$$

$$\xrightarrow[\text{dil. acid}]{2H_2O} \overset{R}{\underset{R'}{\diagdown}}C{=}O + MgBrOH + NH_3$$

Only suitable for ketones.

From Acyl Chlorides

The Grignard reagent must be converted first into the less reactive dialkyl cadmium compound, otherwise the reaction proceeds to yield the tertiary alcohol.

$$2RMgBr + CdCl_2 \xrightarrow[25\,°C]{(C_2H_5)_2O} R_2Cd + 2MgBrCl$$

$$R_2Cd + 2R'COCl \longrightarrow 2 \overset{R}{\underset{R'}{\diagdown}}C{=}O + CdCl_2$$

R and R' may be primary alkyl or aryl groups.

Decarboxylation

Of Calcium Salts

$$(CH_3COO)_2Ca + (HCOO)_2Ca \xrightarrow[400\,°C]{\text{dry distil}} 2CH_3CHO + 2CaCO_3$$

$$(CH_3COO)_2Ca \xrightarrow[400\,°C]{\text{dry distil}} (CH_3)_2CO + CaCO_3$$

Calcium benzenecarboxylate (benzoate) may be employed to prepare the desired aromatic carbonyl compound.

Of Carboxylic Acids

$$CH_3COOH \quad + \; HCOOH \quad \xrightarrow[\text{300 °C}]{\text{pass over MnO cat.,}} \; CH_3CHO + H_2O + CO_2$$

Ethanoic acid   Methanoic acid
(Acetic acid)   (Formic acid)

$$2CH_3COOH \xrightarrow[\text{300 °C}]{\text{MnO cat.,}} (CH_3)_2CO + H_2O + CO_2$$

Other suitable catalysts include ThO_2 and CaO, both of which function at about 400 °C. This technique may be adopted to prepare aromatic carbonyl compounds from benzenecarboxylic (benzoic) acid.

The preparation of aldehydes by either of the above methods is inevitably accompanied by the formation of a certain amount of the appropriate ketone.

Hydrogenation of Acyl Chlorides using a 'Poisoned Catalyst'

Rosenmund Reaction

A palladium/barium sulphate catalyst is deactivated by the addition of a 'poison', e.g. quiniline/sulphur, in order to prevent further reduction to the alcohol.

$$RCOCl \xrightarrow[\text{heat}]{H_2, \text{ 'poisoned' Pd/BaSO}_4 \text{ cat.}} RCHO + HCl$$

This reaction is only suitable for aldehydes.

Preparation of Phenylethanone (Acetophenone): Friedel–Crafts Acylation

$$C_6H_6 + (CH_3CO)_2O \xrightarrow[\text{50 °C}]{\text{AlCl}_3 \text{ cat.}} C_6H_5COCH_3 + CH_3COOH$$

Refer to page 135.

Reactions

The highly polar carbonyl group is predictably susceptible to ionic addition, enabling it to undergo either NUCLEOPHILIC ATTACK ON THE ELECTRON-DEFICIENT CARBON or ELECTROPHILIC ATTACK ON THE ELECTRON-RICH OXYGEN. The former of these two modes of addition is by far the more typical, electrophilic attack only being significant where the reaction takes place in an acidic medium, in which case the oxygen atom donates a lone pair of electrons to a proton, causing the carbon atom to become considerably more positive, and therefore more vulnerable to any subsequent attack by a nucleophile.

$$>C^{\delta+}\!\!=\!O^{\delta-} \;\xrightleftharpoons{H^+}\; >\overset{+}{C}\!\!-\!OH$$
Nucleophile

The susceptibility of the carbonyl carbon to nucleophilic attack is reduced by its attachment to electron-releasing alkyl or aryl groups, which reduce the degree of positive charge on the carbon. Furthermore, the increase in steric hindrance about the carbon by the bulky hydrocarbon groups impedes the approach of the attacking nucleophile and contributes to the reduction in the reactivity. Hence, since aldehydes contain only one hydrocarbon group, the carbonyl carbon in these compounds is more positive and less sterically hindred than that in ketones, and therefore more susceptible to nucleophilic attack.

Ease of nucleophilic attack on the carbonyl carbon atom:

$$
\underset{H}{\overset{H}{>}}C{=}O > \underset{H}{\overset{R}{>}}C{=}O > \underset{R'}{\overset{R}{>}}C{=}O > \underset{H}{\overset{Ar}{>}}C{=}O > \underset{R}{\overset{Ar}{>}}C{=}O > \underset{Ar'}{\overset{Ar}{>}}C{=}O
$$

Where alkyl groups release electrons by inductive effects, aryl groups do so by resonance.

In many instances, the initial adduct formed as a result of nucleophilic addition, notably with hydrazine, NH_2NH_2, and other substituted ammonia types of compounds, is unstable and undergoes spontaneous loss of a water molecule. *Addition–elimination* reactions of this type are referred to as CONDENSATION REACTIONS.

Keto–Enol Tautomerism

A phenomenon commonly encountered in base catalysed reactions is the loss of a proton from an aldehyde or ketone to form a CARBANION (negatively charged carbon atom). On its return, the proton can attach itself to either the negatively charged carbon atom to form the *keto* structure or to the oxygen atom to form the *enol* structure (*see* page 27). Both TAUTOMERS are in dynamic equilibrium with each other and in a chemical reaction can lead to the formation of different products, although in the case of simple aldehydes and ketones this is not so important, as the keto form is much more stable than the enol.

Keto–enol tautomerism provides a further example of PROTOTOPY (*see* page 118).

Comparison of the Addition Reactions of Aldehydes and Ketones with those of Alkenes

$$>C^{\delta+}=O^{\delta-}$$

Polar

$$>C=C<$$

Non-polar

Carbon atom acts as an electron-deficient site, instigating an initial attack by a *nucleophile*.

Double bond acts as a source of electrons instigating an initial attack by an *electrophile*.

In the ensuing reactions *common to both aldehydes and ketones*, the general formula of the carbonyl compound is given as RCOR′, where *R′ represents either the hydrogen atom of the aldehyde or the hydrocarbon group of the ketone*.

Nucleophilic Addition Reactions

Addition of Hydrogen Cyanide: 2-Hydroxyalkanonitrile (Cyanohydrin) Formation

Aldehydes and simple ketones undergo addition of hydrogen cyanide to form 2-hydroxyalkanonitriles (cyanohydrins). The hydrogen cyanide is usually generated during the reaction by the action of dilute sulphuric acid on an alkali metal cyanide, the reaction mixture being maintained at 10–20 °C.

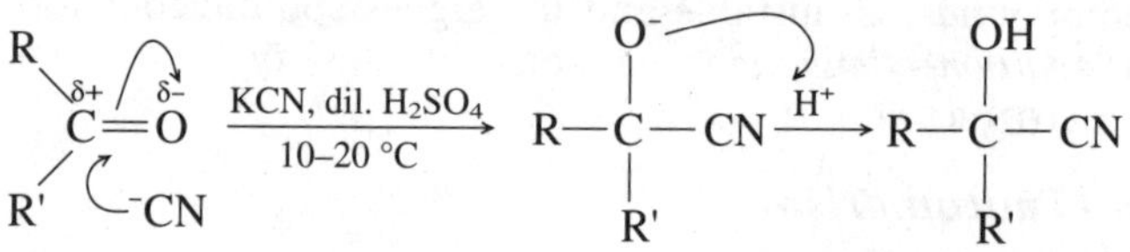

2-Hydroxyalkanonitrile
(Aldehyde cyanohydrin)
or 2-Hydroxy-2-alkylalkanonitrile
(Ketone cyanohydrin)

Alternative techniques include the use of the anhydrous gas in the presence of traces of the alkali metal cyanide and also the preliminary conversion of the aldehyde or ketone into the carbonyl hydrogensulphite compound (*see* below).

Like other nitriles, 2-hydroxyalkanonitriles can be hydrolysed to form the carboxylic acid, in this case the 2- or α-hydroxy acids.

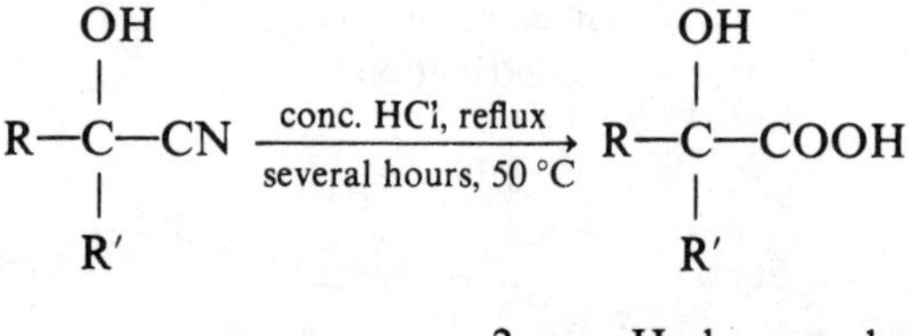

2- or α-Hydroxycarboxylic acid

2-Hydroxypropanonitrile (acetaldehyde cyanohydrin) and 2-hydroxy-2-methylpropanonitrile (acetone cyanohydrin) are both colourless liquids and therefore not ideal for characterization purposes.

Addition of Sodium Hydrogensulphite

Most aldehydes and many ketones, notably methyl ketones, on shaking with excess 40 per cent aqueous sodium hydrogensulphite (an excess is required to maintain the equilibrium position) at room temperature react to yield the carbonyl hydrogensulphite which is isolated as colourless crystals.

$$
\begin{array}{c}
R \\
\diagdown \overset{\delta+}{} \overset{\delta-}{} \\
C=O \xrightleftharpoons[]{\text{room temp}} \\
\diagup \\
R' \\
\;^-SO_3HNa^+
\end{array}
\quad
\begin{array}{c}
O^-Na^+ \\
| \\
R-C-SO_3H \\
| \\
R'
\end{array}
\rightleftharpoons
\begin{array}{c}
OH \\
| \\
R-C-SO_3^-Na^+ \\
| \\
R'
\end{array}
$$

Aldehyde or ketone
hydrogensulphite

This reaction takes place much more readily with aldehydes than with ketones.

The hydrogensulphite products are reasonably soluble in water and when treated with aqueous alkali regenerate the free carbonyl compound, thus providing a useful means of purification.

Carbonyl hydrogensulphite products may be used to prepare 2-hydroxyalkanonitriles (cyanohydrins), therefore eliminating the production of free hydrogen cyanide.

$$
\begin{array}{c}
OH \\
| \\
R-C-SO_3^-Na^+ \\
| \\
R'
\end{array}
\xrightarrow{\text{NaCN}}
\begin{array}{c}
OH \\
| \\
R-C-CN + Na_2SO_3 \\
| \\
R'
\end{array}
$$

Addition of Grignard Reagents

This reaction has already been seen to be a useful and widely applicable method for preparing all three classes of alcohols. Refer to page 170.

$$
\begin{array}{c}
R \\
\diagdown \overset{\delta+}{} \overset{\delta-}{} \\
C=O + R''MgX \\
\diagup \\
R'
\end{array}
\xrightarrow{(C_2H_5)_2O}
\begin{array}{c}
R'' \\
| \\
R-C-O^-MgX^+ \\
| \\
R'
\end{array}
$$

$$
\xrightarrow[\text{dil. acid}]{H_2O}
\begin{array}{c}
R'' \\
| \\
R-C-OH + MgXOH \\
| \\
R'
\end{array}
$$

Methanal	$\longrightarrow$	1° alcohol
Aldehydes	$\longrightarrow$	2° alcohol
Ketones	$\longrightarrow$	3° alcohol

Note the use of aqueous ammonium chloride for hydrolysis in the preparation of tertiary alcohols.

Addition of Alcohols: 1,1-Dialkoxyalkane (Acetal) Formation

On allowing to stand in excess anhydrous alcohol in the presence of a little dry hydrogen chloride catalyst, ALDEHYDES undergo addition to form 1,1-DIALKOXYLAKANES (ACETALS).

$$
\begin{array}{c} R \\ \diagdown \\ C^{\delta+}{=}O^{\delta-} + 2R'OH \\ \diagup \\ H \end{array} \xrightleftharpoons[\text{dil HCl}]{\text{dry HCl}} \begin{array}{c} OR' \\ | \\ R{-}C{-}OR' + H_2O \\ | \\ H \end{array}
$$

A 1,1-dialkoxyalkane
(An acetal)

1,1-Dialkoxyalkanes have the structure of an ether but possess somewhat different properties, as illustrated by the fact that in the presence of dilute hydrochloric acid they undergo acidic cleavage and reform the aldehyde.

The formation of 1,1-dialkoxyalkanes as an intermediate in the preparation of carbonyl compounds from Grignard reagents and 1,1,1-triethoxyalkanes (esters of *ortho* carboxylic acids) has already been mentioned on page 227.

In the absence of a catalyst, the aldehyde and alcohol exist in equilibrium with a type of compound known as 1-ALKOXYALCOHOL (HEMIACETAL).

$$
\begin{array}{c} R \\ \diagdown \\ C^{\delta+}{=}O^{\delta-} + R'OH \rightleftharpoons \\ \diagup \\ H \end{array} \begin{array}{c} OH \\ | \\ R{-}C{-}OR' \\ | \\ H \end{array}
$$

A 1-alkoxyalcohol
(A hemiacetal)

The ketone equivalent of these derivatives (KETALS), are difficult to prepare directly and have to be obtained by other means.

Polymerization

Methanal (formaldehyde) is a rather unpleasant smelling gas and is therefore more conveniently stored in aqueous solution (formalin) or in the form of one of its solid polyoxymethylene polymers; poly(methanal) (paraformaldehyde), $(CH_2O)_n$, where $n \approx 6\text{--}50$, or the cyclic trimer (trioxan), $(CH_2O)_3$.

Poly(methanal) is obtained by evaporating 'formalin'.

$$HOCH_2(CH_2O)_nCH_2OH$$

Poly(methanal)
(Paraformaldehyde)

$$
\begin{array}{c} O \\ \diagup \ \diagdown \\ H_2C \qquad CH_2 \\ | \qquad\quad | \\ O \qquad\quad O \\ \diagdown \ \diagup \\ CH_2 \end{array}
$$

Methanal trimer
(Trioxan)

Both polymers are unstable to heat and are useful only as a source of methanal. *Ethanal (Acetaldehyde)*, in the presence of a few drops of concentrated sulphuric acid, yields a liquid cyclic ethanal trimer (paraldehyde), which has had use as a relatively non-toxic hypnotic drug.

$$3CH_3CHO \xrightleftharpoons{\text{conc. } H_2SO_4}$$

Ethanal trimer
(Paraldehyde)

The reaction is highly exothermic and requires no additional heating. The ethanal can be re-obtained from the pure trimer by adding a drop of concentrated acid to form the equilibrium mixture and progressively distilling off the ethanal.

On treating ethanal with hydrogen chloride at $-20\,^\circ C$, a low yield of an eight-membered ring tetramer (metaldehyde) is obtained.

$$4CH_3CHO \xrightleftharpoons{HCl, \,-20\,^\circ C}$$

Ethanal tetramer
(Metaldehyde)

This tetramer is used for killing slugs and snails ('Snarol').

Ketones and aromatic aldehydes do not polymerize, although propanone *condenses* with itself when distilled with concentrated sulphuric acid forming 1,3,5-trimethylbenzene (mesitylene).

1,3,5-Trimethylbenzene
(Mesitylene)

Addition of Lithium Tetrahydridoaluminate(III) and Sodium Tetrahydridoborate(III)

Refer to pages 171 and 242.

Addition of Ammonia

On passing gaseous ammonia through a dry ethereal solution of an *aliphatic aldehyde* (not methanal), a white, unstable precipitate of the aldehyde ammonia is formed.

$$\underset{H}{\overset{R}{\diagdown}}C^{\delta+}{=}O^{\delta-} + NH_3 \xrightarrow{\text{dry } (C_2H_5)_2O} R{-}\underset{H}{\overset{OH}{\underset{|}{\overset{|}{C}}}}{-}NH_2$$

Aldehyde ammonia

Methanal, aromatic aldehydes and ketones do not form addition compounds with ammonia, but instead yield *complex condensation products*. For example, if an aqueous solution of methanal and ammonia is allowed to evaporate, the condensation product, $(CH_2)_6N_4$, is obtained.

$$6HCHO + 4NH_3 \longrightarrow \text{[structure]} + 6H_2O$$

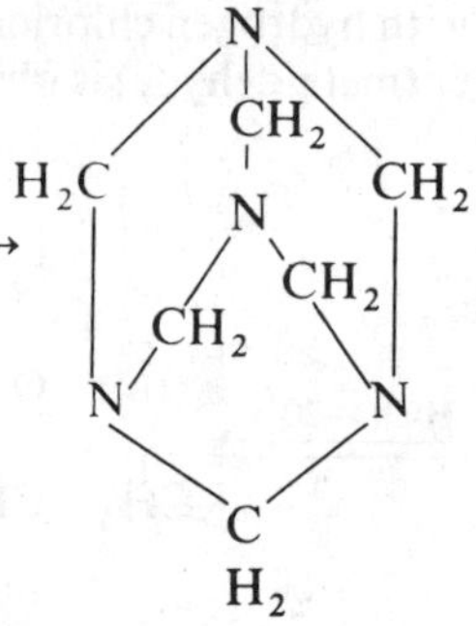

Similarly,

$$3C_6H_5CHO + 2NH_3 \longrightarrow C_6H_5CH{=}N{-}\underset{C_6H_5}{\underset{|}{CH}}{-}N{=}CHC_6H_5 + 3H_2O$$

Condensation (Addition–Elimination) Reactions with Derivatives of Ammonia

Substituted ammonia compounds, e.g. hydroxylamine, NH_2OH, hydrazine, NH_2NH_2, etc. condense with aldehydes and ketones to form a compound containing an IMINE GROUP, $>C{=}N{-}$, together with the elimination of a water molecule.

$$>C{=}\;\boxed{O + H_2}\;N{-} \;\longrightarrow\; >C{=}N{-} + H_2O$$

Imine group

Since a number of these condensation products are easily obtained in a crystalline form, they are used extensively for characterization and identification purposes.

In the free state many amino compounds rapidly deteriorate owing to oxidation, and are preferably stored and handled in the form of their salts, e.g. hydroxylammonium chloride, $HONH_3^+Cl^-$ (cf. phenylamine).

With Hydroxylamine, NH₂OH

Pure hydroxylamine forms colourless deliquescent crystals which decompose above 15 °C to give nitrogen, ammonia and water. However, in the form of one of its more stable salts, it reacts with aldehydes and ketones to form OXIMES, which are crystalline solids. The free hydroxylamine is liberated during the reaction by the presence of sodium ethanoate (acetate) or alkali.

$$\underset{R'}{\overset{R}{>}}C^{\delta+}{=}O^{\delta-} + H_2\ddot{N}OH \xrightarrow{\text{warm}} \underset{R'}{\overset{R}{>}}C{=}NOH + H_2O$$

Hydroxylamine   An oxime

Ethanal and propanone yield *ethanal oxime (acetaldoxime)* and *propanone oxime (acetoxime)* respectively.

Simple aliphatic oximes are too soluble to be precipitated and careful crystallization is necessary in order to obtain them in the solid form.

With Hydrazine, NH₂NH₂

Hydrazine is a colourless liquid possessing two amino groups, and thus, when present in excess, tends to condense with two molecules of the carbonyl compound to yield an AZINE.

$$\underset{R'}{\overset{R}{>}}C^{\delta+}{=}O^{\delta-} + H_2\ddot{N}NH_2 \xrightarrow{-H_2O} \underset{R'}{\overset{R}{>}}C{=}NNH_2$$

Hydrazine   Aldehyde or ketone
hydrazone

$$\xrightarrow[-H_2O]{RCOR'} \underset{R'}{\overset{R}{>}}C{=}NN{=}C\underset{R'}{\overset{R}{<}}$$

An azine

Both hydrazones and azines are crystalline solids.

With Phenylhydrazine, C₆H₅NHNH₂

Phenylhydrazine is a colourless and poisonous liquid and should always be handled in the form of the phenylhydrazinium chloride. On warming with carbonyl compounds dissolved in aqueous alcohol it reacts to yield PHENYLHYDRAZONES.

Phenylhydrazine   Aldehyde or ketone phenylhydrazone

Phenylhydrazone derivatives of simple aliphatic carbonyl compounds are largely oils or low melting point solids but are generally crystalline for aromatic carbonyl compounds.

With 2,4-Dinitrophenylhydrazine, $2,4\text{-}C_6H_3(NO_2)_2NHNH_2$

2,4-Dinitrophenylhydrazine is utilized in BRADY'S REAGENT for the detection of a carbonyl functional group.

For this purpose, it is moistened with methanol and then shaken with a few drops of concentrated sulphuric acid in order to convert it into the yellow sulphate. On adding the carbonyl compound (solids should first be dissolved in methanol) with shaking, the 2,4-*dinitrophenylhydrazone* crystallizes out fairly rapidly although the reaction occurs rather more slowly with ketones than with aldehydes.

2,4-Dinitrophenyl-hydrazine   Aldehyde or ketone 2,4-dinitrophenylhydrazone

Most saturated aliphatic derivatives are yellow or light orange, whereas aryl compounds are somewhat darker.

With Semicarbazide, $NH_2NHCONH_2$

If an aqueous solution of semicarbazide hydrochloride and sodium ethanoate (acetate) is shaken with an aldehyde or ketone in the cold, the SEMICARBAZONE usually crystallizes out within a few minutes.

Semicarbazide   Semicarbazone (usually colourless crystals)

With Primary Amines: Formation of Schiff Bases

Primary amines readily condense with carbonyl compounds to form SCHIFF BASES or ANILS.

$$\begin{array}{c} R \\ \diagdown \\ C^{\delta+} = O^{\delta-} \quad R''\ddot{N}H_2 \\ \diagup \\ R' \end{array} \longrightarrow \begin{array}{c} R \\ \diagdown \\ C = NR'' + H_2O \\ \diagup \\ R' \end{array}$$

Schiff base
or anil

Unless the carbon–nitrogen double bond is stabilized by conjugation with an aromatic nucleus, these bases tend to be unstable in aqueous solution and revert back into the starting reagents. (In a non-aqueous medium they polymerize.)

This means that stable Schiff bases can be formed between the following types of compounds: aliphatic carbonyl compounds and phenylamine (aniline), benzenecarbaldehyde (benzaldehyde) and aliphatic primary amines, benzenecarbaldehyde and phenylamine, and so on.

$$\cdot CH_3CHO + CH_3NH_2 \longrightarrow \text{unstable Schiff base}$$

$$\left.\begin{array}{c} CH_3CHO + C_6H_5NH_2 \\ C_6H_5CHO + CH_3NH_2 \\ C_6H_5CHO + C_6H_5NH_2 \end{array}\right\} \longrightarrow \text{stable Schiff base}$$

Mechanism for Condensation Reactions

Consider an amino derivative, NH_2—G, where G represents the attached group

$$\begin{array}{c} R \\ \diagdown_{\delta+} \\ C = O \quad H_2\ddot{N}-G \\ \diagup^{\delta-} \\ R' \end{array} \longrightarrow \begin{array}{c} O^- \\ | \\ R-C-NH_2^+G \\ | \\ R' \end{array} \xrightarrow{\text{rearranges}} \begin{array}{c} OH \\ | \\ R-C-NHG \\ | \\ R' \end{array}$$

Unstable addition
product

Addition process

$$\Big| -H_2O$$

Elimination
process

$$\begin{array}{c} R \\ \diagdown \\ C = NG \\ \diagup \\ R' \end{array}$$

Some Other Important Reactions of the Carbonyl Group

Chlorination

(1) With Phosphorus Pentachloride
Under anhydrous conditions, aliphatic and simple aromatic carbonyl com-

pounds undergo replacement of the oxygen atom by two chlorines to yield the dichlorohydrocarbon.

$$\begin{array}{c} R \\ \diagdown \\ \diagup \\ R' \end{array} C{=}O + PCl_5 \longrightarrow \begin{array}{c} Cl \\ | \\ R{-}C{-}Cl \\ | \\ R' \end{array} + POCl_3$$

The lower dichloroalkanes are colourless liquids.

(2) Trichloroethanal (Chloral) Formation
On bubbling excess chlorine through *ethanal*, replacement of methyl hydrogen atoms takes place to yield a colourless, oily liquid, trichloroethanal, known as chloral.

$$\begin{array}{c} CH_3 \\ \diagdown \\ \diagup \\ H \end{array} C{=}O + 3Cl_2 \longrightarrow \begin{array}{c} CCl_3 \\ \diagdown \\ \diagup \\ H \end{array} C{=}O + 3HCl$$

Trichloroethanal
(Chloral)

As a result of the electron-withdrawing inductive effects of the three chlorine atoms, the carbonyl carbon is more positive, enabling the compound to react exothermally with water to form a stable crystalline hydrate.

$$\begin{array}{cc} Cl & H \\ | & | \\ Cl{\leftarrow}C{-}C{=}O \\ | & \\ Cl & :OH_2 \end{array} \longrightarrow \begin{array}{cc} Cl & H \\ | & | \\ Cl{-}C{-}C{-}O^- \\ | & | \\ Cl & OH_2^+ \end{array} \longrightarrow \begin{array}{cc} Cl & H \\ | & | \\ Cl{-}C{-}C{-}OH \\ | & | \\ Cl & OH \end{array}$$

2,2,2-Trichloroethanediol
(Chloral hydrate)

If chlorine is bubbled through warm propanone, successive replacement of the methyl hydrogen occurs, yielding a mixture of chloropropanones, e.g. CH_3COCH_2Cl, $ClCH_2COCH_2Cl$ etc.

Under similar conditions, benzenecarbaldehyde (benzaldehyde) is converted into a colourless liquid, benzenecarbonyl (benzoyl) chloride, C_6H_5COCl.

The Trihalomethane (Haloform) Reaction

Methyl carbonyl compounds, i.e. those containing a $\begin{array}{c} CH_3 \\ \diagdown \\ \diagup \end{array} C{=}O$ group, react

readily on gently warming with aqueous solutions of sodium chlorate(I) (hypochlorite) to yield trichloromethane (chloroform). (Note that ethanal is the only aldehyde structurally capable of undergoing this reaction.) If potassium bromide or iodide is included in the reaction mixture, the resulting products are tribromomethane (bromoform), $CHBr_3$, and triiodomethane (iodoform), CHI_3, respectively.

Of these, the TRIIODOMETHANE (IODOFORM) REACTION is visually the more distinctive and is often adopted for test purposes. Triiodomethane is precipitated as fine yellow crystals which possess a characteristic and distinguishable odour.

$$KI + NaOCl \longrightarrow KIO + NaCl$$

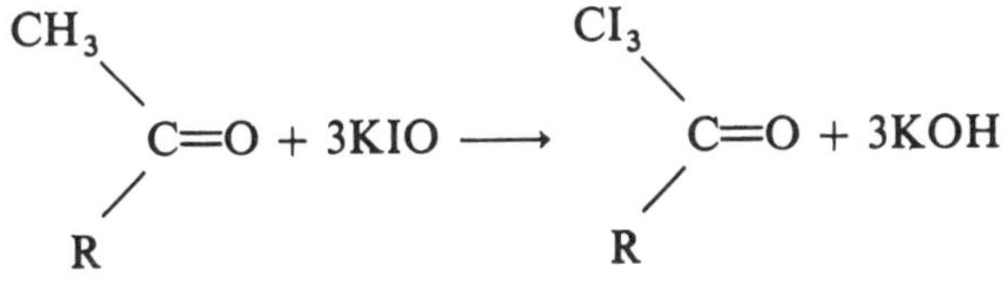

Triiodoketone

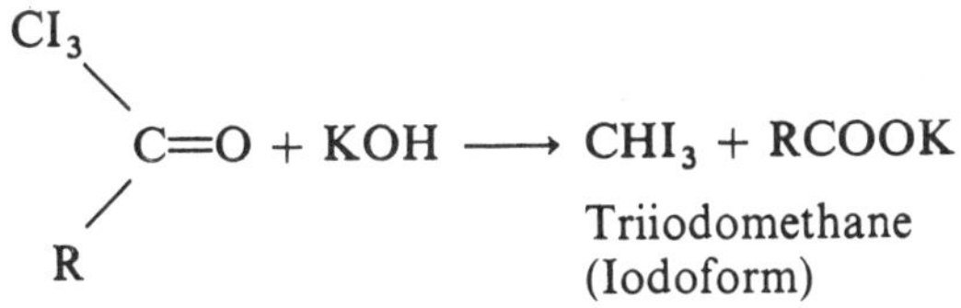

Triiodomethane
(Iodoform)

The trihalomethane (haloform) reaction is also given by compounds containing a $\overset{\displaystyle CH_3}{\diagdown}\text{CHOH}\diagup$ group, since under the reaction conditions it is oxidized to the carbonyl group, $-COCH_3$. This means that it can be performed with ethanol but not methanol, propan-2-ol but not propan-1-ol and so on.

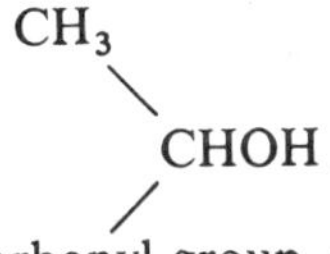

Mechanism for the Trihalomethane (Haloform) Reaction

The reaction is usually base-catalysed and proceeds via the formation of a carbanion. The hydroxide ions are formed in sufficient quantity during the process and no further addition of alkali is necessary.

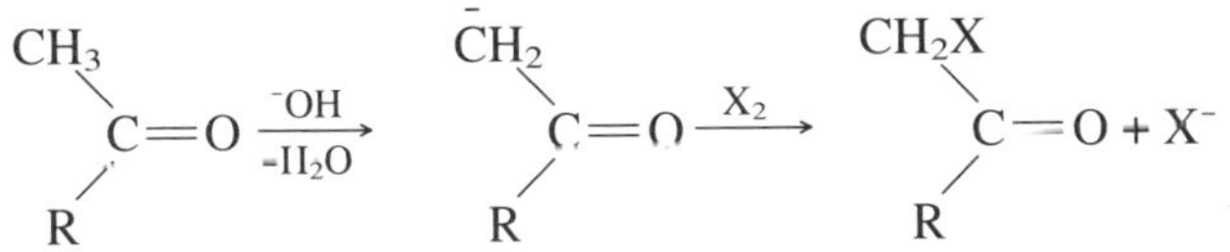

These steps are repeated until the trihalo compound,

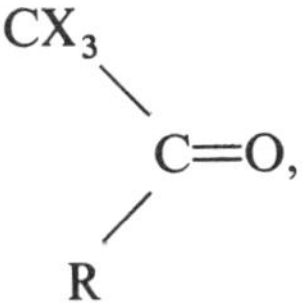

is formed.

The electron-withdrawing inductive effect of the halogen atom causes the stability of the carbanions formed during the reaction to decrease in the order:

$$
\underset{X}{\overset{X}{>}} C \quad > \quad \underset{H}{\overset{X}{>}} C \quad > \quad \underset{H}{\overset{H}{>}} C
$$

thus accounting for the difficulty in stopping the reaction prior to the trihalo stage.

Termination of the mechanism leads to the release of a carboxylate anion (cf. the base-catalysed hydrolysis of ester, *see* page 266).

$$
\underset{R}{\overset{CX_3}{>}} C=O \longrightarrow CX_3 \underset{R}{\overset{O^-}{\underset{|}{\overset{|}{C}}}}-OH \longrightarrow \bar{C}X_3 + RCOOH
$$

$$
\downarrow H_2O
$$

$$
CHX_3 + RCOO^-
$$

An acid-catalysed reaction, involving initial protonation of the oxygen atom, is sometimes employed but is less commonly encountered.

Aldol Condensation

This reaction, like the trihalomethane (haloform) process, is base-catalysed and is confined to those aldehydes and ketones *containing at least one α-hydrogen atom*, i.e. the carbon atom attached to the carbonyl carbon must possess at least one hydrogen. Methanal, HCHO, and benzenecarbaldehyde, C_6H_5CHO, therefore cannot undergo this reaction.

On treating a suitable carbonyl compound with a cold, *dilute* solution of an alkali, it dimerizes to form an aldol, which contains both an aldehyde and an alcohol group.

$$
2CH_3CHO \overset{^-OH}{\rightleftharpoons} CH_3\underset{\underset{OH}{|}}{C}HCH_2CHO
$$

Ethanal
(Acetaldehyde)

3-Hydroxybutanal
An aldol

If the concentration of hydroxide ions is too large, the reaction continues to give eventually a polymeric resin.

Mechanism

The hydroxide ion donates a lone pair to one of the α-hydrogens to form a water molecule and a carbanion, the latter functioning as a nucleophile towards the unionized carbonyl molecule.

$$CH_3CHO \rightleftharpoons \bar{C}H_2CHO + H_2O$$

The reaction is really incorrectly described as a condensation process, as the reacting molecules combine without the overall loss of a water or any other simple molecule.

Cannizzaro Reaction

In direct contrast to the aldol condensation, this reaction only applies to carbonyl compounds *containing no α-hydrogen atoms* and is therefore limited to aromatic and aliphatic compounds in which the carbonyl carbon is attached to a tertiary alkyl carbon atom.

If a suitable aldehyde is treated with a concentrated aqueous solution (40–60 per cent) of alkali at room temperature, it undergoes simultaneous oxidation and reduction to yield the appropriate salt of the carboxylic acid and an alcohol.

Mechanism

Oxidation

Aldehydes are readily oxidized to carboxylic acids by a number of different oxidizing agents, e.g. acidified solutions of potassium manganate(VII) (permanganate) or dichromate(VI), nitric acid, or by passing the vapour, mixed with air, over a finely divided heated copper or platinum catalyst.

$$\underset{H}{\overset{R}{\diagdown}}C{=}O \xrightarrow{\text{[O], acid } K_2Cr_2O_7} RCOOH$$

Aromatic aldehydes are not so readily oxidized as their aliphatic counterparts, but nonetheless benzenecarbaldehyde (benzaldehyde) undergoes light-catalysed autoxidation to benzenecarboxylic (benzoic) acid on exposure to air.

$$C_6H_5CHO \xrightarrow{\text{[O], } h\nu} C_6H_5COOH$$

Ketones are not quite so susceptible to oxidation, and require more vigorous conditions in order to bring about the necessary cleavage of the comparatively strong carbon–carbon single bond.

$$\underset{R'}{\overset{R}{\diagdown}}C{=}O \xrightarrow[\text{KMnO}_4]{\text{hot acid}} RCOOH + R'COOH$$

For unsymmetrical ketones, a mixture of acid products is obtained, resulting from the two possible modes of cleavage.

Because aliphatic aldehydes are easily oxidized by even very mild oxidizing agents such as ammoniacal silver(I) nitrate, Fehling's solution, Schiff's reagent etc., reactions of this type provide a simple means of distinguishing between the two categories of carbonyl compounds.

Reduction

By Lithium Tetrahydridoaluminate(III)

An ethereal solution of this reagent rapidly reduces aldehydes and ketones to primary and secondary alcohols respectively, and involves the *transfer of a hydride ion* from the reducing agent to the carbonyl carbon. The alcohol is liberated by treatment with dilute acid.

$$\underset{[AlH_3{-}H]^-Li^+}{\underset{R'}{\overset{R}{\diagdown}}C\overset{\delta+}{\underset{\delta-}{=}}O} \xrightarrow{(C_2H_5)_2O} \underset{R'}{\overset{O^-}{R{-}\underset{|}{\overset{|}{C}}{-}H}} \xrightarrow[\text{dil. acid}]{H^+} \underset{R'}{\overset{OH}{R{-}\underset{|}{\overset{|}{C}}{-}H}}$$

Sodium tetrahydridoborate(III) (borohydride), $Na^+BH_4^-$, dissolved in water or methanol, as it is insoluble in ether, behaves in a precisely similar manner, although it is somewhat milder in its action.

By Clemmensen Reaction

All classes of carbonyl compounds under consideration are reduced to the appropriate hydrocarbon when treated with amalgamated zinc and concentrated hydrochloric acid.

$$\begin{array}{c} R \\ \diagdown \\ C{=}O + 4[H] \xrightarrow[\text{conc. HCl}]{\text{Zn/Hg}} RCH_2R' + H_2O \\ \diagup \\ R' \end{array}$$

Distinguishing Between Aldehydes and Ketones

Aldehydes and ketones may be easily distinguished by some of the reactions already discussed. For example, the Cannizzaro reaction is only given by aldehydes containing no α-hydrogen atoms, the trihalomethane (haloform) reaction is not given by aldehydes, except ethanol, ketones do not undergo addition with ammonia, and so on.

However, besides these there are several simple test-tube reactions which *utilize the greater reducing properties of aldehydes* in order to distinguish them from ketones. Some of these are described below.

Schiff's Test

A solution is made by treating rosaniline hydrochloride, a magenta dye, with sulphur dioxide until it becomes colourless. Aldehydes restore the red coloration by abstracting sulphurous acid from the reagent, whereas ketones either cause no colour change at all or restore the colour only very slowly.

Simple aldehydes give a positive test within one minute, more complex ones may take thirty minutes, and a number of aromatic ones give a negative result.

Fehling's Test

Fehling's Reagent: a solution of copper(II) sulphate is added to a solution of Rochelle salt, potassium sodium 2,3-dihydroxybutanedioate, in excess sodium hydroxide. A deep blue coloration is obtained on mixing the solutions owing to the formation of a complex copper(II) ion. Aliphatic aldehydes reduce the copper(II) to the reddish-brown copper(I) oxide, which is precipitated.

$$RCHO + 2Cu^{2+} + NaOH + H_2O \xrightarrow{\text{warm}} RCOONa + Cu_2O + 4H^+$$

Reddish-brown
precipitate

Ketones and aromatic aldehydes give no reaction.

Fehling's solution is also commonly employed for detecting reducing sugars (*see* page 287).

Silver Mirror Test

The reagent consists of a solution of silver(I) nitrate in excess ammonia solution. Aldehydes reduce the Ag^+ to silver, which is precipitated and forms a mirror effect in the bottom part of the test-tube. (Residues from this reaction should never be left in the tube as explosive silver(I) azide may form.)

Ethanal reacts almost immediately, but with benzenecarbaldehyde (benzaldehyde) the reaction mixture requires warming.

$$RCHO + 2Ag(NH_3)_2OH \longrightarrow RCOONH_4 + 2Ag + H_2O + 3NH_3$$

'Silver
mirror'

Ketones give no reaction.

A similar reagent which gives the same effect is *Tollen's reagent*: ammonia solution is added dropwise to a solution of silver(I) nitrate in dilute aqueous sodium hydroxide until the brown precipitate just dissolves. Addition of the aldehyde brings about the formation of a silver mirror.

Ammoniacal silver(I) nitrate and Tollen's reagent are both unstable and should always be freshly prepared. Furthermore, there is an explosion hazard if Tollen's reagent is allowed to evaporate to dryness.

Direct Comparison Between the Reactions of Ethanal, Benzenecarbaldehyde and Propanone

In the following reactions, ETHANAL, BENZENECARBALDEHYDE and PROPANONE *all behave in a similar way* towards the same reagent.

(1) Addition of HCN, $NaHSO_3$ and RMgX (aldehydes form the 2° alcohol and ketones the 3° alcohol).

(2) Condensation reactions with, NH_2OH, NH_2NH_2, $C_6H_5NHNH_2$, 2,4-$C_6H_3(NO_2)_2NHNH_2$, $NH_2NHCONH_2$ and RNH_2.

(3) Replacement of the carbonyl oxygen by two chlorines using PCl_5.

(4) Oxidation with acidified solutions of $K_2Cr_2O_7$ and $KMnO_4$.

(5) Reduction with $LiAlH_4$, $NaBH_4$ etc. (aldehydes form the 1° alcohol and ketones the 2° alcohol).

(6) Clemmensen reduction to the hydrocarbon.

In the following reactions, ETHANAL, BENZENECARBALDEHYDE and PROPANONE *behave differently towards the same reagent.*

(1) With NH_3: ethanal undergoes addition whereas benzenecarbaldehyde and propanone both condense with it.

(2) Polymerization: only ethanal polymerizes.

(3) 2,2,2-Trichloroethanal (chloral) formation: formed by ethanal but not with propanone and benzenecarbaldehyde.

(4) Trihalomethane (haloform) reaction: given by ethanal and propanone but not by benzenecarbaldehyde.

(5) Aldol condensation: not given by benzenecarbaldehyde as it contains no α-hydrogen atom.

(6) Cannizzaro reaction: not given by ethanal and propanone as they contain α-hydrogen atoms.

(7) Oxidation with: Schiff's reagent—ethanal restores the colour rapidly, benzenecarbaldehyde more slowly and propanone extremely slowly; Fehling's solution—reaction only given by ethanal; 'silver mirror' reaction—given readily with ethanal, benzenecarbaldehyde requires warming and propanone gives no reaction.

Reactions of Aromatic Aldehydes and Ketones involving Substitution in the Ring

The relative positive charge on the carbonyl carbon atom attracts electrons away from the aromatic nucleus and has the effect of deactivating it with regard to electrophilic substitution. As this withdrawal of electrons affects principally the 2- and 4- positions, the 3- position is left comparatively rich in electrons and it is therefore at this site that electrophilic attack predominantly occurs.

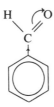

The deactivating effect of the carbonyl group is illustrated by the more vigorous conditions required to bring about substitution. For example, nitration of benzenecarbaldehyde requires a nitrating mixture of *fuming* nitric acid and concentrated sulphuric acid to which the benzenecarbaldehyde is added dropwise, maintaining the temperature below 5 °C. On completion of the addition the reaction mixture is gradually warmed to 40 °C.

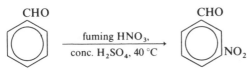

3-Nitrobenzenecarbaldehyde (m.p., 58 °C)
(*m*-Nitrobenzaldehyde)
(Major product)

QUESTIONS

1. With which one of the following reagents does propanone undergo a different *type* of reaction from ethanal?

   A HCN
   B NaHSO$_3$
   C NH$_3$
   D NH$_2$NH$_2$
   E NH$_2$OH

2. Ethanal and propanone react differently with which one of the following?

   A phenylhydrazine
   B Brady's reagent
   C semicarbazide
   D Fehling's solution
   E Schiff bases

3. Which one of the following compounds does not give the triiodomethane (iodoform) test?

   A CH$_3$CHO

   B CH$_3$CH$_2$OH
   C CCl$_3$COCH$_3$
   D CH$_3$CH$_2$CH$_2$OHCH$_3$
   E C$_6$H$_5$CH$_2$CH$_2$OH

4. Give the structural formula and IUPAC name for all the isomeric carbonyl compounds corresponding to C$_4$H$_8$O, and suggest suitable reactions for distinguishing between them.

5. Compare the electronic factors operative in carbonyl compounds with those in alkenes, and explain how they affect the characteristic reactions of each type of compound, emphasizing the reason why different types of reagents participate in each case.

6. Explain why benzenecarbaldehyde is slightly less susceptible to nucleophilic attack than ethanal.

21 *Carboxylic Acids*

SATURATED ALIPHATIC MONOCARBOXYLIC ACIDS form a homologous series corresponding to the general molecular formula, $C_nH_{2n+1}COOH$, or simply RCOOH.

The carboxyl functional group, $-C\!\!\!\overset{\displaystyle O}{\underset{\displaystyle OH}{\big\langle}}$, contains both a *carb*onyl and a *hydr*oxyl functional group—hence the name! These groups modify each other to such an extent that the chemical reactivity of the carboxyl group bears little resemblance to either of its constituent groups.

Aliphatic carboxylic acids as a whole are often referred to as 'fatty' acids since several of the higher homologues, notably hexadecanoic (palmitic) acid, $CH_3(CH_2)_{14}COOH$, octadecanoic (stearic) acid, $CH_3(CH_2)_{16}COOH$, and *cis*-octadec-9-enoic (oleic) acid, $CH_3(CH_2)_7CH{=}CH(CH_2)_7COOH$ are constituents of natural fats and are obtainable from this source.

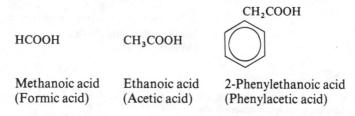

HCOOH	CH₃COOH	CH₂COOH (phenyl)
Methanoic acid (Formic acid)	Ethanoic acid (Acetic acid)	2-Phenylethanoic acid (Phenylacetic acid)

In terms of the quantity of acid consumed, the *most important carboxylic acid* is without doubt ETHANOIC (ACETIC) ACID.

The simplest of the aliphatic series of *dicarboxylic acids* are,

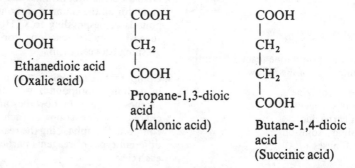

Compounds classified as AROMATIC CARBOXYLIC ACIDS all contain the carboxyl group *attached directly* to an aromatic nucleus, the most important of these being *benzenecarboxylic (benzoic) acid* and *benzene-1,2-dicarboxylic (phthalic) acid*, the latter being a dicarboxylic acid.

Benzenecarboxylic   4-Methylbenzenecarboxylic   Benzene-1,2-dicarboxylic
acid (Benzoic acid)   acid (*p*-Toluic acid)   acid (Phthalic acid)

Nomenclature

Common names are generally derived from the Latin or Greek name of their source of origin.

FORMIC ACID derives its name from the fact that it is obtainable by distilling crushed ants (Lat. *formica*, ant), although it is also present in stinging nettles and certain other plants.

On exposure to the atmosphere, wines, notably sweet ones with a fairly low alcohol content, often become sour and turn to vinegar (French *vinaigre*, sour wine) owing to attack by a bacterium, commonly referred to as the 'vinegar fly'. This micro-organism, instead of allowing the sugar to be converted into alcohol, turns it into acetic (ethanoic) acid (Lat. *acetum*, vinegar).

Derivation of some other common names:

Name	Source	Derivation
Propionic acid	Plant and animal products	Gr. *proto* (first) *pion* (fat)
Butyric acid	Rancid butter	Lat. *butyrum*, butter
Caproic acid	Goat's milk	Lat. *caper*, goat

Positions of substitution in the hydrocarbon chain are denoted by the Greek letters α, β, γ etc.

$$e.g. \quad \overset{\gamma}{CH_3}CH \overset{\beta}{CH_2}\overset{\alpha}{COOH}$$
$$\underset{CH_3}{|}$$

β-Methylvaleric acid

IUPAC names are afforded by taking the name of the appropriate alkane and replacing the ending '-e' with the suffix '-oic' acid. Positions of substitution are denoted in the usual way by numbering the longest unbranched chain containing the carboxyl group.

Formula	IUPAC name	Common name
$HCOOH$	Methanoic	Formic
CH_3COOH	Ethanoic	Acetic
CH_3CH_2COOH	Propanoic	Propionic
$CH_3(CH_2)_2COOH$	Butanoic	*n*-Butyric
$(CH_3)_2CHCOOH$	2-Methylpropanoic	Isobutyric
$CH_3(CH_2)_3COOH$	Pentanoic	*n*-Valeric
$CH_3(CH_2)_{14}COOH$	Hexadecanoic	Palmitic
$CH_3(CH_2)_{16}COOH$	Octadecanoic	Stearic
$C_6H_5CH_2COOH$	2-Phenylethanoic	Phenylacetic

Names of aromatic acids are often related to the appropriate hydrocarbon, e.g. benzenecarboxylic (benzoic) and methylbenzenecarboxylic (toluic) acids, or, like the aliphatic compounds, derived from the name of one of their natural sources.

COOH

Benzenecarboxylic acid
(Benzoic acid)

COOH

CH_3

3-Methylbenzenecarboxylic acid
(*m*-Toluic acid)

Structure of Carboxylic Acids

$$R-C^{\delta +} \overset{\ddot{O}:^{\delta -}}{\underset{\ddot{O} \leftarrow H}{}}$$

In the carbonyl linkage, there is a mesomeric withdrawal of electrons away from the carbon atom towards the more electronegative atom, creating a relative positive charge on the carbon atom. This deficiency of electrons about the carbon atom intensifies the inductive pull of electrons away from the hydrogen atom in the oxygen–hydrogen bond, enhancing the stability of the carboxylate anion, $RCOO^-$, and promoting the release of a proton.

These electronic factors are not operative in alcohols, making the release of a proton considerably more difficult in these compounds, and accounting for their much weaker acidic properties.

The carboxylate anion is a resonance hybrid, the π electrons being delocalized about the two carbon–oxygen bonds, making both bonds equivalent.

$$\left[-C\overset{O}{\underset{O^-}{}} \longleftrightarrow -C\overset{O^-}{\underset{O}{}} \right] \text{ or simply, } \left. -C\overset{O}{\underset{O}{}} \right\} -$$

Hydrogen Bonding

The highly polar carboxylic acid molecules dimerize in the liquid phase and in non-aqueous solvents, e.g. tetrachloromethane (carbon tetrachloride), forming *two hydrogen bonds* between each pair of molecules.

$$R-C\overset{O^{\delta -}---H^{\delta +}-O^{\delta -}}{\underset{O^{\delta -}-H^{\delta +}---O^{\delta -}}{}}C-R$$

The extra degree of hydrogen bonding in aliphatic monocarboxylic acids compared to that in monohydric alcohols of similar relative molecular mass is reflected by the difference in their boiling points, the acids having values about 20 °C higher, and also by the fact that vapour density measurements indicate that ethanoic (acetic) acid exists as a dimer, *even in the vapour phase* at temperatures just above its boiling point.

	M_r	B.p./°C
Ethanoic acid	60	118
Propan-1-ol	60	97
Propanoic acid	74	141
Butan-1-ol	74	117

However, in most hydroxylic solvents, such as water, the dimers dissociate into the monomeric form.

Physical Properties

All simple aliphatic acids as far as C_{10} are liquids at room temperature, although anhydrous ethanoic (acetic) acid freezes to an 'ice-like' solid below 17 °C and is commonly known as *glacial* ethanoic (acetic) acid. Like all the lower members, ethanoic acid possesses a sharp, pungent odour.

Boiling points follow the usual pattern of increasing with increasing relative molecular mass.

Name	Formula	M.p./°C	B.p./°C	Density at 20°C/ $g\ cm^{-3}$
Methanoic	HCOOH	8	101	1.220
Ethanoic	CH_3COOH	17	118	1.049
Propanoic	CH_3CH_2COOH	−21	141	0.992
Butanoic	$CH_3(CH_2)_2COOH$	−7	164	0.964
Pentanoic	$CH_3(CH_2)_3COOH$	−35	186	0.939
Hexanoic	$CH_3(CH_2)_4COOH$	−2	205	0.927
Phenylethanoic	$C_6H_5CH_2COOH$	76	266	—
Benzenecarboxylic	C_6H_5COOH	122	249	—

Aromatic acids are crystalline solids and have higher melting points than their aliphatic counterparts of comparable relative molecular mass.

'Even' members of the aliphatic series have markedly higher melting points than 'odd' members, and x-ray analysis has shown this to be related to the packing of the crystals in the solid.

The first four aliphatic acids are completely miscible with water and, as in the case of the simpler alcohols, this is largely due to the ability of the functional group to form hydrogen bonds with the water molecules. Because of their greater hydrocarbon, and hence covalent, character, the higher homologues become progressively less soluble in water.

Benzenecarboxylic (benzoic) acid is only slightly soluble in cold water but dissolves readily in hot.

All carboxylic acids can be dissolved in suitable organic solvents.

Density follows a general pattern of decreasing with increasing relative molecular mass.

Industrial Source

METHANOIC (FORMIC) ACID is manufactured by the reaction between carbon monoxide and aqueous sodium hydroxide at 200 °C and under high pressure.

$$CO + NaOH \xrightarrow[\text{high press.}]{200\,°C} \quad HCOONa \xrightarrow{\text{dil. acid}} HCOOH$$

Sodium methanoate   Methanoic acid
Sodium formate   (Formic acid)

ETHANOIC (ACETIC) ACID is obtained commercially by the liquid phase air-oxidation of an approximately 5 per cent solution of ethanal (acetaldehyde) in ethanoic (acetic) acid, using a manganese(II) ethanoate (acetate) catalyst.

$$CH_3CHO \xrightarrow[(CH_3COO)_2\ Mn\ cat.]{O_2} CH_3COOH$$

This method is currently being superseded by the liquid phase air-oxidation of C_5–C_7 alkanes, obtainable from petroleum, at a high temperature and pressure. Methanoic, propanoic and butanedioic acids are also obtained as by-products.

BENZENECARBOXYLIC (BENZOIC) ACID is manufactured by the de-carboxylation of benzene-1,2-dicarboxylic (phthalic) anhydride by passing steam into the molten anhydride, containing a metallic benzene-1,2-dicarboxylate (phthalate) catalyst, e.g. chromium(III) benzene-1,2-dicarboxylate.

1,2-Dimethylbenzene
(vapour phase)

A more modern innovation (1965 in the U.K.) is the air-oxidation of methylbenzene (toluene) using a tin(IV) vanadate(V) catalyst.

The principal commercial use of benzenecarboxylic (benzoic) acid nowadays is as a food and drug preservative, accounting for about 80 per cent of the total supply.

Synthetic Preparations

Oxidation of Primary Alcohols

$$RCH_2OH \xrightarrow[K_2Cr_2O_7\ or\ KMnO_4]{[O],\ excess\ acid} RCHO \xrightarrow{[O]} RCOOH$$

Secondary alcohols and ketones give smaller yields and, in the case of unsymmetrical compounds, also a mixture of acid products.

The method is suitable for preparing aromatic as well as aliphatic acids. Refer to page 178.

Grignard Synthesis: Carbonation

Aliphatic acids are obtained by bubbling carbon dioxide into the Grignard reagent and then treating with dilute acid.

$$RMgBr + CO_2 \xrightarrow{(C_2H_5)_2O} RCOOMgBr \xrightarrow[\text{dil. acid}]{H_2O} RCOOH + MgBrCl$$

R may be $1°, 2°, 3°$ or aromatic.

In the preparation of benzenecarboxylic (benzoic) acid, the reagent is added to solid carbon dioxide ('dry ice'), which also serves to cool the reaction mixture.

$$C_6H_5MgBr + CO_2 \xrightarrow{(C_2H_5)_2O} C_6H_5COOMgBr$$
$$\text{'Dry ice'}$$

$$\xrightarrow[\text{dil. acid}]{H_2O} C_6H_5COOH + MgBrCl$$

Hydrolysis of Nitriles

Aliphatic nitriles are generally formed during the reaction from a haloalkane and the alkali metal cyanide in a solvent which dissolves both reactants, usually aqueous alcohol. Complete hydrolysis to the acid may be accomplished by boiling under reflux with an alkali (yielding the carboxylate anion) or with 70 per cent mineral acid (yielding the free acid).

$$RCl + NaCN \xrightarrow{\text{aq. alcohol}} RCN + NaCl$$

$$RCN \underset{-H_2O}{\overset{+H_2O}{\rightleftharpoons}} RCONH_2 \underset{-H_2O}{\overset{+H_2O}{\rightleftharpoons}} RCOO^-NH_4^+$$

Both modes of hydrolysis involve the intermediate formation of the amide, which may, if desired, be isolated by performing only partial hydrolysis of the nitrile.

Similarly, benzenecarbonitrile (benzonitrile), C_6H_5CN, undergoes hydrolysis to benzenecarboxylic acid.

Hydrolysis of Esters: Saponification

The ester is boiled under reflux with concentrated aqueous sodium hydroxide.

$$\underset{\text{Ester}}{RCOOR'} + NaOH \rightleftharpoons RCOO^-Na^+ + R'OH$$
$$\downarrow \text{dil. acid}$$
$$RCOOH$$

Cannizzaro Reaction

This reaction is only undergone by aromatic aldehydes and those aliphatic ones containing no α-hydrogen atoms.

$$2C_6H_5CHO + NaOH \longrightarrow C_6H_5COO^-Na^+ \qquad + C_6H_5CH_2OH$$
$$(40-60\%) \qquad \text{Sodium benzenecarboxylate}$$
$$\text{(Sodium benzoate)}$$
$$\downarrow \text{dil. acid}$$
$$C_6H_5COOH$$

Refer to page 241.

Synthesis of Benzenecarboxylic (Benzoic) Acid using Methylbenzene (Toluene) and its Derivatives

From Methylbenzene (Toluene)

$$C_6H_5CH_3 \xrightarrow[\text{heat}]{MnO_2, H_2SO_4} C_6H_5COOH$$

From (Chloromethyl)benzene (Benzyl Chloride)

$$C_6H_5CH_2Cl \xrightarrow[\text{(2) dil. acid to precipitate}]{\text{(1) alkaline } KMnO_4} C_6H_5COOH$$

From (Trichloromethyl)benzene (Benzotrichloride)

$$C_6H_5CCl_3 \xrightarrow[\text{Fe powder cat., 50 °C}]{Ca(OH)_2} C_6H_5C(OH)_3 \xrightarrow{-H_2O} C_6H_5COOH$$

Reactions

The reactions of carboxylic acids almost invariably involve the hydroxyl group, which either undergoes the loss of a proton, i.e. functions as an acid, or is replaced by another atom or group.

The side-chain reactions of aromatic acids are fundamentally similar to those of the aliphatic series, although functional group reactions of 2-*substituted* compounds are difficult and 2,6-*substituted* acids virtually impossible to perform by normal techniques owing to the high degree of steric hindrance.

Despite being about 10^{10}–10^{11} times stronger in acidic strength than alcohols, carboxylic acids are only partially ionized in aqueous solution owing to the predominantly covalent nature of the molecules, and are only very weak in comparison with the mineral acids.

$$RCOOH + H_2O \rightleftharpoons RCOO^- + H_3O^+$$

For example, a molar solution of ethanoic (acetic) acid is only approximately 0.4 per cent ionized whereas a solution of sulphuric acid of the same molarity is about 62 per cent ionized.

However, the comparative strengths of carboxylic acids is attributable to the stability of the carboxylate anion, represented below as a resonance hybrid of two canonical forms. The resonance energy assists the ionization process, and hence the release of the proton.

The two canonical forms may be conveniently represented by the single structure:

which illustrates the equivalence of both carbon–oxygen bonds and also the equal distribution of the negative charge between the oxygen atoms.

A guide to the relative strengths of the different carboxylic acids is caused by the varying degree of positive charge upon the carboxyl carbon atom within a molecule of each compound. As the extent of this charge increases, so does the ease with which electrons are withdrawn from the oxygen atom of the hydroxyl group, thus promoting the release of the proton.

This phenomenon is governed primarily by the inductive effects of aliphatic groups or the resonance contribution of aromatic groups.

Acidic strength decreases in the order:

$$Cl_3CCOOH > HCOOH > C_6H_5COOH > CH_3 \rightarrow COOH$$

$$> CH_3CH_2 \rightarrow COOH$$

The greater acidic strength of benzenecarboxylic (benzoic) acid compared with that of ethanoic (acetic) acid is attributable to the greater stability of the benzenecarboxylate (benzoate) ion afforded by resonance.

Name	Formula	pK$_a$
Methanoic	HCOOH	3.75
Ethanoic	CH$_3$COOH	4.76
Propanoic	CH$_3$CH$_2$COOH	4.87
Butanoic	CH$_3$(CH$_2$)$_2$COOH	4.82
Phenylethanoic	C$_6$H$_5$CH$_2$COOH	4.31
Benzenecarboxylic	C$_6$H$_5$COOH	4.20
Ethanoic	CH$_3$COOH	4.76
Chloroethanoic	CH$_2$ClCOOH	2.86
Dichloroethanoic	CHCl$_2$COOH	1.29
Trichloroethanoic	CCl$_3$COOH	0.65
Benzenecarboxylic	C$_6$H$_5$COOH	4.20
2-Methylbenzenecarboxylic	2-CH$_3$C$_6$H$_4$COOH	3.91
3-Methylbenzenecarboxylic	3-CH$_3$C$_6$H$_4$COOH	4.24
4-Methylbenzenecarboxylic	4-CH$_3$C$_6$H$_4$COOH	4.34
2-Hydroxybenzenecarboxylic (salicyclic)	2-HOC$_6$H$_4$COOH	2.99
3-Hydroxybenzenecarboxylic	3-HOC$_6$H$_4$COOH	4.08
4-Hydroxybenzenecarboxylic	4-HOC$_6$H$_4$COOH	4.58

Name	Formula	pK_a
2-Aminobenzenecarboxylic	$2\text{-}NH_2C_6H_4COOH$	6.97
3-Aminobenzenecarboxylic	$3\text{-}NH_2C_6H_4COOH$	4.78
4-Aminobenzenecarboxylic	$4\text{-}NH_2C_6H_4COOH$	4.92
2-Chlorobenzenecarboxylic	$2\text{-}ClC_6H_4COOH$	2.94
3-Chlorobenzenecarboxylic	$3\text{-}ClC_6H_4COOH$	3.83
4-Chlorobenzenecarboxylic	$4\text{-}ClC_6H_4COOH$	3.99
2-Nitrobenzenecarboxylic	$2\text{-}NO_2C_6H_4COOH$	2.17
3-Nitrobenzenecarboxylic	$3\text{-}NO_2C_6H_4COOH$	3.45
4-Nitrobenzenecarboxylic	$4\text{-}NO_2C_6H_4COOH$	3.43

The effect of further substitution in the aromatic ring of benzenecarboxylic acid upon its degree of ionization has been fairly extensively studied. Substituents in the 2- position, irrespective of their electron-releasing or withdrawing properties, almost invariably increase the degree of ionization, indicating that factors other than inductive and resonance effects, such as solvation, are operative and contribute to the strength of the acid. A notable exception to this general pattern is the basic amino group, 2-aminobenzenecarboxylic acid being markedly weaker in acidic strength than benzenecarboxylic acid.

A better correlation between the electronic effects of the substituent group and the strength of the acid is given for those groups substituted in the 3- and 4-positions. For example, in 3- and 4-methylbenzenecarboxylic (toluic) acids, the electron-releasing effect of the methyl group is transmitted to the carboxyl group, and the corresponding increase in electron density within this group is accompanied by a slight decrease in its tendency to lose a proton.

Effect of the Medium on Acidic Properties

In a *basic medium*, the base donates a pair of electrons to the acidic proton, thus promoting the ionization process.

$$RCOOH \rightleftharpoons RCOO^- + H^+$$

$$\Big\updownarrow :B$$

$$HB^+$$

Another possible effect whereby the base, acting as a nucleophile, attacks the electron-deficient carbon atom, is much less likely.

In an *acidic medium*, protonation of either oxygen may occur to form the cations II and III, which exist in equilibrium with each other.

However, since the carbonyl oxygen is somewhat richer in electrons, protonation at this site is much more facile and the equilibrium position lies very much in favour of II, which itself exists as a resonance hybrid of two canonical forms.

This phenomenon causes electrons to be withdrawn from the carboxyl carbon, thus increasing its positive nature and promoting its susceptibility to nucleophilic attack.

Salt Formation

The characteristic acidic properties are illustrated by the ease with which all carboxylic acids, irrespective of whether they are water-soluble or not, liberate hydrogen in the presence of metals, and carbon dioxide when added to either sodium carbonate or hydrogencarbonate.

$$2RCOOH + Mg \longrightarrow (RCOO^-)_2Mg^{2+} + H_2$$

$$2RCOOH + Na_2CO_3 \longrightarrow 2RCOO^-Na^+ + CO_2 + H_2O$$

$$RCOOH + NaHCO_3 \longrightarrow RCOO^-Na^+ + CO_2 + H_2O$$

In fact, the degree of acidity of most of these compounds is sufficient for it to be estimated quantitatively by titrating against standard alkali.

$$RCOOH + NaOH \longrightarrow RCOO^-Na^+ + H_2O$$

In all cases, the carboxylic acid can be regenerated by treating the salt with dilute mineral acid.

$$RCOONa + HCl \longrightarrow RCOOH + NaCl$$

Esterification

The significance of this process and the use of isotopic labelling to demonstrate alkoxy–hydrogen fission in the alcohol (acyl–hydroxy fission in the acid) has already been discussed on page 177.

Similarly, for benzenecarboxylic (benzoic) acid

Methylbenzenecarboxylate
(Methyl benzoate)

Mechanism for the Esterification Process with Primary and Some Secondary Alcohols: Fischer–Speier Method

(2)

$$R-\overset{\overset{\displaystyle OH}{|}}{\underset{\underset{\displaystyle OH}{|}}{C^+}} \quad R'\ddot{O}H \quad \rightleftharpoons \quad R-\overset{\overset{\displaystyle OH}{|}}{\underset{\underset{\displaystyle OH}{|}}{C}}-\overset{+}{O}R' \quad \underset{\text{transfer}}{\overset{\substack{\text{intramolecular}\\ \text{proton}}}{\rightleftharpoons}} \quad R-\overset{\overset{\displaystyle OH}{|}}{\underset{\underset{\displaystyle \overset{+}{O}H_2}{|}}{C}}-OR'$$

(3)

$$R-\overset{\overset{\displaystyle OH}{|}}{\underset{\underset{\displaystyle \overset{+}{O}H_2}{|}}{C}}-OR' \quad \rightleftharpoons \quad R-\overset{\overset{\displaystyle OH}{|}}{\underset{+}{C}}-OR' + H_2O$$

(4)

$$R-\overset{\overset{\displaystyle \overset{H}{O}}{|}}{\underset{+}{C}}-OR' \quad H_2\ddot{O}: \quad \rightleftharpoons \quad R-\overset{\overset{\displaystyle O}{\|}}{C}-OR' + H_3^+O$$

The overall reaction is reversible, although it is far more satisfactory to hydrolyse the ester under alkaline conditions (saponification). This process is discussed in the section on esters.

Halogenation

Bubbling chlorine through boiling ethanoic (acetic) acid in the presence of either iodine or red phosphorus in sunlight yields chloroethanoic acid, which when isolated is a colourless and corrosive crystalline solid (m.p., 61 °C).

$$I_2 + 3Cl_2 \longrightarrow 2ICl_3$$

$$CH_3COOH + ICl_3 \xrightarrow{105-110\,°C} CH_2ClCOOH + ICl + HCl$$

Chloroethanoic
acid

$$ICl + Cl_2 \longrightarrow ICl_3$$

Dichloro- and trichloroethanoic acids are obtained by successive substitution of the alkyl hydrogen atoms. The trichloro derivative is best obtained at a temperature of about 160 °C.

$$CH_2ClCOOH \xrightarrow[\text{elevated temp}]{Cl_2, I_2} CHCl_2COOH \xrightarrow[\text{elevated temp}]{Cl_2, I_2} CCl_3COOH$$

Dichloroethanoic   Trichloroethanoic
acid   acid

although these derivatives are preferably obtained by the oxidation of 2,2,2-trichloroethanediol (chloral hydrate), $CCl_3CH(OH)_2$ by fuming nitric acid.

$$CCl_3CH(OH)_2 + [O] \xrightarrow{\text{fuming HNO}_3} CCl_3COOH + H_2O$$

Dichloroethanoic acid is conveniently prepared by reacting 2,2,2-trichlorodiol with calcium carbonate in the presence of a small amount of sodium cyanide followed by acidification with concentrated hydrochloric acid.

$$2CCl_3CH(OH)_2 + 2CaCO_3 \xrightarrow{\text{NaCN}} (CHCl_2COO)_2Ca + CaCl_2 + 2CO_2 + 2H_2O$$

$$(CHCl_2COO)_2Ca + 2HCl \longrightarrow 2CHCl_2COOH + CaCl_2$$

Chlorination and bromination of higher acids, in the presence of a small amount of phosphorus trihalide (Hell–Volhard–Zelinsky reaction), occurs solely in the 2-position.

$$RCH_2COOH \xrightarrow[\text{warm}]{Br_2,\ PCl_3} RCHBrCOOH \xrightarrow{Br_2,\ PCl_3} RCBr_2COOH$$

2-Halocarboxylic acids are all stronger acids than those from which they are derived, owing to the electron-withdrawing inductive effects of the halogen atoms, which promote the withdrawal of electrons from the oxygen–hydrogen bond.

Conversion into Acyl Chlorides

Both aliphatic and aromatic carboxylic acids readily undergo replacement of a hydroxyl group on reacting with PCl_3, PCl_5 and $SOCl_2$ to yield the acyl chloride.

$$RCOOH + PCl_5 \longrightarrow RCOCl + POCl_3 + HCl$$

Acyl
chloride

$$RCOOH + SOCl_2 \longrightarrow RCOCl + HCl + SO_2$$

Conversion into acyl chlorides is one of the most common reactions that carboxylic acids are made to undergo, the reaction with sulphur dichloride oxide (thionyl chloride) being especially convenient as the two other products are both gaseous and easily removed from the reaction mixture.

Reduction

Carboxylic acids are not easily reduced and are immune to most of the common reducing agents.

However, lithium tetrahydridoaluminate(III) and diborane, B_2H_6, form intermediate compounds with the acids which suitably modify the properties of the hydroxyl group. In the case of lithium tetrahydridoaluminate(III), the intermediate is an alkoxide from which the alcohol is liberated by hydrolysis.

$$4RCOOH + 3LiAlH_4 \xrightarrow{(C_2H_5)_2O} (RCH_2O)_4AlLi + 2LiAlO_2 + 4H_2$$
$$\downarrow 4H_2O$$
$$4RCH_2OH + Al(OH)_3 + LiOH$$

Amide Formation

At an elevated temperature, ammonium carboxylates, prepared by reacting the carboxylic acid with ammonium carbonate, undergo dehydration in the presence of the free acid to yield the amide.

$$2RCOOH + (NH_4)_2CO_3 \longrightarrow 2RCOO^-NH_4^+ + CO_2 + H_2O$$

$$RCOO^-NH_4^+ \xrightarrow[\text{heat, 100–200 °C}]{\text{excess RCOOH}} RCONH_2 + H_2O$$

In the absence of the free acid, the yield is poor because, like all ammonium salts, the carboxylate dissociates on warming.

$$RCOO^-NH_4^+ \rightleftharpoons RCOOH + NH_3$$

Decarboxylation of the Sodium Salts

(1) Heating with 'sodalime'

$$RCOONa + NaOH \xrightarrow{\text{fuse}} RH + Na_2CO_3$$
$$\text{Sodalime}$$

Refer to page 92.

(2) Kolbé Synthesis

$$2RCOONa + 2H_2O \xrightarrow[\text{aq. CH}_3\text{OH}]{\text{electrolysis}} \underbrace{R\!-\!R + 2CO_2}_{\text{Anode}} + \underbrace{2NaOH + H_2}_{\text{Cathode}}$$

This reaction is only suitable for preparing symmetrical alkanes. Refer to page 92.

QUESTIONS

1. Which of the following compounds is the strongest acid?

   A benzenecarboxylic acid
   B trichloroethanoic acid
   C carbonic acid
   D sodium hydrogensulphate
   E phenol

2. Without referring to tables, arrange the following groups of acids in decreasing order of acidity.

   A ethanoic, methanoic, butanoic, propanoic
   B benzenecarboxylic, ethanoic, 2-aminobenzenecarboxylic, 2-nitrobenzenecarboxylic
   C ethanoic, chloroethanoic, trichloroethanoic, trifluoroethanoic

3. Explain by means of electronic considerations why the carbonyl group of carboxylic acids is virtually inert to addition reactions.

4. Discuss and compare the reactivity of the hydroxyl group in alcohols and in monocarboxylic acids.

5. In what way does the medium affect the ease of nucleophilic attack upon the carboxylic carbon atom of monocarboxylic acids? Illustrate your answer with reference to specific examples.

6. Give the mechanism for the esterification of a monocarboxylic acid with a primary alcohol.

22 Derivatives of Monocarboxylic Acids: Acid Chlorides, Anhydrides, Esters and Amides

Acyl chlorides (acid chlorides), anhydrides, esters and amides are all polar compounds in which the hydroxyl group of the carboxylic acid has been replaced by —Cl, —OOCR', —OR', —NH$_2$ (—NHR' or —NR$_2'$) respectively.

| Acyl chloride | Acid anhydride | Ester | Amide |

R and R' may be either alkyl or aryl.

The R—C(=O)— group, common to all such derivatives is called the ACYL GROUP.

General Comparative Properties

Physical

Chlorides, anhydrides and esters have normal boiling points, being similar in value to those of aldehydes and ketones of comparable relative molecular mass. Amides possess a fairly high degree of intermolecular hydrogen bonding, causing them to have higher than expected boiling points and at normal temperatures to exist as solids. This ability to form hydrogen bonds can be extended to water molecules, allowing amides to be much more soluble than the other derivatives. (Simple chlorides and anhydrides undergo spontaneous hydrolysis in water.)

Reactivity

The reactions are characterized by nucleophilic substitution of the halogen, carboxylate, alkoxy or amino groups and show similarities to the condensation (addition–elimination) reactions of aldehydes and ketones. All the substituent groups possess lone pairs of electrons which are conjugated with the carbonyl group. As the electronegativity of the group increases, the degree of conjugation decreases and the electron availability about the carbonyl oxygen is reduced.

Order of electronegativity of the substituent groups:

$$-Cl > -OOCR' > -OR' > -NH_2$$

However, the overall polarity of the carbonyl group is enhanced by the more electronegative substituents owing to the simultaneous withdrawal of electrons away from the carbon atom, making it more susceptible to nucleophilic attack.

Order of reactivity of the acid derivatives:

$$\text{Acyl chloride} > \text{Acid anhydride} > \text{Ester} > \text{Amide}$$

Acid Chlorides

Nomenclature

Each aliphatic compound is named by dropping the ending '-ic' from either the IUPAC or the common name of the corresponding carboxylic acid and adding the suffix '-yl' followed by the word 'chloride'.

Formula	IUPAC name	Common name
CH_3COCl	Ethanoyl chloride	Acetyl chloride
CH_3CH_2COCl	Propanoyl chloride	Propionyl chloride

Aromatic acyl chlorides may be considered as chlorides of the aromatic carbonyl, or named, like the aliphatic compounds, by replacing the ending '-ic' of the systematic or common name by '-yl', and adding the word chloride.

e.g. C_6H_5COCl Benzenecarbonyl chloride or Benzoyl chloride

Physical Properties

All simple members are colourless liquids. The more volatile compounds possess a sharp, pungent smell and have an irritating effect upon the eyes and mucous membranes.

Name	Formula	B.p./°C	Density at 20°C/ $g\,cm^{-3}$
Ethanoyl chloride	CH_3COCl	51	1.105
Propanoyl chloride	CH_3CH_2COCl	80	1.065
Benzenecarbonyl chloride	C_6H_5COCl	197	1.210

Ethanoyl (acetyl) chloride fumes in moist air owing to hydrolysis and liberates hydrogen chloride.

As a whole, acyl chlorides are generally insoluble in water, and a number of aliphatic compounds, like ethanoyl chloride, are decomposed by it.

Synthetic Preparations

Acyl chlorides are usually prepared from the corresponding carboxylic acid using PCl_3, PCl_5 or $SOCl_2$ (*see* page 257). the latter reagent being especially useful as the other products are both gases and easily removed from the reaction mixture.

$$RCOOH + SOCl_2 \longrightarrow RCOCl + HCl + SO_2$$

Reactions

The reactions of aliphatic acyl halides are fundamentally similar to those of carboxylic acids, the halogen readily undergoing nucleophilic substitution by —OH, —OR', NH_2 (NHR' or NR'_2) etc. The mechanisms for these processes may be likened to those for the *condensation (addition–elimination) reactions* of aldehydes and ketones.

Benzenecarbonyl (benzoyl) chloride, and other aromatic acyl chlorides, are much less reactive, owing to the reduction in the positive nature of the carbonyl carbon caused by resonance.

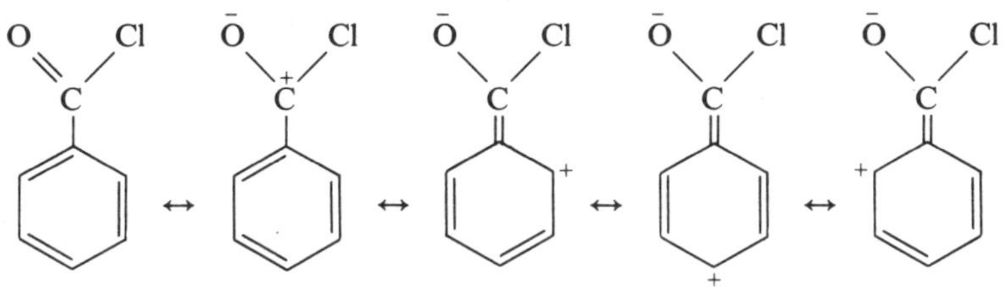

Hydrolysis

$$RCOCl + H_2O \rightarrow RCOOH + HCl$$

Ester Formation

With alcohols and phenols

$$RCOCl + R'OH \longrightarrow RCOOR' + HCl$$

Esterification with phenol requires an alkaline medium.

Refer to page 186.

Amide Formation

With ammonia and amines ($R'NH_2$ and R_2NH)

$$RCOCl + 2NH_3 \longrightarrow RCONH_2 + NH_4Cl$$

$$RCOCl + R'NH_2 \longrightarrow RCONHR' + HCl$$

Refer to page 211.

Mechanism for the Condensation (Addition–Elimination) Reaction of Acyl Chlorides

The mechanisms for all of these processes and equivalent ones involving acid anhydrides are basically similar.

Examples

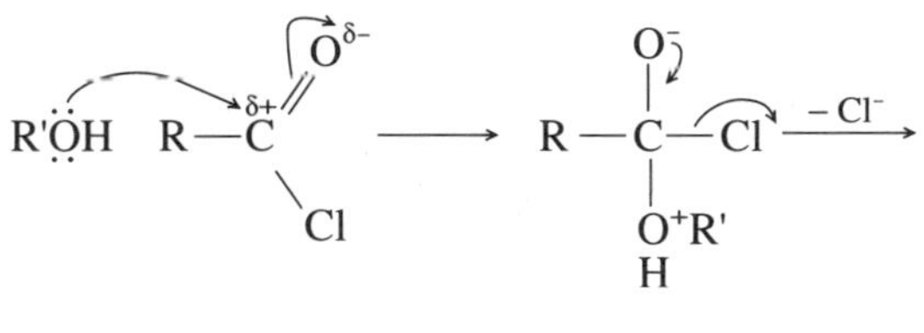

$$R-C \overset{O}{\underset{\underset{H}{O^+R'}}{\|}} \quad \xrightarrow{-H^+} \quad R-C \overset{O}{\underset{OR'}{\|}}$$

The reaction is similar with H_2O.

$$(2) \quad R'\overset{..}{N}H_2 \quad R-C \overset{O^{\delta-}}{\underset{Cl}{\|}} \quad \longrightarrow \quad R-\overset{O^-}{\underset{\underset{H}{N^+HR'}}{\overset{|}{C}}}-Cl \quad \xrightarrow{-Cl^-}$$

$$R-C \overset{O}{\underset{\underset{H}{\overset{+}{N}HR'}}{\|}} \quad \xrightarrow{-H^+} \quad R-C \overset{O}{\underset{NHR'}{\|}}$$

The reaction is similar with NH_3 and R'_2NH.

Aldehyde Formation: Rosenmund Reaction

$$RCOCl \xrightarrow[\text{'poisoned' Pd/BaSO}_4 \text{ cat.}]{H_2, \text{ heat}} RCHO + HCl$$

Refer to page 228.

Ketone Formation

(1) Friedel–Crafts acylation

$$RCOCl + C_6H_6 \xrightarrow{AlCl_3 \text{ cat.}} C_6H_5COR + HCl$$

Refer to page 135.

(2) Using dialkylcadmium compounds

$$2R'MgBr + CdCl_2 \xrightarrow{(C_2H_5)_2O} R'_2Cd + 2MgBrCl$$

$$R'_2Cd + 2RCOCl \xrightarrow{(C_2H_5)_2O} 2 \underset{R'}{\overset{R}{\diagdown}}C{=}O + CdCl_2$$

Refer to page 227.

Anhydride Formation

Anhydrides are formed with sodium salts of carboxylic acids.

$$CH_3COONa + CH_3COCl \xrightarrow{\text{distil}} (CH_3CO)_2O + NaCl$$

The reactants are heated until the anhydride distils over.

Reduction to Alcohols

$$RCOCl + 2H_2 \xrightarrow[\text{1,2-dimethylbenzene solvent}]{\text{colloidal Pt or Pd cat.}} RCH_2OH + HCl$$

Bubbled
through

Acid Anhydrides

These are compounds in which a water molecule has been eliminated from two carboxylic acid molecules. Methanoic (formic) acid is exceptional in that it yields carbon monoxide on dehydration.

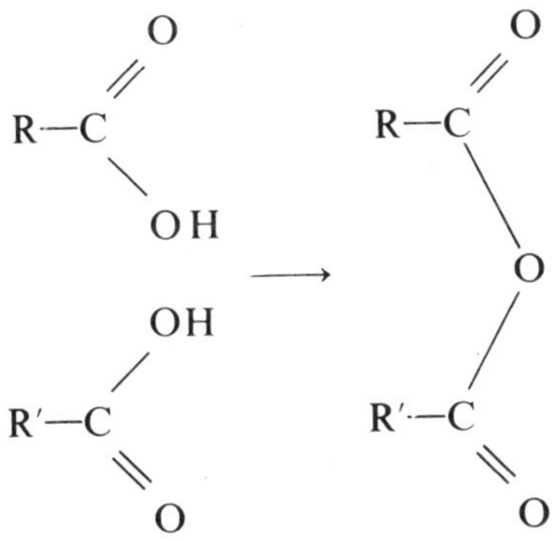

When R and R′ are identical the compound is described as a *symmetrical or simple anhydride* and when different as an *unsymmetrical or mixed anhydride*.

Nomenclature

Simple compounds are named by taking either the IUPAC or common name of the carboxylic acid containing the same acyl group and replacing the word acid with 'anhydride'. For mixed anhydrides, each acyl group is named separately.

Formula	IUPAC name	Common name
$(CH_3CO)_2O$	Ethanoic anhydride	Acetic anhydride
$(CH_3CO)O(COCH_2CH_3)$	Ethanoic propanoic anhydride	Acetic propionic anhydride

Aromatic anhydrides are similarly named as derivatives of their parent acid.

e.g. $(C_6H_5CO)_2O$—Benzenecarboxylic anhydride or Benzoic anhydride

Physical Properties

All simple aliphatic compounds derived from monocarboxylic acids and containing less than thirteen carbon atoms are colourless liquids. Ethanoic (acetic) anhydride possesses a sharp, pungent smell rather like that of ethanoic acid. Benzenecarboxylic (benzoic) and other aromatic anhydrides are solids.

Despite the lack of hydrogen bonding, they have higher boiling points than their parent acids, many of which dimerize to give almost the same effective relative molecular mass.

Name	Formula	M.p./°C	B.p./°C	Density at 20 °C/ g cm^{-3}
Ethanoic anhydride	$(CH_3CO)_2O$	−72	140	1.082
Propanoic anhydride	$(CH_3CH_2CO)_2O$	−45	168	1.022
Benzenecarboxylic anhydride	$(C_6H_5CO)_2O$	42	360	0.967

The lone pairs of electrons on the oxygen atoms are not sufficiently localized to enable them to form hydrogen bonds with water molecules (illustrated by the comparatively high resonance energy of 7.2 kJ mol^{-1}) and it is probably for this reason that anhydrides are insoluble in water, although many aliphatic ones undergo immediate hydrolysis to yield the acid.

Industrial Source

Ethanoic (acetic) anhydride is manufactured on a very large scale, especially in the United States of America.

The pyrolysis of both ethanoic (acetic) acid and propanone (acetone) yields a highly reactive gas called ethenone (ketene),

$$CH_3COOH \xrightarrow[\text{triethyl phosphate(V) cat.}]{650\text{--}700\,°C \text{ reduced press.}} CH_2{=}C{=}O + H_2O$$

Ethenone
(Ketene)

$$CH_3COCH_3 \xrightarrow{750\text{--}860\,°C} CH_2{=}C{=}O + CH_4$$

which when condensed by rapid cooling is absorbed in ethanoic acid in a scrubbing tower to form the anhydride.

$$CH_2{=}C{=}O + CH_3COOH \longrightarrow (CH_3CO)_2O$$

Another important process is the air-oxidation of ethanal (acetaldehyde) using a cobalt(III) ethanoate (acetate)/copper(II) ethanoate (acetate) catalyst at 50 °C.

$$2CH_2CHO + O_2 \xrightarrow[\text{ethanoates cat., 50 °C}]{\text{cobalt(III) and copper(II)}} (CH_3CO)_2O + H_2O$$

The water is removed from the system by using an entrainer such as ethyl ethanoate (acetate).

Synthetic Preparation

From the Acyl Chloride and the Sodium Salt

$$RCOCl + RCOONa \longrightarrow (RCO)_2O + NaCl$$

The reactants are heated until the anhydride distils over.

From the Sodium Salt and Phosphorus Trichloride Oxide (Phosphoryl Chloride)

$$4RCOONa + POCl_3 \longrightarrow 2(RCO)_2O + NaPO_3 + 3NaCl$$
(Excess)

The reaction is fundamentally similar to the one above since the process involves the formation of the acyl chloride as an intermediate.

Reactions

The reactions of acid anhydrides are similar to those of acyl chlorides, although in practice they are very much less reactive. Whereas acyl chlorides generally evolve hydrogen chloride, anhydrides liberate the carboxylic acid.

Hydrolysis

$$(RCO)_2O + H_2O \longrightarrow 2RCOOH$$

Ester Formation

Esters are formed from alcohols and phenols.

$$(RCO)_2O + R'OH \longrightarrow RCOOR' + RCOOH$$

Esterification with phenol requires an alkaline medium. Refer to page 186.

Amide Formation

Amides are formed from ammonia and amines ($R'NH_2$ and R'_2NH)

$$(RCO)_2O + 2NH_3 \longrightarrow RCONH_2 + RCOO^-NH_4^+$$

$$(RCO)_2O + R'NH_2 \longrightarrow RCONHR' + RCOOH$$

Refer to page 211.

Ketone Formation: Friedel–Crafts Acylation

$$C_6H_6 + (RCO)_2O \xrightarrow[\text{cat.}]{AlCl_3} C_6H_5COR + RCOOH$$

Refer to page 135.

Esters

Nomenclature

Esters are named by taking either the IUPAC or common name of the parent carboxylic acid and replacing the ending '-ic' with the suffix '-ate', preceding this with the name of the alkyl or aryl group of the appropriate alcohol or phenol.

Formula	IUPAC name	Common name
$HCOOCH_3$	Methyl methanoate	Methyl formate
$CH_3COOCH_2CH_3$	Ethyl ethanoate	Ethyl acetate
$CH_3COOC_6H_5$	Phenyl ethanoate	Phenyl acetate

The simplest ester derived from benzenecarboxylic (benzoic) acid is METHYL BENZENECARBOXYLATE (BENZOATE), $C_6H_5COOCH_3$.

Physical Properties

Simple esters are colourless liquids possessing pleasant fruity odours and are commonly used in scenting perfumes and flavouring food.

Name	Formula	B.p./°C	Density at 20°C/g cm³
Methyl methanoate	$HCOOCH_3$	32	0.974
Ethyl methanoate	$HCOOCH_2CH_3$	54	0.912
Methyl ethanoate	CH_3COOCH_3	57	0.933
Ethyl ethanoate	$CH_3COOCH_2CH_3$	77	0.901
Ethyl benzenecarboxylate	$C_6H_5COOCH_2CH_3$	213	1.047

Boiling points are normal. Methyl and ethyl esters are completely un-associated liquids and therefore have much lower boiling points than their associated parent acid, despite having higher relative molecular masses.

Name	M_r	B.p./°C
Methanoic acid	46	101
Methyl methanoate	60	32
Ethanoic acid	60	118
Ethyl ethanoate	88	77

Methyl methanoate is very soluble in water, but there is a rapid and progressive decline in the solubility of the higher compounds as they increase in relative molecular mass. Esters of aromatic carboxylic acids are virtually insoluble.

Synthetic Preparation

The majority of esters are prepared by reacting an alcohol or phenol with a carboxylic acid (Fischer–Speier esterification reaction), acyl chloride or acid anhydride.

$$RCOOH + R'OH \xrightleftharpoons{H^+} RCOOR' + H_2O$$

$$RCOCl + R'OH \longrightarrow RCOOR' + HCl$$

$$(RCO)_2O + R'OH \longrightarrow RCOOR' + RCOOH$$

With the exception of direct esterification, i.e. Fischer method, the other reactions proceed more or less to completion.

Industrial applications of the Fischer-Speier method utilize a much smaller proportion of sulphuric acid than is used in the laboratory.

Reactions

Replacement of the alkoxy group, —OR′, by weak nucleophiles occurs under acid or base catalysed conditions, which are necessary in order to enhance the electron deficiency of the carboxyl carbon atom.

Hydrolysis

Hydrolysis into acids can be brought about by either acid or base catalysis, the mechanism for the acid catalysed process being the exact opposite to that for esterification.

$$RCOOR' + H_2O \underset{\text{reflux}}{\overset{H^+ \text{ or } OH \text{ cat.}}{\rightleftharpoons}} RCOOH + R'OH$$

The process is more satisfactorily performed under alkaline conditions and is referred to as SAPONIFICATION because it is a type of reaction used in preparing soaps.

'Soapy detergents', as opposed to 'soapless detergents' (*see* page 277), are generally considered as alkali metal derivatives of carboxylic acids which contain between 10 and 18 carbon atoms, and are usually manufactured by the alkaline hydrolysis of vegetable oils and animal fats.

Mechanism for Saponification

Amide Formation : Ammonolysis

The reaction can be carried out with ammonia dissolved in an alcoholic medium, in which case it is accelerated by the presence of alkoxide ions, RO^-, or alternatively by using concentrated aqueous ammonia containing dissolved ammonium salts which serve to promote the reaction by acting as proton donors.

$$RCOOR' + NH_3 \xrightarrow[\substack{\text{or } NH_4^+ \text{ in conc.} \\ \text{aq. solution}}]{RO^- \text{ in alcohol}} RCONH_2 + R'OH$$

With Grignard Reagents : Formation of Ketone and Tertiary Alcohols

Refer to page 170.

Transesterification: Ester Exchange

This is the process whereby one alcohol replaces another in an ester. The reaction may be catalysed by an acid (H_2SO_4 or dry HCl) or by the basic alkoxide ion, RO^-

$$RCOOR' + R''OH \underset{\text{reflux}}{\overset{H^+ \text{ or } RO^- \text{ cat.}}{\rightleftharpoons}} RCOOR'' + R'OH$$

Reduction to Alcohols

$$RCOOR' + 4[H] \xrightarrow[(C_2H_5)_2O]{LiAlH_4,} RCH_2OH + R'OH$$

Reduction may also be brought about by catalytic hydrogenation using a copper(II) oxide/copper(II) chromate(VI) catalyst heated to 250 °C.

Sodium tetrahydridoborate(III), $NaBH_4$, is not sufficiently reactive to perform this reduction.

Replacement of the Carboxylate Group

Dry hydrogen bromide, concentrated aqueous hydrogen iodide, or concentrated sulphuric acid brings about cleavage of the carboxylate ion to yield the carboxylic acid,

Amides

Amides are monoacyl derivatives of ammonia, and may be classified as primary ($RCONH_2$), secondary ($RCONHR'$) or tertiary ($RCONR'_2$) according to the number of alkyl or aryl groups attached to the nitrogen atom.

Nomenclature

Each compound is named by replacing the ending '-oic acid' (IUPAC) or '-ic acid' (common) of the corresponding carboxylic acid with the suffix '-amide'.

Formula	IUPAC name	Common name
CH_3CONH_2	Ethanamide	Acetamide
$CH_3CONHCH_3$	N-Methylethanamide	N-Methylacetamide

The simplest amide formed from benzenecarboxylic (benzoic) acid is BENZENECARBOXAMIDE (BENZAMIDE), $C_6H_5CONH_2$.

Physical Properties

With the exception of methanamide (formamide) all primary amides, $RCONH_2$, are crystalline solids, due largely to fairly strong intermolecular hydrogen bonding.

Name	Formula	M.p./°C	B.p./°C
Methanamide	$HCONH_2$	3	193
Ethanamide	CH_3CONH_2	82	221
Benzenecarboxamide	$C_6H_5CONH_2$	132	290

Both primary and secondary amides are associated in the liquid phase and have high boiling points. As tertiary amides contain no *N*-hydrogen atoms, they are unable to form hydrogen bonds and have normal boiling points.

A further consequence of hydrogen bonding is that the simpler aliphatic amides (containing less than six carbons) are reasonably soluble in water.

Benzenecarboxamide is very soluble in hot water but only slightly soluble in cold. All amides are virtually insoluble in hydrocarbon solvents.

Industrial Source

Amides are usually prepared by ammonolysis of acid derivatives or by the pyrolysis of ammonium salts. (Refer to page 257 and below.)

Synthetic Preparation of Primary Amides

Ammonolysis of Acid Derivatives

$$RCOCl + 2NH_3 \longrightarrow RCONH_2 + NH_4Cl$$

$$(RCO)_2O + 2NH_3 \longrightarrow RCONH_2 + RCOO^-NH_4^+$$

Pyrolysis of Ammonium Salts

$$2RCOOH + (NH_4)_2CO_3 \longrightarrow 2RCOO^-NH_4^+ + CO_2 + H_2O$$

$$RCOO^-NH_4^+ \underset{\text{heat 100–200 °C}}{\overset{\text{excess RCOOH}}{\rightleftharpoons}} RCONH_2 + H_2O$$

Partial Hydrolysis of Nitriles

$$RCN \xrightarrow[\text{or 70\% acid}]{\text{boil with aq. alc. NaOH}} RCONH_2$$

Refer to page 251.

Reactions

The lone pair of electrons on the nitrogen atom gives amides a slightly basic character. Owing to resonance between the two canonical forms,

More stable form

these electrons are not as readily available for donation as in amines, and amides are consequently much less basic (pK_b of ethanamide = 15.1).

Hydrolysis

(1) With dilute acid:

$$RCONH_2 + H_2O + H^+ \xrightarrow{\text{heat}} RCOOH + NH_4^+$$

(2) With aqueous alkali:

$$RCONH_2 + {}^-OH \xrightarrow{\text{heat}} RCOO^- + NH_3$$

The mechanism for the hydrolysis of amides is similar to that of esters.

Hofmann Degradation Reaction

On warming a primary amide with bromine and a concentrated aqueous solution of an alkali, rearrangement and the elimination of a carboxyl group occurs to yield a primary amine.

$$RCONH_2 + Br_2 + 4NaOH \longrightarrow RNH_2 + 2NaBr + Na_2CO_3 + 2H_2O$$

Mechanism

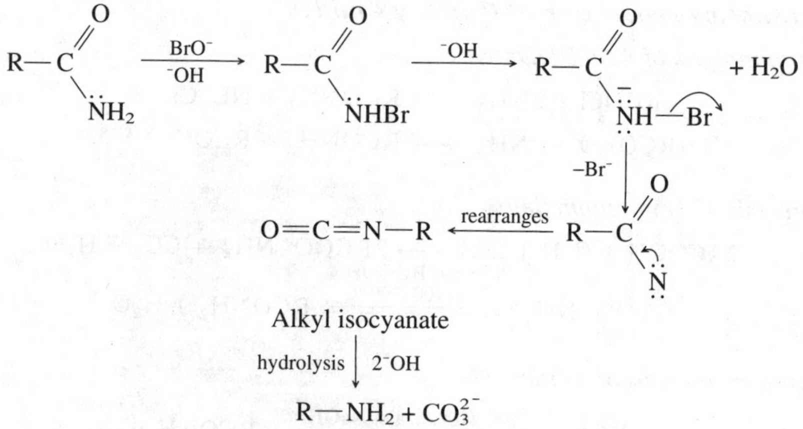

Alkyl isocyanate

$$R-NH_2 + CO_3^{2-}$$

Dehydration using Phosphorus(V) Oxide

$$RCONH_2 \xrightarrow[\text{distil}]{P_2O_5} RCN + H_2O$$

With Nitrous Acid

$$RCONH_2 \xrightarrow[(\text{NaNO}_2/\text{dil. HCl})]{\text{HONO}} RCOOH + N_2 + H_2O$$

Carbamide (Urea), $H_2N-\overset{\overset{\displaystyle O}{\|}}{C}-NH_2$

Carbamide (urea) is a white, crystalline diamide derivative of carbonic acid. It has the distinction of being the first organic compound to be prepared deliberately in the laboratory when Wöhler (1828) obtained it by evaporating an aqueous solution of ammonium cyanate (*see* page 2).

$$NH_4OCN \xrightarrow{\text{evaporate}} \overset{\displaystyle O}{\overset{\displaystyle \|}{H_2N-C-NH_2}}$$

Ammonium	Carbamide
cyanate	(Urea)

It is synthesized in large quantities in Britain by compressing carbon dioxide and an excess of ammonia at a high pressure and a temperature of 200 °C, and is

$$CO_2 + 2NH_3 \rightleftharpoons H_2N-\overset{\displaystyle O}{\overset{\displaystyle \|}{C}}-ONH_4 \rightleftharpoons H_2N-\overset{\displaystyle O}{\overset{\displaystyle \|}{C}}-NH_2 + H_2O$$

Ammonium
carbamate

used mainly for manufacturing carbamide–methanal (urea–formaldehyde) resins (*see* page 314), although small quantities are used in fertilizers and drugs.

Reactions

Carbamide acts as a weak monobasic acid, forming cations of the type, $[(NH_2)_2COH]^+$ *with concentrated strong acids.*

With nitrous acid, it yields nitrogen and carbon dioxide.

$$(NH_2)_2C{=}O + 2HONO \longrightarrow CO_2 + 2N_2 + 3H_2O$$

In the presence of acids, bases, or the enzyme urease, carbamide undergoes *hydrolysis*:

$$(NH_2)_2C{=}O + H_2O \begin{cases} \xrightarrow{H^+} NH_4^+ + CO_2 \\ \xrightarrow{^-OH} NH_3 + CO_3^{2-} \\ \xrightarrow{\text{urease}} NH_3 + CO_2 \end{cases}$$

With sodium halate(I) (hypohalous) solutions, it yields the carbonate and nitrogen.

$$(NH_2)_2C{=}O + 3BrO^- + 2OH^- \longrightarrow CO_3^{2-} + 3Br^- + N_2 + 3H_2O$$

On gentle heating, carbamide leaves a white solid called *biuret*.

$$2(NH_2)_2C{=}O \longrightarrow (NH_2C{=}O)_2NH + NH_3$$
Biuret

The product, on dissolving in aqueous alkali and treating with copper(II) sulphate, gives a pink or violet coloration.

QUESTIONS

1. Which one of the following compounds is the most commonly employed and easy-to-handle laboratory ethanoylating (acetylating) agent?

   A ethanal
   B ethanoyl chloride
   C ethanoyl anhydride
   D ethanoic acid
   E sodium ethanoate

2. Which one of the following compounds has the most pronounced amphoteric character?

   A CH_3CH_2OH

B C_6H_5OH
C $CH_3CH_2NH_2$
D CH_3CONH_2
E $HOCH_2COOH$

3. Give the structural formulae of *nine* isomeric esters corresponding to the formula $C_5H_{10}O_2$.

4. How might the following conversions be brought about?

A $RCONH_2 \longrightarrow RCH_2NH_2$
B $RCONH_2 \longrightarrow RCN$

C $RCOOR' \longrightarrow RCONH_2 + R'OH$
D $(RCO)_2O \longrightarrow RCONHR'$
E $RCOCl \longrightarrow RCHO$

5. Compare and contrast the addition–elimination (condensation) reactions of acid anhydrides and acyl chlorides with those of aldehydes and ketones.

6. Discuss and compare the reactivity of the halogen atom in haloalkanes and acyl chlorides, and similarly for the C—O—C linkage in ethers and esters.

23 **Sulphonic Acids**

AROMATIC SULPHONIC ACIDS, which are of considerably greater importance than their aliphatic counterparts, are polar compounds in which the *sulphur atom* of the sulphonic acid group, —SO_3H, is attached directly to the benzene ring.

Nomenclature

Names are afforded by attaching the ending 'sulphonic acid' to the name of the compound to which the acid group is substituted.

Benzenesulphonic   4-Methylbenzenesulphonic   2-Chlorobenzenesulphonic
acid   acid (*p*-Toluenesulphonic acid) acid

2-, 3- and 4-Aminobenzenesulphonic acids
(Orthanilic acid)   (Metanilic acid)   (Sulphanilic acid)

Physical Properties

Sulphonic acids are relatively non-volatile compounds, many of which decompose at temperatures below their boiling point, although they can usually be successfully distilled under reduced pressure.

The melting points of the anhydrous acids are lower than those of the corresponding carboxylic acids.

Name	M.p./°C	B.p./°C
Benzenesulphonic acid	50	
2-Methylbenzenesulphonic acid	68	128
4-Methylbenzenesulphonic acid	104	140
4-Aminobenzenesulphonic acid	288	

Owing to their highly hygroscopic nature, the anhydrous form is difficult to obtain, and the acids are usually isolated in the free state as hydrated crystals.

However, it is generally found to be more convenient to store and use them in the form of their sodium salts.

As a family, they are more soluble in water than any other series of organic compounds, completely dissociating into ions. Because of their polar nature, they are virtually insoluble in hydrocarbon solvents but are more soluble in organic oxygen-containing compounds.

Industrial Source

Aromatic compounds are usually prepared by direct sulphonation, the precise conditions depending upon the activating or deactivating nature of any substituents already present in the ring.

Nowadays, sulphuric acid is gradually being superseded by stabilized liquid sulphur(VI) oxide (sulphur trioxide) as a sulphonating agent, but as yet this reagent by itself is utilized only in a minority of syntheses.

As previously stated, the acids are usually isolated in the form of their sodium salts. This is accomplished by 'salting-out' or 'liming-out'. For example, since benzenesulphonic acid is of comparable strength to hydrochloric acid, an equilibrium is established on adding an excess of sodium chloride to an aqueous solution of the acid.

$$C_6H_5SO_3H + NaCl \rightleftharpoons C_6H_5SO_3Na + HCl$$

The presence of excess sodium ions reduces the solubility of the sodium benzenesulphonate, thus enabling the latter to be crystallized out.

In the 'liming-out' process, slaked lime is added to an aqueous solution of the reaction mixture, removing excess sulphuric acid in the form of the insoluble calcium sulphate which is separated by filtration. The subsequent addition of sodium carbonate to the filtrate removes the calcium ions by precipitating calcium carbonate, thus leaving the sodium sulphonate in solution.

The sulphonate can then be separated by partially evaporating the remaining solution and crystallizing out.

Synthetic Preparations

Like the industrial syntheses, the aromatic acids are generally prepared by direct sulphonation.

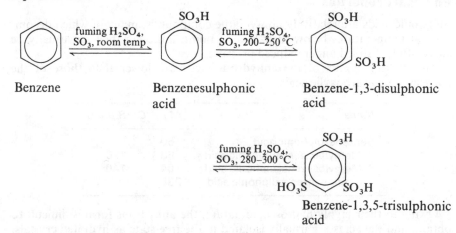

Benzene   Benzenesulphonic acid   Benzene-1,3-disulphonic acid

Benzene-1,3,5-trisulphonic acid

The deactivating effect of the acid group makes further sulphonation more difficult and the preparation of the 1,3- and 1,3,5-derivatives therefore requires higher temperatures.

Methylbenzene (toluene) being ring-activated by the electron-releasing methyl group, undergoes sulphonation much more readily, and this reaction can be performed under ice-cold conditions.

Methylbenzene	4-Methylbenzenesulphonic acid
(Toluene)	(p-Toluenesulphonic acid)
	Major product

Reactions

Sulphonic acids are comparable in acid strength to the mineral acids (pK_a of benzenesulphonic acid $= 2.5$), being completely ionized in aqueous solution.

$$ArSO_3H \longrightarrow ArSO_3^- + H^+$$

The acid strength is enhanced by the presence of electron-withdrawing groups in the ring, especially in the 2- and 4- positions.

Reactions of the Sulphonic Acid Group

Salt Formation

$$2C_6H_5SO_3H + Mg \longrightarrow (C_6H_5SO_3^-)_2Mg^{2+} + H_2$$

$$C_6H_5SO_3H + KOH \longrightarrow C_6H_5SO_3^-K^+ + H_2O$$

$$2C_6H_5SO_3H + Na_2CO_3 \longrightarrow 2C_6H_5SO_3^-Na^+ + H_2O + CO_2$$

$$C_6H_5SO_3H + NaHCO_3 \longrightarrow C_6H_5SO_3^-Na^+ + H_2O + CO_2$$

Hydrolysis

Unlike nitration, the sulphonation process is reversible, and hence benzene can be re-obtained slowly from benzenesulphonic acid by boiling with excess water. The rate can be increased to a more practical level by reacting it in a sealed tube with superheated steam and a mineral acid catalyst at 150–170 °C.

$$C_6H_5SO_3H + H_2O \Longrightarrow C_6H_6 + H_2SO_4$$

Sulphonyl Chloride Formation

Good yields (75–80 per cent) can be obtained by employing methods similar to those used to prepare the chlorides of carboxylic acids.

$$3C_6H_5SO_3Na + PCl_5 \xrightarrow{170-180\,°C} 3C_6H_5SO_2Cl + 2NaCl + NaPO_3$$

Benzenesulphonyl chloride

Benzenesulphonyl chloride may be isolated as a solid (m.p. $14\,^\circ$C, b.p. $252\,^\circ$C) at temperatures below $14\,^\circ$C.

Ester Formation

Esters are sometimes prepared for purposes of identification.

$$C_6H_5SO_3Na + (CH_3)_2SO_4 \xrightarrow{150\text{--}160\,^\circ C} C_6H_5SO_3CH_3 + CH_3NaSO_3$$

Methyl
benzenesulphonate

$$C_6H_5SO_2Cl + CH_3OH \xrightarrow{OH^-\ cat.} C_6H_5SO_3CH_3 + HCl$$

Phenol Formation

Fusion of the sodium salt with solid sodium hydroxide followed by treatment with dilute acid gives good yields of phenols.

$$C_6H_5SO_3Na + NaOH \xrightarrow{fuse} C_6H_5ONa + NaHSO_3$$

$$\downarrow \begin{array}{l} dil. \\ HCl \end{array}$$

$$C_6H_5OH + NaCl$$

Benzenecarbonitrile (Benzonitrile) Formation

$$C_6H_5SO_3Na + NaCN \xrightarrow{fuse} C_6H_5CN + Na_2SO_3$$

Benzenecarbonitrile
(Benzonitrile)

Formation and Uses of Sulphonic Acids as Intermediates

Sulphonic acids are sometimes prepared as intermediate compounds to enable other groups to be more easily or more efficiently substituted.

Refer to the preparation of 2,4,6-trinitrophenol (picric) acid, page 188.

Formation of Soluble Azo-Dyes

Azo-dyes, formed by the interaction of a diazonium salt and a phenol, are usually only slightly soluble in water and therefore of little practical importance. However, the introduction of a sulphonic acid group into the molecule renders the dye water soluble without having any adverse effect upon the colour. Refer to pages 136 and 216.

Ring Substitution

The $-SO_3H$ group is 3-*directing* since it withdraws electrons from the ring and therefore deactivates it with regard to electrophilic substitution.

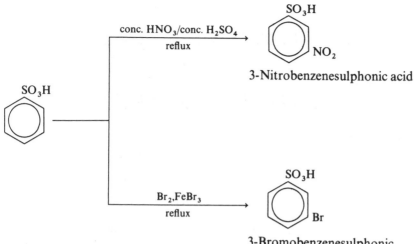

3-Nitrobenzenesulphonic acid

3-Bromobenzenesulphonic acid

Soapless Detergents

'Soapless detergents' vary considerably in their chemical nature, although the majority are sodium salts of alkylbenzenesulphonic acids. (The alkyl side-chain generally contains about 12 to 18 carbon atoms.) The detergents exist in both liquid and solid forms and are manufactured principally from petroleum. They have advantages over 'soapy detergents' (*see* page 267) in that they are immediately effective in hard water and, as they are salts of a fairly strong acid and a strong base, they are almost neutral in aqueous solution. ('Soapy detergents', being salts of a weak acid and a strong base, hydrolyse to give a slightly alkaline solution.)

QUESTIONS

1. Without referring to tables, state which of the following sulphonic acids possesses the lowest pK_a value.

    A $4\text{-ClC}_6\text{H}_4\text{SO}_3\text{H}$
    B $3\text{-HOC}_6\text{H}_4\text{SO}_3\text{H}$
    C $2\text{-NH}_2\text{C}_6\text{H}_4\text{SO}_3\text{H}$
    D $4\text{-NO}_2\text{C}_6\text{H}_4\text{SO}_3\text{H}$
    E $3\text{-NO}_2\text{C}_6\text{H}_4\text{SO}_3\text{H}$

2. Starting with 4-methylbenzenesulphonic acid, outline how you would prepare

    A 4-methylbenzenesulphonyl chloride
    B methylbenzene
    C 4-methylphenol
    D ethyl 4-methylbenzenesulphonate

3. Account for the observation that 1,3-dimethylbenzene, $C_6H_4(CH_3)_2$, undergoes sulphonation much more rapidly than either of its isomers.

24 Amino Acids, Proteins and Polypeptides

Proteins are high relative molecular mass polyamides. The name is derived from the Greek, *proteios*, meaning first or primary, and relates to their essential rôle in all living cells. They are the principal constituent of skin, hair, blood, muscles, nerves, enzymes and hormones, and are present in cheese, milk, eggs, meat and many other foods. One of these proteins, insulin, is produced by the pancreas to control the amount of sugars in the body; failure of the gland to produce sufficient insulin causes the amount of sugars in the blood stream to build up to a dangerously high level, and is accompanied by a decline in the quantity of glucose (glycogen) stored in the liver. A condition of this type is known as diabetes mellitus, and patients suffering from it require periodic injections of insulin in order to restore the balance.

Proteins which yield only 2- or α-amino acids on hydrolysis are classified as SIMPLE PROTEINS, and those which yield 2-amino acids together with some other product with characteristics different from those of proteins are classified as CONJUGATED PROTEINS.

Further classification tends to be crude and is based upon solubility.

Fibrous proteins are insoluble in water and possess a function similar to that of cellulose in plants, acting as the principal structural component of animal cells. These include collagen (found in skin, tendons and bones, and which yields gelatine when boiled with water), keratins (proteins of hair, nails, horns and feathers), elastins (elastic tissues of tendons and arteries), and fibroin (a protein of silk).

Globular proteins form a colloidal solution with water but are soluble in acids, bases and salts. On boiling in these solvents, the change incurred is irreversible and known as *denaturation*, causing a reduction in the degree of solubility. Examples of globular proteins include the albumins (found in egg white) and casein and lactalbumin (found in milk). The change in the nature of the white of an egg on boiling provides a typical example of denaturation.

The Peptide Linkage

All proteins contain the POLYPEPTIDE CHAIN. Acid or enzyme (trypsin) hydrolysis readily breaks proteins down into amino acids, and since the only functional groups present are the amino and the carboxyl groups, it becomes evident that each unit must be linked by means of a group analogous to an amide group. This is referred to as the PEPTIDE LINKAGE.

A polypeptide which would yield the 2-amino acid, $RCH(NH_2)COOH$, on hydrolysis may be represented as,

$$
\begin{array}{c}
\text{O} \quad \left[\begin{array}{c} \text{H} \quad \text{H} \end{array}\right. \quad \text{R} \quad \text{O} \quad \text{H} \\
\| \qquad | \qquad \diagup \qquad \| \qquad | \\
\text{C} \qquad \text{N} \qquad \text{C} \qquad \text{C} \qquad \text{N} \\
\diagdown \quad \diagup \quad \diagdown \quad \diagup \quad \diagdown \quad \diagup \quad \diagdown \\
\text{C} \quad \text{C} \qquad \text{N} \qquad \text{C} \\
\diagup \quad \diagdown \quad \| \quad | \quad \diagup \quad \diagdown \\
\text{H} \qquad \text{R} \quad \text{O} \left.\right] \quad \text{H} \quad \text{H} \qquad \text{R}
\end{array}
$$

the peptide linkage being indicated by the square brackets.

2- or α-Amino Acids

2- or α-Amino acids are yielded as the final products of the hydrolysis of proteins, and a number of them are actually synthesized in this way by the human body. However, certain amino acids cannot be formed by the metabolism from external food sources but are nonetheless vital to life. These are referred to as the *essential amino acids.*

The compounds themselves are bifunctional, containing a basic amino group and an acidic carboxyl group, and not surprisingly, exhibit amphoteric properties. They may be classified as *neutral, basic* or *acidic* according to the number of amino and carboxyl groups they contain. By far the most common class are the neutral compounds, which contain an equal number of amino and carboxyl groups (usually only one of each). The basic and the acidic compounds respectively contain an extra amino or carboxyl group.

Nomenclature

Amino acids are named systematically by considering them as amino derivatives of carboxylic acids. However, many are still referred to by their original names, which generally give no indication of their acidic properties, but refer rather to their relationship with amines. These names have the ending '-ine'.

$$NH_2CH_2COOH$$

$$CH_3CHCOOH$$
$$\qquad\quad |$$
$$\qquad\quad NH_2$$

Aminoethanoic acid
(Glycine)

2-Aminopropanoic acid
(Alanine)

Exceptions to this general rule with regard to common nomenclature occur amongst the acidic amino acids:

$$HOOCCH_2CHCOOH$$
$$\qquad\qquad |$$
$$\qquad\qquad NH_2$$

$$HOOC(CH_2)_2CHCOOH$$
$$\qquad\qquad\qquad |$$
$$\qquad\qquad\qquad NH_2$$

Aminobutanedioic acid
(Aspartic acid)

2-Aminopentanedioic acid
(Glutamic acid)

Stereochemistry

With the sole exception of aminoethanoic acid (glycine), all 2-amino acids contain a chiral centre and consequently can exist in optically active forms. The enantiomers of 2-aminopropanoic acid (alanine) and their inherent optical activity are shown on page 30.

The products of laboratory syntheses are, however, generally optically inactive owing to the formation of racemates containing equal proportions of each enantiomer.

Physical Properties

Aminoethanoic acid (glycine) is a white, sweet-tasting solid (m.p. 235 °C) which is soluble in water but insoluble in most organic liquids, suggesting a high degree of polarity in the molecule.

Synthetic Preparation

Direct Ammonolysis

The simplest amino acid, aminoethanoic acid, is usually obtained by the hydrolysis of a protein such as gelatine or by direct ammonolysis of a chlorocarboxylic acid with a concentrated solution of ammonia.

$$ClCH_2COOH \ + \ 2NH_3 \longrightarrow NH_2CH_2COOH \ + \ NH_4Cl$$

Chloroethanoic   Aminoethanoic acid
acid   (Glycine)

2-Hydroxyalkanonitrile (Cyanohydrin) Synthesis (Strecker Synthesis)

This process involves the addition of hydrogen cyanide, in the presence of ammonia, to an aldehyde to form a 2-hydroxyalkonitrile (cyanohydrin), the hydroxyl group of which is immediately replaced by an amino group to yield a 2-aminoalkanonitrile. On acid hydrolysis, the latter yields an 2-amino acid.

$$RCHO + HCN \longrightarrow RCH(OH)CN \xrightarrow{NH_3} RCH(NH_2)CN$$

                2-Hydroxalkanonitrile   Aminoalkanonitrile
                   (Cyanohydrin) $\Big\downarrow$ dil. acid

$$RCH(NH_2) \ COOH$$

2-Amino acid

Aminoethanoic acid (glycine), NH_2CH_2COOH, is obtained from methanal (formaldehyde). The hydrogen cyanide and ammonia are both initially obtained from the dissociation of ammonium cyanide.

$$NH_4 + NaCN \longrightarrow NH_4CN + NaCl$$
$$NH_4CN \rightleftharpoons NH_3 + HCN$$

Reactions

The reactions of aminoethanoic acid are typical of a compound containing both an amino and a carboxyl group.

In solution, it exists in equilibrium with its tautomer, *a dipolar ion or Zwitterion* (literally 'between ion'), formed by the intramolecular migration of the acidic proton.

$$NH_2CH_2COOH \rightleftharpoons NH_3^+ CH_2COO^-$$

Zwitterion,
a dipolar ion

The equilibrium lies very much towards the right-hand side, and the amphoteric nature of this species is illustrated by the following scheme, showing its relative stability in both acidic and basic media.

$$NH_2CH_2COO^- \underset{OH^-}{\overset{H^+}{\rightleftharpoons}} NH_3^+CH_2COO^- \underset{OH^-}{\overset{H^+}{\rightleftharpoons}} NH_3^+CH_2COOH$$

Aminoethanoate	Zwitterion	An ammonium
anion		*cation*

Conjugate base | | | Conjugate acid

In acidic media, aminoethanoic acid exists as the cation, $NH_3^+CH_2COOH$, whereas in a basic medium it functions as the anion, $NH_2CH_2COO^-$. At the intermediate point, the dipolar ion possesses no net charge and this position is referred to as the ISOELECTRIC POINT.

The acidic and basic strengths of aminoethanoic acid are extremely low compared with those of carboxylic acids and most aliphatic amines.

Aminoethanoic acid. $pK_a = 9.87$ (cf ethanoic acid $pK_a = 4.76$)
Aminoethanoic acid. $pK_b = 4.13$ (cf methylamine, $pK_b = 3.36$)

Reactions of the Amino Group

Salt Formation

Salts are formed with mineral acids:

$$NH_2CH_2COOH + HCl \longrightarrow [NH_3^+CH_2COOH]Cl^-$$

(Carboxymethyl)ammonium chloride
(Glycine hydrochloride)

With Nitrous Acid

$$NH_2CH_2COOH + HONO \longrightarrow HOCH_2COOH \quad + \quad N_2 \quad + \quad H_2O$$

Hydroxyethanoic acid
(Glycollic acid)

Acylation

The amino group reacts with ethanoic (acetic) anhydride or ethanoyl (acetyl) chloride:

$$NH_2CH_2COOH + (CH_3CO)_2O \longrightarrow CH_3CONHCH_2COOH + CH_3COOH$$

2-Ethanamidoethanoic acid
(α-Acetamidoacetic acid)

Aminoethanoic acid undergoes benzenecarbonylation (benzoylation) with benzenecarbonyl (benzoyl) chloride to yield benzenecarboxamidoethanoic (hippuric) acid, $C_6H_5CONHCH_2COOH$.

Peptide Synthesis

Peptides can be formed by the combination of a number of amino acids. One of the simplest methods is to condense the ester of one amino acid with the acid chloride of another. This is followed by hydrolysis of the ester group of the product and then replacing the chlorine with an amino group.

$$NH_2CH_2COOCH_2CH_3 + ClCH_2COCl$$

$$\xrightarrow{\hspace{2cm}} ClCH_2CONHCH_2COOCH_2CH_3$$

$$\xrightarrow{\text{dil. acid}} ClCH_2CONHCH_2COOH$$

$$\xrightarrow{NH_3 \text{ solution}} NH_2CH_2CONHCH_2COOH$$

This series can be repeated to give further peptides, but the sequence becomes progressively more difficult.

One of the most universal means of detecting proteins is the *biuret test* (*see* page 271).

Reactions of the Carboxyl Group

Salt Formation

Salts are formed with alkalis and carbonates:

$$NH_2CH_2COOH + NaOH \longrightarrow NH_2CH_2COONa + H_2O$$

$$2NH_2CH_2COOH + K_2CO_3 \longrightarrow 2NH_2CH_2COOK + H_2O + CO_2$$

Esterification

This reaction is fundamentally similar to the reactions of carboxylic acids, with the exception that the mineral acid catalyst ultimately unites with the ester.

$$NH_2CH_2COOH + CH_3CH_2OH \underset{\longleftarrow}{\overset{HCl}{\longrightarrow}} [NH_3^+CH_2COOCH_2CH_3]Cl^- + H_2O$$

QUESTIONS

1. In solution, aminoethanoic acid (glycine), NH_2CH_2COOH, is better represented as $NH_3^+CH_2COO^-$. This suggests that

   A it can function as a strong acid
   B it can function as a strong acid or a strong base
   C it can function as weak acid or a weak base
   D in the solid state it is completely non-polar
   E it is insoluble in all organic liquids

2. Outline the synthesis of amino acids from:

   A an aldehyde
   B a carboxylic acid

3. Explain the amphoteric nature of aminoethanoic acid (glycine) in terms of its dipolar ion, illustrating your answer with reference to specific reactions.

25 Carbohydrates

As the name implies, carbohydrates contain carbon, hydrogen and oxygen only, and correspond to a general molecular formula, $C_xH_{2y}O_y$ or $C_x(H_2O)_y$. They are, in effect, polyhydroxy aldehydes or ketones.

Carbohydrates are extensively distributed in nature in both plants and animals in which they play vital rôles. For example, starch functions as a source of stored food, providing both warmth and energy, and another carbohydrate, cellulose, is the principal structural component of the cell walls of plants. Cellulose is also an important industrial raw material, being used for manufacturing synthetic fibres and plastics.

Plants obtain starch and cellulose from glucose which in turn is photosynthesized, in the presence of chlorophyll, from carbon dioxide and water.

$$6CO_2 + 6H_2O \xrightarrow[\text{chlorophyll}]{\text{sunlight}} C_6H_{12}O_6 + 6O_2$$
$$\text{Glucose}$$

The plant then receives its energy by the reverse process, respiration, in which glucose is burnt up.

$$C_6H_{12}O_6 + 6O_2 \xrightarrow{\text{respiration}} 6CO_2 + 6H_2O + \text{energy}$$
$$\text{Glucose}$$

Human beings obtain their glucose from the food they eat, notably in the form which is present in bread, cakes, potatoes and cereals in general.

Classification and Nomenclature

Carbohydrates may be classified according to one of the following three categories.

Monosaccharides

Monosaccharides contain no more than six carbon atoms and do not undergo acid hydrolysis.

The most common and important monosaccharides are the isomers glucose and fructose, which have a molecular formula, $C_6H_{12}O_6$.

Disaccharides

Disaccharides contain twelve carbon atoms, and on acid hydrolysis one molecule yields two monosaccharide molecules, e.g. the isomers sucrose, maltose and lactose which have a molecular formula, $C_{12}H_{22}O_{11}$.

Mono- and disaccharides are collectively known as sugars (Lat. *saccharon*, sugar) and are distinguished by their sweet taste.

Polysaccharides

Polysaccharides are high relative molecular mass polymers composed of large numbers of sugar molecules linked together into chains by means of a linking oxygen atom. On acid hydrolysis polysaccharides yield a large number of monosaccharide molecules, e.g. cellulose, starch, inulin and glycogen, the latter being a reserve carbohydrate of animals distributed throughout the protoplasm and stored in the liver.

Carbohydrates are, in effect, polyhydroxy aldehydes and ketones, although the common names, which are specific for each particular stereochemical structure and are still popular for the more abundant compounds, give little indication of this. Even the international system is in itself not fully descriptive unless the stereochemical features of each compounds are known.

The systematic names of monosaccharides are afforded by classifying them as either ALDOSES or KETOSES according to the type of carbonyl group they contain. In each of these categories, the number of carbon atoms in each unit is indicated by placing the prefix tri-, tetr-, pent- or hex- before the ending '-ose'.

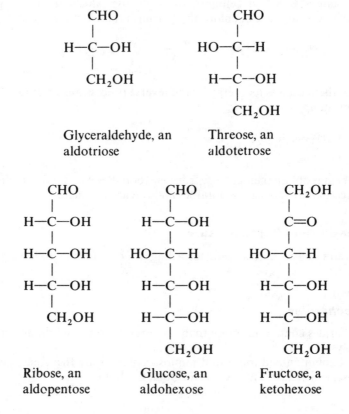

Configuration

Glyceraldehyde contains a central chiral carbon atom. For each of its optical isomers the (+) and (−) signs, specifying the direction in which each one rotates plane-polarized light, give no indication of the way in which the groups are attached to the chiral carbon. The absolute configuration of the two isomers is therefore shown by placing a D or an L in front of the name.

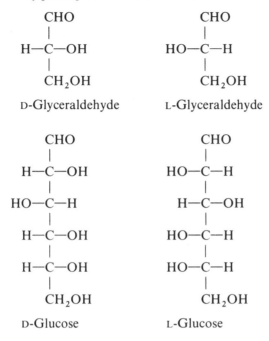

CHO
|
H—C—OH
|
CH₂OH

D-Glyceraldehyde

CHO
|
HO—C—H
|
CH₂OH

L-Glyceraldehyde

CHO
|
H—C—OH
|
HO—C—H
|
H—C—OH
|
H—C—OH
|
CH₂OH

D-Glucose

CHO
|
HO—C—H
|
H—C—OH
|
HO—C—H
|
HO—C—H
|
CH₂OH

L-Glucose

Since all monosaccharides are in effect higher homologues of one of the enantiomers of glyceraldehyde, they are called D-compounds if related to D-glyceraldehyde and L-compounds if related to L-glyceraldehyde. It is conventional to write the structures of sugars with the carbonyl group at, or near, the top, and the comparison with the enantiomers of glyceraldehyde is made by considering the lowest chiral carbon atom.

The most common and important hexoses are D-(+)-*glucose* and D-(−)-*fructose*, which are respectively sometimes referred to as DEXTROSE and LAEVULOSE on account of their optical properties. The further implications of these stereochemical features are beyond the scope of this text.

It is important to remember that although these molecular projections are illustrated in two dimensions, in reality, they are, of course, three dimensional. For example, glyceraldehyde is tetrahedral about the chiral carbon atom.

Monosaccharides

The most abundant naturally occurring monosaccharides are pentoses and hexoses of which glucose and fructose are undoubtedly the most important. These are found in ripe grapes ('grape sugars') as well as in many other fruits, and also in nectar and honey. Mild acid or enzyme hydrolysis breaks down all disaccharides and polysaccharides into their monosaccharide components.

Glucose (Dextrose), $C_6H_{12}O_6$

Glucose can be obtained, together with fructose, by warming cane sugar (sucrose) or starch with a mineral acid, or with the enzyme invertase.

$$C_{12}H_{22}O_{11} + H_2O \xrightarrow[\text{or invertase}]{\text{dil. acid}} C_6H_{12}O_6 + C_6H_{12}O_6$$

Sucrose Glucose Fructose

$$(C_6H_{10}O_5)_n + nH_2O \xrightarrow[\text{diastase/maltase}]{\text{dil. acid or}} nC_6H_{12}O_6$$

Starch Glucose

The fructose can be separated by dissolving it in excess ethanol leaving the glucose, which is virtually insoluble in ethanol, to be crystallized from the aqueous solution. This process is usually aided by 'seeding' with a few crystals of glucose, which also serves to prevent supersaturation occurring.

Glucose is also formed as an intermediate in the fermentation of starch-containing compounds in the manufacture of ethanol (*see* page 169).

Industrially, glucose is manufactured by hydrolysing starch with dilute hydrochloric acid under pressure.

Structure and Constitution of Glucose

The molecule contains four chiral centres. C_2, C_3, C_4 and C_5 of the acyclic (chain) form, creating the possibility for the existence of sixteen stereoisomers, all of which have been isolated. However, only four exist naturally and, of these, D-(+)-glucose (dextrose) is by far the most common. Of the others, only two are reasonably abundant, namely (+)-*mannose*, obtained by hydrolysis of a number of polysaccharides, e.g. ivory nuts (a seed of the Taqua palm), and (+)-*galactose*, obtained by hydrolysis of the disaccharide lactose ('milk sugar') and also of a number of polysaccharides.

In solution, the acyclic form of glucose exists in equilibrium with two isomeric cyclic structures, referred to as α- and β-glucose.

α-Glucose Acyclic form β-Glucose

Both of these cyclic structures are dextrorotatory, but to differing degrees, the specific rotation of a freshly prepared solution of the α-isomer being $+112°$ and that of the β-isomer being $+18.7°$. Stereoisomers of this type, which differ only in the configuration of the C_1 atom (the carbonyl carbon atom of the acyclic form), are called ANOMERS. In this context the word applies only to ALDOSES. The carbon atom about which this structural modification takes place is called the *anomeric carbon atom*.

The existence of these anomers accounts for the variation in the degree of rotation of a freshly prepared solution of either one of them with time. This phenomenon is known as *mutarotation* and results from the structural change within the molecule. On standing, equilibrium becomes established and the specific rotation of the solution becomes constant at $+52.7°$.

Further evidence for the cyclic structure of glucose has been advanced by x-ray analysis of the crystals.

Physical Properties of Glucose

Glucose possesses a sweet taste but this is not quite so immediately distinctive as that of fructose and sucrose.

It is extremely soluble in water but virtually insoluble in alcohol. On crystallizing from warm solutions (98 °C), it yields anhydrous crystals (m.p. 146 °C), and from cold solutions it forms a monohydrate (m.p. 86 °C).

Reactions of Glucose

Glucose undergoes many of the reactions typical of carbonyl compounds, forming hydroxynitriles (cyanohydrins), oximes and phenylhydrazones. The reducing properties of certain sugars with, for example, Fehling's solution and Tollen's reagent, are utilized in their detection, and the formation of osazones provides a useful means of characterization and identification. Furthermore, the reactions of sugars in general provide a considerable amount of information about the structure of the molecules, this being clearly exemplified for glucose by its ability to form α- and β-cyclic glucosides (*see* page 289).

Oxidation

Like aldehydes, glucose is a strong reducing agent, and on warming it readily reduces Fehling's solution, ammoniacal silver(I) nitrate and Tollen's reagent. In addition, it is also oxidized by bromine water to gluconic acid and by the more powerful nitric acid to the dicarboxylic acid, glycaric acid (saccharic acid).

$$\begin{array}{cc}
\text{COOH} & \text{COOH} \\
| & | \\
(\text{CHOH})_4 & (\text{CHOH})_4 \\
| & | \\
\text{CH}_2\text{OH} & \text{COOH} \\
\\
\text{Gluconic acid} & \text{Glycaric acid} \\
& \text{(Saccharic acid)}
\end{array}$$

Reduction

With hydrogen and a nickel catalyst, or sodium tetrahydridoborate(III), or sodium amalgam and water, etc., glucose yields the hexahydric alcohol, sorbitol.

$$\begin{array}{ccc}
\text{CHO} & & \text{CH}_2\text{OH} \\
| & & | \\
(\text{CHOH})_4 & \xrightarrow{2[H]} & (\text{CHOH})_4 \\
| & & | \\
\text{CH}_2\text{OH} & & \text{CH}_2\text{OH} \\
& & \text{Sorbitol}
\end{array}$$

Further evidence for the existence of a straight-chain structure for glucose is provided by its reduction to hexane by hydrogen iodide and red phosphorus at 100 °C.

Acylation

On reacting with excess ethanoic (acetic) anhydride or ethanoyl (acetyl) chloride in the presence of an anhydrous zinc chloride catalyst, glucose yields a pentaethanoyl derivative, indicating the presence of five hydroxyl groups in the molecule.

$$\begin{array}{l} \text{CHO} \\ | \\ (\text{CHOH})_4 \\ | \\ \text{CH}_2\text{OH} \end{array} + 5(\text{CH}_3\text{CO})_2\text{O} \xrightarrow[\text{cat.}]{\text{anhyd. ZnCl}_2} \begin{array}{l} \text{CHO} \\ | \\ (\text{CHOOCCH}_3)_4 \\ | \\ \text{CH}_2\text{OOCCH}_3 \end{array} + 5\text{CH}_3\text{COOH}$$

Pentaethanoyl glucose
(Pentaacetyl glucose)

Addition Reactions of the Carbonyl Group

Glucose forms a hydroxynitrile (cyanohydrin) with *hydrogen cyanide* but gives no reaction with sodium hydrogensulphite. Acid hydrolysis of the hydroxynitrile derivative followed by reduction with hydriodic acid, yields heptanoic acid, further indicating the existence of a straight-chain structure.

$$\begin{array}{l} \text{CHO} \\ | \\ (\text{CHOH})_4 \\ | \\ \text{CH}_2\text{OH} \end{array} \xrightarrow{\text{HCN}} \begin{array}{l} \text{CN} \\ | \\ \text{CHOH} \\ | \\ (\text{CHOH})_4 \\ | \\ \text{CH}_2\text{OH} \end{array} \xrightarrow[\text{(2) HI}]{\text{(1) dil. acid}} \begin{array}{l} \text{COOH} \\ | \\ \text{CH}_2 \\ | \\ (\text{CH}_2)_4 \\ | \\ \text{CH}_2\text{OH} \end{array}$$

Glucose   Hydroxynitrile   Heptanoic acid
derivative
(Glucose
cyanohydrin)

Condensation Reactions of the Carbonyl Group

Hydroxylamine and *hydrazine* condense with glucose to form an oxime and a hydrazone respectively.

$$\begin{array}{l} \text{CHO} \\ | \\ (\text{CHOH})_4 \\ | \\ \text{CH}_2\text{OH} \end{array} + \text{NH}_2\text{OH} \longrightarrow \begin{array}{l} \text{CH}{=}\text{NOH} \\ | \\ (\text{CHOH})_4 \\ | \\ \text{CH}_2\text{OH} \end{array} + \text{H}_2\text{O}$$

Glucose oxime

At room temperature, *phenylhydrazine* reacts with glucose to form the phenylhydrazone, which remains in solution. However, on warming to 100 °C in the presence of a large excess of phenylhydrazine, a yellow precipitate of glucose phenylosazone is formed.

$$
\begin{array}{ccc}
CHO & CH{=}NNHC_6H_5 & CH{=}NNHC_6H_5 \\
| & | & | \\
(CHOH)_4 \xrightarrow{C_6H_5NHNH_2} & (CHOH)_4 \xrightarrow{C_6H_5NHNH_2} & C{=}NNHC_6H_5 \\
| & | & | \\
CH_2OH & CH_2OH & (CHOH)_3 \\
& & | \\
& & CH_2OH
\end{array}
$$

| | Glucose phenylhydrazone (remains in solution) | Glucose phenylosazone (yellow precipitate) |

Osazone formation is particularly useful for characterization and identification purposes.

Glucoside Formation

(*See* 1-Alkoxyalcohol (hemiacetal) formation, page 232.)

Unlike aldehydes, which in the presence of an acid catalyst undergo addition of alcohols to form 1-alkoxyalcohols (hemiacetals) and may subsequently yield the 1,1-dialkoxyalcohol (acetal) by further addition, glucose forms with methanol a crystalline solid which contains only one methyl group.

This product contains no aldehyde group, as indicated by its inability to reduce Fehling's solution or to form osazones with phenylhydrazine, and exists in two anomeric forms. This behaviour can be accounted for in terms of the α- and β-cyclic structures of glucose being in dynamic equilibrium.

α-Glucose Acyclic form β-Glucose

Methyl α-glucose Methyl β-glucose

Methyl α- and methyl β-glucose are called GLYCOSIDES, the anomeric carbon atom sometimes being referred to as the *glycosidic carbon*.

Fermentation

$$C_6H_{12}O_6 \xrightarrow[15\,°C]{\text{zymase}} 2CH_3CH_2OH + 2CO_2$$

Refer to page 169.

Dehydration

When strongly heated, glucose chars and leaves a black, carbon residue. Alternatively, treatment with warm concentrated sulphuric acid brings about fairly rapid dehydration yielding a black mass of sugar carbon.

$$C_6H_{12}O_6 \xrightarrow[-6H_2O]{\text{conc. } H_2SO_4} 6C$$

$$\text{Glucose} \qquad\qquad \text{Sugar carbon}$$

Fructose (Laevulose), $C_6H_{12}O_6$

The naturally occurring form of fructose is laevorotatory (hence its alternative name, laevulose), and is usually found mixed with glucose.

It can be obtained, together with glucose, from the acid or enzyme hydrolysis of cane sugar and separated, as already explained, by dissolving in alcohol.

Industrially, it is manufactured as the only product by the acid hydrolysis of *inulin*, a polysaccharide present in dahlia tubers, artichokes and dandelion roots.

$$(C_6H_{10}O_5)_n + nH_2O \xrightarrow[\text{heat}]{\text{dil. } H_2SO_4} nC_6H_{12}O_6$$

$$\text{Fructose}$$

Structure and Constitution of Fructose

As in the case of glucose, there is evidence for the existence of both chain and cyclic structures of fructose, the former containing three chiral centres (indicated below by the asterisks).

$$
\begin{array}{c}
CH_2OH \\
| \\
C{=}O \\
| \\
HO{-}{*}C{-}H \\
| \\
H{-}{*}C{-}OH \\
| \\
H{-}{*}C{-}OH \\
| \\
CH_2OH
\end{array}
$$

In the crystalline form, only one type of fructose is known, namely the six-membered, cyclic, β-isomer.

The properties of fructose in solution are much more complex than those of glucose, the β-isomer existing in equilibrium with the cyclic α-isomer, with the open-chain structure, and also with a five-membered ring structure. Cyclic isomers of the α- and β-type, differing in configuration of the C_2 atom, i.e. the carbonyl atom of the acyclic structure, are called EPIMERS, and the phenomenon is referred to as EPIMERISM. This category of isomerism is specifically associated with KETOSES.

The six-membered ring structure of fructose is known as a *fructopyranose* and the five-membered ring as a *fructofuranose*.

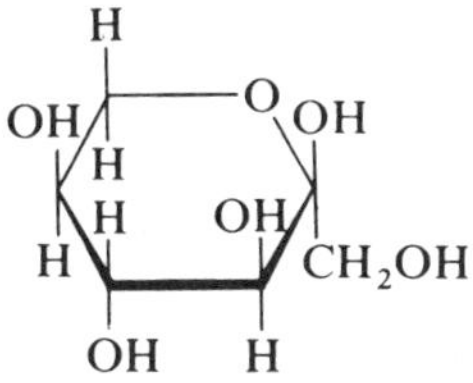

β-fructopyranose,
a six-membered ring structure

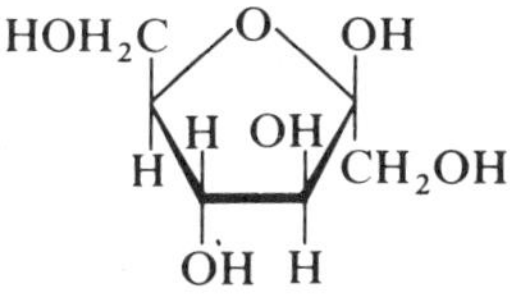

β-fructofuranose,
a five-membered ring structure

More generally, sugars which contain a six-membered ring structure, including the oxygen atom, are referred to as PYRANOSE compounds, and those containing a five-membered ring structure are called FURANOSE compounds, the names being derived from the heterocyclic (i.e. pertaining to a ring structure containing more than one type of atom) compounds PYRAN and FURAN.

Pyran

Furan

These are examples of a special kind of aromatic compound, and may therefore be represented as either of the above structures.

The hexagonal ring structures of glucose and fructose are not in fact flat, the normal pyranose conformation being the *chair* form, as with cyclohexane (*see* page 33).

Physical Properties of Fructose

Fructose is the sweetest of all sugars and is more soluble in water than glucose. It is also reasonably soluble in alcohol, a property which has already been seen to be useful in separating it from glucose, from which it is obtained as colourless anhydrous crystals (m.p. 95 °C).

Reactions of Fructose

Reactions of fructose are fundamentally similar to those of glucose.

Oxidation

In many ways, fructose reflects the reducing powers of an aldehyde, reducing Fehling's solution, ammoniacal silver(I) nitrate and Tollen's reagent, which are not normally affected by ketones. It is not, however, oxidized by bromine water, indicating the absence of an aldehyde group.

Reduction

Like glucose, fructose is reduced to sorbitol.

Acylation

On treating in the same way as described for glucose (*see* page 288). it yields the pentaethanoyl derivative, indicating the presence of five hydroxyl groups in the molecule.

Addition and Condensation Reactions of the Carbonyl Group

Fructose forms a hydroxynitrile derivative (cyanohydrin) with hydrogen cyanide and condenses with hydroxylamine and hydrazine. When warmed with excess phenylhydrazine it yields an osazone, fructose phenylosazone, which is analogous to the corresponding glucose derivative.

Fermentation and Dehydration

Fermentation and dehydration take place as for glucose.

Disaccharides

All disaccharides have the molecular formula $C_{12}H_{22}O_{11}$, the most common being sucrose (cane or beet sugar), maltose (malt sugar) and lactose (milk sugar) which are simply structural isomers of each other. Of these, the most familiar is undoubtedly sucrose.

They are hydrolysed by dilute acid or enzyme action to monosaccharides, with which they share a great number of common reactions.

The molecules of all disaccharides contain chiral carbon atoms, and optical isomers of most of them are known.

Natural Sources of Disaccharides

Sucrose occurs naturally in fruit and plants, the principal source being cane and beet sugar which contain as much as 15 per cent sucrose. Sugar cane is grown in tropical or sub-tropical climates, such as those of the Caribbean or Queensland, whereas sugar beet grows mostly in more temperate zones, for example Northern Europe.

The canes or beet are first shredded and crushed between rollers before extracting with water warmed to about 80 °C. The spent cane, *bagasse*, is used mainly as a fuel or as a source of cellulose for manufacturing synthetic fibres and plastics. The brown syrupy solution obtained is partly purified by treating with lime and carbon dioxide. The precipitated calcium carbonate, in addition to absorbing and carrying down the majority of suspended proteinic impurities, also provides an alkaline medium which prevents any hydrolysis of the disaccharide to glucose and fructose.

After partial evaporation under reduced pressure, the crystalline raw sugar, *brown sugar*, which contains about 95 per cent sucrose, is separated from the mother liquor, *molasses*, in centrifugal baskets. The molasses is used to make treacle or fermented to industrial alcohol and rum. It is also used for manufacturing silage, which provides a useful food for cattle.

The more familiar, and highly pure, white, crystalline form of sucrose is obtained from the final crystallization after treating the raw sugar with steam and then filtering through columns of decolorizing animal charcoal under reduced pressure.

Maltose is formed as an intermediate in the fermentation of starch (*see* page 169) and **lactose** is present in the milk of mammals to the extent of about 5 per cent.

Structure and Constitution of Disaccharides

Disaccharides may be considered as glycosides in which the alcohol substituent is replaced by another monosaccharide, attached via one of its hydroxyl groups.

Maltose and lactose molecules consist of two hexose (or pyranose) units whereas sucrose has a hexose–pentose (or pyranose–furanose) structure.

α-Maltose molecule

Sucrose molecule

Both maltose and lactose exist in α- and β-forms, undergo mutarotation in solution, and are capable of reducing Fehling's solution etc. and forming osazones. These facts all indicate that the structures of the molecules contain a potential 'free' carbonyl group and a hemiacetal ring structure.

Sucrose does not exist in anomeric forms and is a non-reducing sugar, indicating the total absence of a 'free' carbonyl group.

Physical Properties

Sucrose, maltose and lactose are all readily soluble in water, from which they can easily be separated as colourless, crystalline solids, but are virtually insoluble in alcohol. All three are dextrorotatory and are used mainly as foodstuffs.

If sucrose is heated above its melting point, 160 °C, and cooled, it re-solidifies to a solid mass known as '*barley sugar*'. On raising the temperature to about 200 °C, some water molecules are lost and a somewhat softer, brownish substance, *caramel*, is obtained.

Reactions

Many of the reactions of sucrose, maltose and lactose provide a useful means of distinguishing between them.

Hydrolysis

Maltose undergoes acid or enzyme hydrolysis to glucose only, whereas *lactose*, whose molecules contain a glucose structure attached to a galactose structure, yields both of these monosaccharides.

$$C_{12}H_{22}O_{11} + H_2O \xrightarrow[\text{or maltase}]{\text{dil. acid}} 2C_6H_{12}O_6$$

Maltose   Glucose

$$C_{12}H_{22}O_{11} + H_2O \xrightarrow[\text{or lactase}]{\text{dil. acid}} C_6H_{12}O_6 + C_6H_{12}O_6$$

Glucose   Galactose

The *hydrolysis of sucrose*, which is itself dextrorotatory, yields equal proportions of glucose and fructose, known as *invert sugar*, but since the laevorotatory power of fructose is greater than the dextrorotatory power of glucose, an equimolecular mixture of these isomers is therefore laevorotatory overall. Consequently, the extent of the dextrorotatory power of sucrose diminishes as the hydrolysis proceeds until it eventually becomes laevorotatory.

$$C_{12}H_{22}O_{11} + H_2O \xrightarrow[\text{or invertase}]{\text{dil. acid}} C_6H_{12}O_6 + C_6H_{12}O_6$$

Sucrose   Glucose   Fructose

Invert sugar

The process is referred to as INVERSION, and can easily be followed by means of a polarimeter. A study of the acid-catalysed process shows the rate of reaction to be directly proportional to the concentration of the acid.

The enzymes maltase, lactase and invertase are all present in yeast.

Oxidation

Whereas maltose and lactose are both readily oxidized by Fehling's solution, ammoniacal silver(I) nitrate and Tollen's reagent, sucrose is not since it is incapable of forming a 'free' carbonyl group, unless it has previously been hydrolysed to the more powerfully reducing monosaccharides, glucose and fructose. Furthermore, unlike maltose and lactose, which are both oxidized to maltobionic acid and lactobionic acid respectively, sucrose is unaffected by bromine water.

However, on warming with the more powerful oxidizing agent dilute nitric acid, sucrose is oxidized to ethanedioic (oxalic) acid.

Acylation

Sucrose, maltose and lactose all yield an octaethanoyl (octaacetyl) derivative on heating with ethanoic (acetic) anhydride, confirming the presence of eight hydroxyl groups.

Condensation with Phenylhydrazine

Maltose and lactose both form a phenylosazone with phenylhydrazine, but the lack of reducing power and the total absence of a carbonyl group in sucrose is further indicated by its inability to undergo these reactions.

Dehydration

All three disaccharides, on heating above their melting points or by warming with concentrated sulphuric acid, yield a black mass of sugar carbon.

$$C_{12}H_{22}O_{11} \xrightarrow[-11H_2O]{\text{conc. } H_2SO_4} 12C$$

Polysaccharides

Polysaccharides are high relative molecular mass polymers corresponding to a general molecular formula $(C_6H_{10}O_5)_n$ and containing a large number of monosaccharide units linked together in the same way as disaccharides, i.e. by means of a common linking oxygen atom.

Some of the most important and best known polysaccharides include starch, cellulose, inulin and glycogen.

In the vast majority of cases, the actual relative molecular mass is not known and is extremely difficult even to estimate, since all the molecular units in the polymer are not identical in size. Furthermore, changes in structure occur quite readily, even under very mild treatment.

Most are generally insoluble in both water and organic solvents and degradation by hydrolysis is necessary in order to bring them into solution.

Starch

Starch is a polyglucose found in potatoes, rice, cereals and in green plants in general. In animals it functions as a reserve food which can be broken down by the enzymes diastase (amylase) and ptyalin present in saliva, to maltose and dextrin. Further hydrolysis of maltose by the enzyme, maltase, yields glucose. Dextrin is a gum-like substance, 'British gum', and is used in adhesives.

$$(C_6H_{10}O_5)_n + nH_2O \xrightarrow{\text{diastase}} \frac{n}{2} C_{12}H_{22}O_{11}$$

Starch   Maltose

$$C_{12}H_{22}O_{11} + H_2O \xrightarrow{\text{maltase}} 2C_6H_{12}O_6$$

Maltose   Glucose

Starch is apparently insoluble in cold water, but on warming it forms a colloidal mixture which can be separated into two fractions. Examination of these indicates that about 20 per cent is in fact soluble. The *soluble starch*, known as AMYLOSE, has a markedly lower relative molecular mass than the *insoluble form*, known as AMYLOPECTIN, which contains a high degree of branching.

Starch (Amylose), a polyglucose

Reactions of Starch

Starch does not reduce Fehling's solution, ammoniacal silver(I) nitrate or Tollen's reagent, nor does it form an osazone with phenylhydrazine.

With iodine, starch forms an intense dark blue substance which disappears on warming and then reappears on cooling, providing a sensitive test for either iodine or starch.

Cellulose

Cellulose is the principal structural component of the cell walls of plants and, like starch, is a polyglucose containing 1000–1500 glucose units.

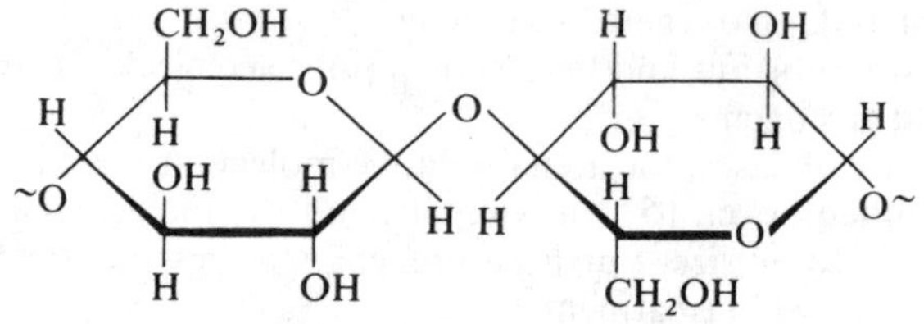

Cellulose, a polyglucose

It is obtained from the cotton plant, wood, straw, bagasse etc., and plays a very important role in the polymers industry (*see* page 299).

QUESTIONS

1. Which one of the following compounds is capable of being oxidized by bromine water?

   A glucose
   B fructose
   C maltose
   D lactose
   E sucrose

2. Give the structures and names, where possible, of the principal products formed when glucose and fructose react with

   A sodium tetrahydridoborate(III)
   B ethanoic (acetic) anhydride
   C methanol
   D a large excess of phenylhydrazine
   E HCN followed by hydrolysis and reduction with HI

3. Briefly discuss the chemical evidence which suggests the existence of a cyclic glucose structure.

4. What do you understand by the terms *anomerism* and *epimerism*? Illustrate your answer with reference to glucose and fructose.

5. Outline the chemical evidence available which suggests the total absence of a 'free' carbonyl group in sucrose.

26 Polymers

The term polymer (Gr. *poly*, many; *meros*, parts) is generally reserved to describe compounds composed of at least several hundred repeating units and possessing relative molecular masses in excess of 5000, although in its broadest sense, polymerization is often used to refer to comparatively simple processes (as has already been seen) such as the cyclization of ethyne, methanal and ethanal.

Different texts group polymers in various ways, two of the more popular systems being to categorize them in terms of either their chemical mode of formation or by their physical properties and form.

The term ELASTOMER is usually applied to rubbers or rubber-like materials which possess definite elastic properties, i.e. the ability to undergo deformation on the application of a force and then to regain the original shape on removing the force. Poly(ethene), although it may be stretched, does not regain its original shape and therefore cannot be placed in this category.

Polymers classified as FIBRES can usually be drawn out as threads and then spun and woven.

PLASTICS are solid compounds which are capable of being moulded, whereas RESINS are solids or semisolids, usually transparent or translucent and possessing a characteristic lustre, which are incapable of being moulded.

The classification of polymers according to these definitions is not strictly adhered to since the terms are often interchangeable. It is mainly for this reason, and to help avoid unnecessary ambiguity, that polymers in this chapter have been classified according to the type of chemical process by which they are formed.

Chemically, there are fundamentally two modes of polymerization: ADDITION POLYMERIZATION in which the product is theoretically an integral multiple of the monomeric reactant molecule(s) and consequently has the same percentage composition, e.g. poly(ethene), poly(phenylethene) (polystyrene); and CONDENSATION POLYMERIZATION, which occurs between two different types of monomers, both of which are usually at least bifunctional in the same group, i.e. each reactant molecule contains a minimum of at least two of the same functional groups, usually in the terminal positions, e.g. Nylon 6.6, and polyesters such as Terylene. If one of the reactants is more than bifunctional, polymerization occurs in three dimensions forming a massively cross-linked structure.

Condensation processes always result in the formation of a copolymer.

Organosilicon polymers (silicones) provide a different, but nonetheless important, type of condensation polymer and are discussed towards the end of this chapter.

Types of Linkages in Polymers

~A—A—A— A—A—A—A~   *Linear polymer,*
                        e.g. poly(ethene)

~A—B—A—B—A—B—A~   *Linear alternating copolymer*
                        e.g. Nylon

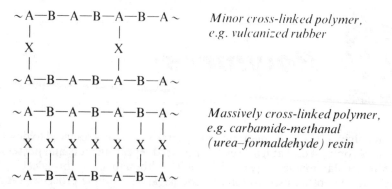

In the above cross-linked polymers, the adjacent groups A, B and X, may be the same or different. Furthermore, the number of units that X represents can vary, and may be numerous.

In addition to forming linear alternating copolymers, copolymerization sometimes occurs to form *random copolymers* and *block polymers*.

$\sim$A—B—A—A—B—B—A$\sim$ *Random copolymer*

$\sim$A—A—A—A—B—B—B$\sim$ *Block polymer*

Copolymers may be formed as a result of either an addition process, e.g. SBR rubber, or a condensation process, e.g. Nylon 6.6.

Copolymerization between two different types of monomers, both of which are capable of forming an addition polymer in their own right, very often leads to the formation of a material that exhibits the beneficial properties of the polymers of both individual monomers, e.g. Vinyon, which is a copolymer of chloroethene (vinyl chloride) and ethenyl ethanoate (vinyl acetate) (*see* page 307).

Effects of Cross-Linking on Physical Properties

Linear polymers and copolymers contain no linkages between the individual chains, although they may possess many branches, and therefore on heating the distance between each chain may increase markedly, causing the polymer to soften and become more flexible. Since the only binding forces between the polymeric chains are weak intermolecular attractions, it requires only a very small change in temperature to overcome them and bring about softening. On cooling, the process is reversed. Polymers of this type are called **thermoplastics or thermosoftening plastics**, e.g. poly(ethene) and poly(chloroethene) (polyvinyl chloride, PVC).

Cross-linked polymers are not softened as easily, since the individual chains are actually bound to each other, and they set hard on heating and cannot be re-melted. Compounds of this type are described as **thermosetting plastics**, e.g. carbamide-methanol (urea-formaldehyde) and phenol-methanal resins. These require very strong heating in order to bring about any form of chemical change.

Polymers with massively cross-linked structures are virtually incapable of softening, although those with only minor cross-linking often exhibit thermo-properties which are intermediate between those of linear and massively cross-linked structures.

Natural and Synthetic Polymers

Nowadays, vast numbers of different types of polymers are made synthetically, although certain natural products such as rubber, wool, cotton and silk are used in what is virtually their raw form, and a great many more can be regenerated from cotton-wool, wood, straw, bagasse etc., by treating with Schweitzer's reagent, an ammoniacal solution of copper(II) hydroxide (Cuprammonium process). The alkaline solution of cellulose is squirted through fine jets into dilute sulphuric acid to destroy the tetraamminecopper(II) complex; the cellulose is precipitated, and can be withdrawn as a thread and spun into a rayon fibre.

Treatment of the above cellulose product with ethanoic (acetic) acid causes hydroxyl groups in the cellulose to be replaced by ethanoate (acetate) groups (Acetate process), and forms a non-flammable material which has a shiny appearance and low water-absorption properties. Different forms of this polymer include cine film and Tricel.

A more favoured technique than the use of the tetraamminecopper(II) complex in the U.K. and U.S.A. is the Viscose process in which the sodium salt of cellulose is treated with carbon disulphide to form a xanthate, which forms a viscous, colloidal solution in dilute alkali. After some time, during which several complex reactions occur, the cellulose is regenerated by treating with dilute acid. This polymer can be obtained as a rayon yarn or in the form of sheets (Cellophane) which can be made soft and pliable by passing them through a solution of propane-1,2,3-triol (glycerol).

A great many more synthetic fibres, artificial silks, lacquers, plastics etc., can be obtained from cellulose. Its derivatives include cellulose nitrate lacquers, cellulose mixed esters, cellulose nitrate plastics and cellulose ethers.

Conditions for Polymerization

The exact conditions used for producing a number of materials commercially are often a closely guarded secret known only to the manufacturers, especially with regard to details as to the nature of the catalyst employed, so that precise information cannot always be stated for every process.

Certain techniques, although basically simple in principle, require extreme conditions, e.g. low-density poly(ethene) requires pressures of up to 3000 atmospheres, and as a result are difficult therefore to simulate in the laboratory. However, many other processes are comparatively simple, both in principle and to perform, and can be carried out under normal or fairly moderate conditions of temperature and pressure, e.g. making Nylon 6.6, Nylon 6.10, phenol–methanal and carbamide–methanal (urea–formaldehyde) resins.

In order to govern the number of repeating units, the degree of branching, or the extent of cross-linking between the chains, the conditions under which a process takes place can often be controlled to 'tailor-make' polymers to suit the purpose for which they are to be applied. For example, the various forms of Nylon can be manufactured as either a fibre or as a solid block, and poly(ethene) can be obtained as a high-density, rigid, crystalline plastic or as a less dense and more flexible material.

There are now so many different polymers available that it would be impossible to discuss more than just a few of them. This chapter attempts to outline the techniques for preparing some of the more important and commonly encountered materials.

Addition Polymers

Natural Rubber

Raw rubber is obtained from LATEX, which is extensively distributed in nature and occurs as a colloidal solution in a white fluid, from which it can be coagulated by simply adding ethanoic (acetic) acid. The vast majority of all latex used commercially is obtained from the rubber tree, *Hevea brasiliensis*, which is a native of the Amazon region of Brazil but is nowadays grown on plantations in different parts of the world, e.g. Ceylon and Malaya.

Natural rubber is a type of hydrocarbon known as a polyterpene, $(C_5H_8)_n$, and exists in two isomeric forms.

cis-Poly(2-methylbuta-1,3-diene)
(*cis*-Polyisoprene)
elastic form

trans-Poly(2-methylbuta-1,3-diene)
(*trans*-Polyisoprene)
non-elastic form

The *cis* isomer has considerable elastic properties whereas the *trans* isomer form, known as gutta-percha (*trans*-poly(methylbuta-1,3-diene)), is non-elastic and when heated above 100 °C, softens to a plastic-like material. Uses of gutta-percha include the coverings for underwater cables and golf balls.

In its raw form, natural rubber contains only a limited number of cross-linkages between each polymeric chain and, as such, exhibits *thermoplastic properties*, i.e. it softens and becomes sticky on heating. On cooling, it becomes hard and brittle.

Vulcanized rubber

These problems can be largely overcome by vulcanizing. This technique was first discovered and introduced by Charles Goodyear (1838), and requires heating the raw rubber with up to 8 per cent sulphur, which forms cross-linkages between the polymeric chains. The *Cold Cure* process of vulcanizing uses a $2\frac{1}{2}$ per cent solution of disulphur dichloride and carbon disulphide.

Accelerators for vulcanizing, which may be organic or inorganic, are used to increase the rate of combination and to allow the process to take place at lower temperatures.

Vulcanized rubber has greater tensile strength, durability and elastic properties over a wide range of temperatures.

The life of rubber articles can be considerably prolonged by the presence of another type of additive, known as *anti-oxidants*, which retard the process of autoxidation. Certain aldehyde–phenylamine (aniline) condensation products are used for this purpose and have an added advantage in that they also possess an accelerating action.

Synthetic Rubbers

The first synthetic rubber to be marketed (U.S.A., 1932) was POLY(2-CHLOROBUTA-1,3-DIENE) (NEOPRENE). Unfortunately, this suffers from the disadvantage that, even today, it is still much more expensive to produce than natural rubber, and is therefore not generally suitable for manufacturing articles such as tyres etc., although since it possesses a high resistance to chemicals and autoxidation it does have certain specialized uses.

The polymer is obtained from ethyne, as outlined below.

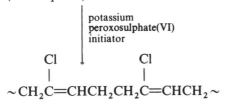

Allowing for the isomeric rearrangement, 1-buten-3-yne (vinyl acetylene) undergoes addition of hydrogen chloride in accordance with Markownikoff's rule (*see* page 107).

The structure is similar to that of gutta-percha, but differs in that the molecules are less sterically hindered and are therefore more flexible and have greater elastic properties.

Copolymers of Buta-1,3-diene

The cheapest commercial source of buta-1,3-diene is the vapour-phase catalytic dehydrogenation of butane, but-1-ene and but-2-ene.

$$CH_3CH_2CH_2CH_3 \xrightarrow[\text{600 °C, 1 atm}]{\text{Al}_2\text{O}_3/\text{Cr}_2\text{O}_3 \text{ cat.}} CH_3CH=CHCH_3$$

Butane   But-2-ene

$$\xrightarrow[\text{phosphates(V) cat.}]{\text{calcium and nickel(II)}} CH_2=CHCH=CH_2$$

Buta-1,3-diene

Buta-1,3-diene forms a number of useful copolymers, two of which are outlined below.

BUNA RUBBER was developed in Germany during the period 1927–33 and was the first high relative molecular mass buta-1,3-diene rubber to be manufactured. The process utilizes sodium as a polymerization catalyst, and in fact the name is contracted from the names of the monomer and the catalyst, *bu*ta-1,3-diene and *na*trium (sodium).

$$CH_2=CHCH=CH_2 + 2Na$$
$$\longrightarrow NaCH_2CH=CHCH_2Na$$
$$\xrightarrow{CH_2=CHCH=CH_2} NaCH_2CH=CHCH_2-CH_2-CH=CHCH_2Na$$
$$\xrightarrow{CH_2=CHCH=CH_2} \text{etc.}$$

SBR (GRS, Buna S or Cold Rubber) is without doubt one of the most universally important and useful synthetic all-purpose rubbers. It is obtained by the free-radical copolymerization of buta-1,3-diene (70 per cent) and phenylethene (styrene) (30 per cent), and was developed during World War II in order to replace unavailable natural rubber.

$$\sim CH_2CH=CHCH_2-CH_2CH=CHCH_2-CH_2CHCH_2=CHCH_2 \sim$$
$$| $$
$$C_6H_5$$

SBR rubber

This product, which can be vulcanized in the same way as natural rubber, has a greater durability than most other synthetic rubbers and is used commercially for manufacturing tyres.

Harder rubbers can be obtained by increasing the percentage composition of styrene.

Poly(ethene) (Polythene)

Simple alkenes polymerize to form a family of long-chain addition polymers. These are strong, flexible solids which may adopt many forms and have a seemingly infinite number of domestic and commercial applications.

POLY(ETHENE) is produced by a number of different techniques, each one producing a polymer with slightly different characteristics. Earlier processes all utilized extremely high pressures, ranging from 1000 to 3000 atmospheres, and temperatures of 200–400 °C.

The *ICI High Pressure Process* requires ethene, containing a trace of oxygen, which serves as a free-radical initiator, to be subjected to a pressure in excess of

1500 atmospheres and a temperature of about 200 °C. The thermal decomposition of organic peroxides may also be used to initiate the reaction.

$$nCH_2\!\!=\!\!CH_2 \xrightarrow[\text{1500 atm, 200 °C}]{O_2\text{initiator}} \sim CH_2\!-\!CH_2\!-\!CH_2\!-\!CH_2 \sim$$

Poly(ethene)

$$n \approx 1000$$

The material produced by this process contains a comparatively large number of branched methyl groups, and is described as *low-density poly(ethene)* ($0.92\,g\,cm^{-3}$).

The *Zeigler Process* requires much more moderate conditions of 50–75 °C and 2–7 atmospheres. Ethene is passed into a hydrocarbon medium containing a suspension of titanium(IV) chloride and triethylaluminium which functions as a catalyst. On completion of the reaction, the catalyst is decomposed by dilute acid and the polymer separated by filtration.

The *Phillips Process* again utilizes a hydrocarbon medium, but in this case the catalyst is chromium(III) oxide promoted by a mixture of silicon(IV) oxide (90 per cent) and aluminium oxide (10 per cent). The conditions of 150–180 °C and 30–35 atmospheres are somewhat more stringent than those employed for the Zeigler process, and the polymeric chains contain rather more branched methyl groups, although still considerably less than those formed by the high pressure technique.

The Zeigler and Phillips products are referred to as *high-density poly(ethene)s* (0.945–$0.96\,g\,cm^{-3}$), and have the polymeric molecules packed more regularly and more closely together to give a more rigid and highly crystalline material, possessing greater tensile strength. In addition, both of these materials have higher softening temperatures than low-density poly(ethene)s, the softening range of Zeigler polymer being 120–128 °C and that of the Phillips polymer being 130–136 °C.

High density poly(ethene)s are formed via *ionic mechanisms*, the principles of these being fundamentally similar to those described for the polymerization of phenylethene (styrene) (*see* page 304).

A copolymer of ethene and ethenyl ethanoate (vinyl acetate) possesses properties closely resembling, and often better than, those of PVC.

Poly(propene)

Poly(propene) can be obtained as both low and high relative molecular mass polymers. The low relative molecular mass compounds are produced by passing propene over a phosphoric(V) acid catalyst on an inert support heated to about 200 °C and subjected to a moderate pressure. This yields a mixture of the trimer, which is used in petrol, and the tetramer.

High relative molecular mass poly(propene) were first prepared in Italy by Giulio Natta (1955). The techniques are very similar to those used for manufacturing high-density poly(ethene).

The polymer obtained consists mainly of a mixture of two isomeric forms, *isotactic* poly(propene) (major constituent), in which all the methyl groups are contained on the same side of the polymeric chain, and *atactic* poly(propene), in which the methyl groups are randomly distributed along the chain.

The isotactic polymer has a number of advantageous properties, being a very low density ($0.906\,g\,cm^{-3}$), highly crystalline material which possesses a very high tensile strength and a high softening temperature (165–175 °C).

The percentage composition of each type of isomer, including other isomers of poly(propene), can be controlled by varying the nature of the catalyst.

Poly(tetrafluoroethene) (PTFE, Teflon, Fluon)

Tetrafluoroethene is obtained commercially by the pyrolysis of chlorodifluoromethane, which, like certain other chlorofluoro-derivatives of methane and ethane, is a valuable refrigerant and is known as *Freon*-22.

$$2CHClF_2 \xrightarrow{700\text{–}900\,°C} CF_2{=}CF_2 \quad + \quad 2HCl$$

Chlorodifluoromethane　　　　Tetrafluoroethane

Polymerization of tetrafluoroethene requires the presence of peroxide initiators and a pressure of 45–50 atmospheres.

$$n CF_2{=}CF_2 \xrightarrow[45\text{–}50\ \text{atm}]{\text{peroxide initiators}} \sim CF_2{-}CF_2{-}CF_2{-}CF_2 \sim$$

PTFE, Teflon

Although Teflon is a thermoplastic it has a high softening point of 327 °C, and is comparatively stable at temperatures in excess of 400 °C. Furthermore, the polymer is also highly resistant to chemicals and possesses an extremely low coefficient of friction, making it especially suitable for manufacturing non-stick cooking utensils and low-friction bearings.

Poly(phenylethene) (Polystyrene)

Benzene provides a useful raw material for commercially obtaining phenylethene (styrene). It undergoes a Friedel–Crafts alkylation reaction with ethene to yield ethylbenzene, which is then cracked to phenylethene.

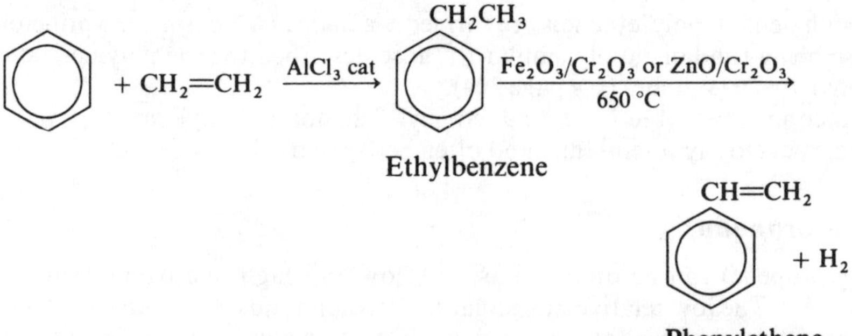

Ethylbenzene

Phenylethene
(Styrene)

Free-radical polymerization of phenylethene (styrene) is brought about by a di(benzenecarboxyl)peroxide (di(benzoyl)peroxide) initiator at a temperature of 85–100 °C.

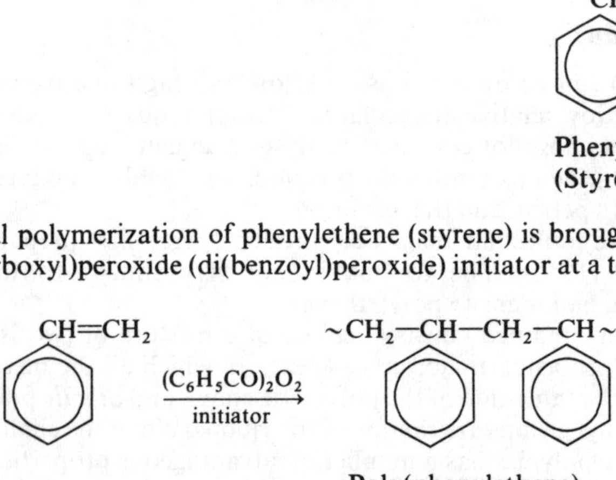

Poly(phenylethene)
(Polystyrene)

This produces a thermoplastic which is soluble in benzene. However, the presence of a trace amount of diethenylbenzene (divinylbenzene), $CH_2=CHC_6H_4CH=CH_2$, causes a high degree of cross-linking to occur and form a material that is no longer a thermoplastic nor soluble in benzene.

Mechanism of Free-Radical Polymerization

The process is initiated by the generation of free radicals, $M\cdot$, by thermal or photochemical (photolytic) decomposition of substances such as organic peroxides, hydroperoxides, azo compounds or even oxygen. The radicals then react with unsaturated monomer molecules to form new free radicals.

$$(1)\ M\cdot + CH_2{=}\underset{\underset{R}{|}}{CH} \longrightarrow MCH_2{-}\underset{\underset{R}{|}}{\dot{C}H} \qquad \text{Chain initiation}$$

The new free radicals then undergo a chain reaction by successively adding on to other monomeric molecules.

$$(2)\ MCH_2{-}\underset{\underset{R}{|}}{\dot{C}H} \xrightarrow{CH_2=CHR} MCH_2\underset{\underset{R}{|}}{CH}CH_2\underset{\underset{R}{|}}{\dot{C}H} \xrightarrow{CH_2=CHR} \text{etc.} \quad \begin{array}{l}\text{Chain}\\ \text{propagation}\end{array}$$

The chain is terminated by any of several types of processes: for example by combination of two free radicals to form an inactive polymer (3), or by collision with a third body, S, (4), which may be any of the other molecules present in the system, or by disproportionation (5).

$$(3)\ M(CH_2\underset{\underset{R}{|}}{CH})_x CH_2\underset{\underset{R}{|}}{\dot{C}H} + M(CH_2\underset{\underset{R}{|}}{CH})_y CH_2\underset{\underset{R}{|}}{\dot{C}H}$$

$$\rightarrow M(CH_2\underset{\underset{R}{|}}{CH})_x CH_2\underset{\underset{R}{|}}{CH}{-}\underset{\underset{R}{|}}{CH}CH_2(CH_2\underset{\underset{R}{|}}{CH})_y M$$

$$(4)\ M(CH_2\underset{\underset{R}{|}}{CH})_x CH_2\underset{\underset{R}{|}}{\dot{C}H} + \underset{\substack{\text{'Third}\\\text{body'}}}{HS} \rightarrow M(CH_2\underset{\underset{R}{|}}{CH})_x CH_2\underset{\underset{R}{|}}{CH_2} + S^* \quad \begin{array}{l}\text{Chain}\\ \text{termination}\end{array}$$

$$(5)\ 2M(CH_2\underset{\underset{R}{|}}{CH})_x CH_2\underset{\underset{R}{|}}{\dot{C}H} \rightarrow M(CH_2\underset{\underset{R}{|}}{CH})_x CH_2\underset{\underset{R}{|}}{CH_2} + M(CH_2\underset{\underset{R}{|}}{CH})_x \underset{\underset{R}{|}}{CH}{=}\underset{\underset{R}{|}}{CH}$$

The combination of free radicals is a highly exothermic process, the surplus energy being dissipated about the bulk of the molecules or transferred to a third body.

The free-radical process is by far the most important mode of polymerization but suffers from the fact that it is extremely sensitive to the presence of impurities. Reactions are usually aided by the addition of 'stabilizers' such as cyclohexadiene-1,4-dione (1,4-benzoquinone).

Polymers formed via free-radical mechanisms include low-density poly(ethene), poly(phenylethene) (polystyrene), PTFE, poly(ethenyl) (polyvinyl) compounds and Perspex, [poly(methyl 2-methylpropenoate)].

Poly(phenylethene) (polystyrene) can be obtained as a transparent solid, but the precise nature of the solid is influenced considerably by the nature of the catalyst and the reaction conditions. It has a high resistance to chemicals and can be expanded to form the familiar, extremely low-density, solid foam by generating gas in the syrup during polymerization. It is used for thermal and electrical insulators, packing protectives, making theatrical properties, decorative purposes and a whole variety of other uses.

In order to keep phenylethene (styrene) in the monomeric form, it has to be stored containing small quantities of certain stabilizers to protect it from undergoing free-radical addition, since polymerization can take place even on contact with air, especially if the phenylethene is in a highly purified state.

In addition to the free-radical process, it can also be obtained via *ionic mechanisms*.

Ionic Polymerization

There are two basic types of ionic polymerization:

(1) *cationic polymerization*, which proceeds via the formation of *carbocation* (*carbonium ion*) and is usually acid catalysed; and

(2) *anionic polymerization*, which proceeds via the formation of a *carbanion* and is usually base catalysed.

Phenylethene (styrene) can be polymerized by either process.

Cationic Mechanism

$$HClO_4 \rightleftharpoons H^+ + ClO_4^-$$

$$CH_2{=}CH \xrightarrow{H^+} CH_3{-}\overset{+}{C}H \xrightarrow{C_6H_5CH=CH_2} CH_3{-}CH{-}CH_2{-}\overset{+}{C}H$$
$$\mid \qquad\qquad \mid \qquad\qquad\qquad \mid \qquad\quad \mid$$
$$C_6H_5 \qquad\quad C_6H_5 \qquad\qquad\qquad C_6H_5 \qquad C_6H_5$$

$$\xrightarrow{C_6H_5CH=CH_2} \text{etc.}$$

Anionic Mechanism

Reaction is catalysed by sodamide, $NaNH_2$, in liquid ammonia.

$$CH_2{=}CH \xrightarrow{NH_2^-} NH_2{-}CH_2{-}\overset{-}{C}H \xrightarrow{C_6H_5CH=CH_2} NH_2{-}CH_2{-}CH{-}CH_2{-}\overset{-}{C}H$$
$$\mid \qquad\qquad\qquad \mid \qquad\qquad\qquad\qquad \mid \qquad\quad \mid$$
$$C_6H_5 \qquad\qquad C_6H_5 \qquad\qquad\qquad\qquad C_6H_5 \qquad C_6H_5$$

$$\xrightarrow{C_6H_5CH=CH_2} \text{etc.}$$

The rate of polymerization and position of the equilibrium depend upon the nature of the solvent, which is usually non-polar.

Ionic processes have the advantage in that they are far less susceptible to impurities than free-radical reactions.

Most of the earlier and commercially viable polymerization processes involve a free-radical mechanism, and it is only since 1953 that the ionic type have come into prominence.

Ethenyl (Vinyl) Polymers

Ethenyl (vinyl) compounds are usually obtained as derivatives of ethyne (acetylene). Refer to Chapter 12, 'Alkynes'.

Poly(chloroethene) (Polyvinyl Chloride, PVC)

There are two principal methods for obtaining chloroethene (vinyl chloride):

(1) $CH{\equiv}CH + HCl$ $\xrightarrow[\substack{\text{charcoal cat.}\\ 120-180\,°C}]{\text{HgCl}_2\text{activated}}$ $CH_2{=}CHCl$
anhyd. Chloroethene
(Vinyl chloride)

(2) $CH_2{=}CH_2 + Cl_2$ $\xrightarrow[\text{solvent, 50\,°C}]{\substack{\text{metal chloride cat.,}\\ \text{CH}_2\text{ClCH}_2\text{Cl}}}$ $CH_2Cl{-}CH_2Cl$
Ethene 1,2-Dichloroethane
(Ethylene dichloride)

$\xrightarrow{500\,°C}$ $CH_2{=}CHCl + HCl$

The former of these two processes is the more economical and is therefore the one usually adopted.

The free-radical mechanism is initiated by heating the chloroethene, suspended under water, with potassium peroxosulphate(VI) or hydrogen peroxide.

$$nCH_2{=}CHCl \xrightarrow[\text{initiator}]{\text{peroxide}} {\sim}CH_2{-}\underset{\underset{Cl}{|}}{C}H{-}CH_2{-}\underset{\underset{Cl}{|}}{C}H{\sim}$$

Poly(chloroethene)
(Polyvinyl chloride, PVC)

PVC is a thermosoftening plastic which can easily be moulded, and it is used in the manufacture of plastic raincoats, curtains, furniture coverings, records, water piping and guttering, and numerous other commonly encountered articles.

Poly(ethenyl ethanoate) (Polyvinyl Acetate, PVA)

The principal sources of ethenyl ethanoate (vinyl acetate) are:

(1) $CH{\equiv}CH + CH_3COOH$ $\xrightarrow[\text{cat., 160-170\,°C}]{(\text{CH}_3\text{COO})_2\text{Zn, charcoal}}$ $CH_2{=}CHOOCCH_3$
Ethyne Ethenyl ethanoate
(Vinyl acetate)

(2) $2CH_2{=}CH_2 + 2CH_3COOH + O_2$

$\xrightarrow[\text{5-10 atm}]{\text{Pd cat., 200\,°C}}$ $2CH_2{=}CHOOCCH_3 + 2H_2O$

Free-radical polymerization can be brought about by ultra-violet light, peroxides, trioxygen (ozone), tetraethyllead(IV) etc.

$$nCH_2{=}CHOOCCH_3 \xrightarrow[\text{initiator}]{\text{peroxide}} \sim CH_2{-}\underset{\underset{OOCCH_3}{|}}{CH}{-}CH_2{-}\underset{\underset{OOCCH_3}{|}}{CH}\sim$$

Poly(ethenyl ethanoate)
(Polyvinyl acetate, PVA)

Each ethanoate (acetate) group possesses exactly the same chemical characteristics as those of simple esters and as a result the polymer readily undergoes acid hydrolysis to poly(ethenol) (polyvinyl alcohol) on warming.

PVA is used in sheets as the middle layer of Triplex safety glass. It also possesses considerable adhesive properties, but its uses are limited in this respect as it tends to be too soft for many practical applications.

Vinyon

Vinyon is a copolymer of chloroethene (vinyl chloride) and ethenyl ethanoate (vinyl acetate).

$$nCH_2{=}CHCl + nCH_2{=}CHCOOH \xrightarrow[\text{initiator}]{\text{peroxide}}$$

$$\sim CH_2{-}\underset{\underset{Cl}{|}}{CH}{-}CH_2{-}\underset{\underset{OOCCH_3}{|}}{CH}{-}CH_2{-}\underset{\underset{Cl}{|}}{CH}{-}CH_2{-}\underset{\underset{OOCCH_3}{|}}{CH}\sim$$

Vinyon

Vinyon fibre exhibits the flexible properties of PVA and has the strength of PVC, although its uses are still limited owing to its comparatively low softening temperature of 65 °C.

Saran

Saran is a copolymer of 85 per cent 1,1-dichloroethene (vinylidene chloride) and 15 per cent chloroethene (vinyl chloride). It is very similar in texture to Vinyon fibre but has the advantage of having a markedly higher softening point (120–140 °C).

$$nCH_2{=}CCl_2 + CH_2{=}CHCl \longrightarrow \sim CH_2{-}\underset{\underset{Cl}{|}}{CH}{-}CH_2{-}\underset{\underset{Cl}{|}}{CCl}\sim$$

1,1-Dichloroethene   Saran

Poly(ethenol) (Polyvinyl Alcohol)

Poly(ethenol) is obtained by the acid hydrolysis of poly(ethenyl ethanoate). The reaction mixture is maintained at 57–59 °C, at which point the methyl ethanoate (acetate) formed distils over allowing the process to go to completion.

$$\underset{\displaystyle \sim CH_2-\underset{\displaystyle OOCCH_3}{\overset{|}{CH}}-CH_2-\underset{\displaystyle OOCCH_3}{\overset{|}{CH}}\sim}{}\quad \xrightarrow[57-59\,°C]{dil.\ H_2SO_4}\quad \sim CH_2-\underset{\displaystyle OH}{\overset{|}{CH}}-CH_2-\underset{\displaystyle OH}{\overset{|}{CH}}\sim$$

Poly(ethenol)
(Polyvinyl alcohol)

It provides a useful intermediate for preparing other polymers, and is also used in a number of other contexts, e.g. making water-soluble coatings and adhesives.

Poly(propenonitrile) (Polyacrylonitrile, Orlon)

The ammo-oxidation of propene provides probably the most efficient and economical method for preparing propenonitrile (acrylonitrile or vinyl cyanide) commercially and has generally superseded other processes. Propene, ammonia, air and steam are passed over a suitable catalyst, e.g. bismuth(III) molybdate(IV) or dodecamolybdophosphate(V) (phosphomolybdate) on silicon, mixed oxides of molybdenum and cobalt on aluminium oxide, or any one of many others, heated to about 450 °C.

$$2CH_2{=}CHCH_3 + 2NH_3 + 3O_2 \xrightarrow[450\,°C]{catalyst} 2CH_2{=}CHCN + 6H_2O$$

Propene $\qquad\qquad\qquad\qquad$ Propenonitrile
(Acrylonitrile or
Vinyl cyanide)

Other methods include:

$$CH{\equiv}CH + HCN \xrightarrow[HCl,\ 80-90\,°C]{CuCl,aq.\ NH_4Cl} CH_2{=}CHCN$$

$$CH_3CHO + HCN \longrightarrow CH_3CH(OH)CN \xrightarrow[-H_2O]{H_3PO_4,\ 600\,°C} CH_2{=}CHCN$$

$$CH_2{=}CH_2 \xrightarrow[Ag\ cat.]{O_2} \underset{O}{\overset{CH_2-CH_2}{\diagdown\diagup}} \xrightarrow{HCN} HOCH_2CH_2CN \xrightarrow[-H_2O]{NaHSO_4,\ heat}$$

$$CH_2{=}CHCN$$

The hydrogen cyanide necessary for the above processes is usually manu-actured from methane and ammonia.

$$2CH_4 + 2NH_3 + 3O_2 \xrightarrow[1000\,°C]{Pt/Rh\ cat.} 2HCN + 6H_2O$$

(Air)

Propenonitrile (acrylonitrile) is used principally for manufacturing acrylic fibres which can be spun into threads from suitable solvents, e.g. *N,N*-dimethylethanamide (*N,N*-dimethylformamide) and *N,N*-dimethyl-ethanamide (*N,N*-dimethylacetamide). One such material *Orlon*, a woolly textured fibre, is used principally for making 'woollen' garments.

$$n CH_2{-}CHCN \xrightarrow[initiator]{peroxide} \sim CH_2-\underset{\displaystyle CN}{\overset{|}{CH}}-CH_2-\underset{\displaystyle CN}{\overset{|}{CH}}\sim$$

Poly(propenonitrile)
(Polyacrylonitrile)

A modified fibre, *Acrilan*, is obtained from poly(propanonitrile) (polyacrylonitrile) by treating it with ethenyl ethanoate (vinyl acetate).

A copolymer of propenonitrile and chloroethene, *Dynel (Vinyon N)*, can be spun into a thread from a propanone (acetone) solvent.

Fairly large quantities of the monomer are used for manufacturing buta-1,3-diene–propenonitrile rubbers and, to a lesser extent, for making plastics.

A fairly recent innovation is an electrolytic technique whereby propenonitrile can be converted into hexane-1,6-dinitrile (adiponitrile), from which hexane-1,6-diamine (hexamethylene diamine), which is one of the substituent monomers of Nylon 6.6, can be obtained by reduction.

$$2CH_2{=}CHCN + H_2 \xrightarrow{\text{electrolysis}} NC(CH_2)_4CN$$

Hexane-1,6-dinitrile
(Adiponitrile)

$$\xrightarrow{4[H]} H_2N(CH_6)_6NH_2$$

Hexane-1,6-diamine
(Hexamethylene diamine)

Perspex (Poly(methyl 2-methylpropenoate)

Perspex is a strong, transparent thermoplastic which has a variety of uses although it is probably most frequently encountered as a replacement for glass.

It is obtainable from propanone (acetone).

$$(CH_3)_2CO \xrightarrow{HCN} (CH_3)_2C(OH)CN \xrightarrow{98\%\ H_2SO_4} CH_2\overset{\displaystyle CH_3}{\underset{}{C}}CONH_2 \cdot H_2SO_4$$

$$\begin{array}{c} CH_3 \\ | \\ {\sim}CH_2-C-CH_2-C\sim \\ | \qquad\quad | \\ COOCH_3\ COOCH_3 \end{array} \xleftarrow[\text{initiator}]{\text{peroxide}} \begin{array}{c} CH_3 \\ | \\ CH_2{=}CCOOCH_3 \end{array}$$

Poly(methyl-2-methylpropenoate)
Perspex

Methyl 2-methylpropenoate

Condensation Polymers

Polyesters

Polyesters are formed by the interaction of a dicarboxylic acid and a diol (a dihydric alcohol), both containing terminal functional groups, e.g. butanedioic (succinic acid) and ethane-1,2-diol (ethylene glycol).

Probably the best known and most important polyester is that of benzene-1,4-dicarboxylic (terephthalic) acid and ethane-1,2-diol, which when spun into the form of a textile fibre is better known as TERYLENE (Dacron or Fortrel). The fibre has properties which have certain advantages over those of natural fibres. For example, fabrics containing Terylene (about 50–75 per cent) and wool are soft and capable of retaining an almost permanent crease, and are therefore popular for manufacturing items of clothing. Terylene may also be obtained in the form of transparent sheets.

The polymer can be obtained from benzene-1,4-dicarboxylic (terephthalic) acid, 1,4-$HOOCC_6H_4COOH$, and ethane-1,2-diol using an acid catalyst to promote the esterification process. The acyl chloride may be used instead of the acid reactant, in which case no catalyst is required.

Transesterification, involving the alcoholysis of dimethyl benzene-1,4-dicarboxylate with ethane-1,2-diol is also commonly utilized as a method of manufacturing the fibre.

$$\text{COOCH}_3\text{-C}_6\text{H}_4\text{-COOCH}_3 + 2\text{HOCH}_2\text{CH}_2\text{OH} \xrightarrow[-2\text{CH}_3\text{O}]{\text{H}^+ \text{ cat.}} \text{COOCH}_2\text{CH}_2\text{OH-C}_6\text{H}_4\text{-COOCH}_2\text{CH}_2\text{OH} + 2\text{CH}_3\text{OH}$$

Dimethyl benzene-1,4-dicarboxylate (Dimethyl terephthalate)

Ethane-1,2-diol (Ethylene glycol)

Dihydroxyethyl benzene-1,4-dicarboxylate (Hydroxyethyl terephthalate)

excess ethane-1,2-diol removed by distillation

$$\sim\overset{\text{O}}{\overset{\|}{\text{C}}}-\!\!\!\langle C_6H_4 \rangle\!\!\!-\overset{\text{O}}{\overset{\|}{\text{C}}}-\text{OCH}_2\text{CH}_2\text{O}\sim$$

Terylene
(A polyester)

Nylon 6.6

NYLON 6.6 is the most popular of all the various available forms of Nylon, and has the distinction of being the first synthetic fibre to be produced commercially (1940) by simple condensation.

It is manufactured from hexane-1,6-dioic (adipic) acid, dissolved in tetrachloromethane (carbon tetrachloride) and an aqueous solution of hexane-1,6-diamine.

$$n\text{H}_2\text{N(CH}_2)_6\text{NH}_2 + n\text{HO}-\overset{\text{O}}{\overset{\|}{\text{C}}}(\text{CH}_2)_4\overset{\text{O}}{\overset{\|}{\text{C}}}-\text{OH} \xrightarrow[\text{crystallize}]{\text{CCl}_4/\text{H}_2\text{O}}$$

Hexane-1,6-diamine

Hexane-1,6-dioic acid (Adipic acid)

$$n\left[\overset{+}{\text{H}_3}\text{N(CH}_2)_6\overset{+}{\text{NH}_3}-\overset{\text{O}}{\overset{\|}{\overset{-}{\text{O}}\text{C}}}(\text{CH}_2)_4\overset{\text{O}}{\overset{\|}{\text{CO}}}^- \right] \xrightarrow[-2n\text{H}_2\text{O}]{200-300\,°\text{C}}$$

$$\sim\text{HN(CH}_2)_6\text{NH}-\overset{\text{O}}{\overset{\|}{\text{C}}}(\text{CH}_2)_4\overset{\text{O}}{\overset{\|}{\text{C}}}\sim$$

Nylon 6.6
(A polyamide)

The polymer is known as Nylon 6.6 since each of the constituent monomers contains six carbon atoms.

The reaction may be performed equally well using hexanedioyl dichloride (adipyl chloride), $ClOC(CH_2)_4COCl$, although this compound is usually only encountered in laboratory preparations. In this case, the polymer is produced together with the elimination of hydrogen chloride instead of water.

NYLON 6.10, which closely resembles the 6.6 polymer, can also be obtained from hexane-1,6-diamine, but using decane-1,10-dioic acid (sebacic acid), $HOOC(CH_2)_8COOH$ (ten carbons) or decane-1,10-dioyl dichloride (sebacoyl chloride), $ClOC(CH_2)_8COCl$, instead of hexane-1.6-dioic acid (adipic) acid. This polymer is especially useful for making synthetic bristles.

Apart from its great versatility, either in the form of a fibre or as a solid block, one of the great attributes of Nylon 6.6 is the low cost involved in obtaining both reactants from relatively cheap sources, e.g. benzene, cyclohexane, cyclohexanol, phenol (which can be easily hydrogenated to cyclohexanol) and cyclohexanone.

Nowadays, hexane-1,6-dioic acid is generally manufactured by the liquid phase air-oxidation of cyclohexane, using cobalt(II) ethanoate (acetate), dissolved in ethanoic (acetic) acid, as a catalyst.

$$\text{Cyclohexane} \xrightarrow[\text{cat., 95 °C, high press}]{O_2,(CH_3COO)_2Co/CH_3COOH} \text{Hexane-1,6-dioic acid (Adipic acid)}$$

Hexane-1,6-diamine is obtained by the reduction of hexane-1,6-dinitrile (adiponitrile), which is obtainable as a derivative of hexane-1,6-dioic acid, or from cyanoethene (vinyl cyanide) (page 310), or from ethyne via the formation of tetrahydrofuran, or from buta-1,3-diene.

$$\text{Hexane-1,6-dioic acid (Adipic acid)} \xrightarrow[\text{vapour phase}]{\text{excess } NH_3, BPO_4 \text{ cat.}} \text{Diammonium hexane-1,6-dioate (Ammonium adipate)} \xrightarrow[-2H_2O]{\text{heat}}$$

Hexane-1,6-diamine $\xleftarrow{4H_2}$ Hexane-1,6-dinitrile (Adiponitrile) $\xleftarrow[-2H_2O]{\text{heat}}$ Hexane-1,6-diamide (Ammonium adipamide)

NYLON 6, sometimes known by the German name, PERLON L, is a polyamide fibre which also possesses properties practically identical to those of the 6.6 polymer. It can be prepared from cyclohexanone, and is softer and has a lower melting point than Nylon 6.6.

Cyclohexanone → (H₂NOH) Cyclohexanone oxime → (20% oleum, heat) 6-Aminohexanoic acid lactam (Caprolactam) ⇌ (tautomers) 6-Aminohexanoic acid lactam (ε-Aminocaprolactam)

$$\sim NH-\overset{\overset{\displaystyle O}{\|}}{C}-(CH_2)_5-NH-\overset{\overset{\displaystyle O}{\|}}{C}-(CH_2)_5 \sim$$

Nylon 6

← (n molecules with a trace of water, prolonged heating 260–275 °C)

Polyurethanes

These polymers contain the urethane group, $-O-\overset{\overset{\displaystyle O}{\|}}{C}-NH-$, and are detained by reacting a diisocynanate with an appropriate diol possessing terminal functional groups. The extent of cross-linking, and hence elasticity, of this type of polymer can be predetermined, and may be increased by choosing a diol containing functional group substituents in the carbon chain of the monomer.

Polyurethanes are used extensively for manufacturing durable paints and varnishes. In addition, both flexible and rigid foams can be manufactured from 2,4- and 2,6-methylbenzene diisocyanates, $CH_3C_6H_3(NCO)_2$, the latter being obtainable from methylbenzene (toluene).

PERLON U is a spun, synthetic, polyurethane fibre which bears a close resemblance to Nylon and is manufactured from hexane-1,6-diisocyanate and butane-1,4-diol.

$$nO=C=N(CH_2)_6N=C=O + nHO(CH_2)_4OH \longrightarrow$$

Hexane-1,6-diisocyanate   Butane-1,4-diol

$$\sim O-\overset{\overset{\displaystyle O}{\|}}{C}-NH(CH_2)_6NH-\overset{\overset{\displaystyle O}{\|}}{C}-O(CH_2)_4 \sim$$

Perlon U

Uses of the fibre are limited owing to its comparatively low melting point (175–180 °C), and it is therefore unsuitable for making articles of clothing.

Phenol–Methanal (Phenol–Formaldehyde) Resins

Condensation between phenol and methanal (formaldehyde) in either an acidic or, preferably, an alkaline solution yields a hard thermosetting plastic, BAKELITE (*see* page 193), which was the first polymer of its type to be produced commercially.

Various other resins may be obtained by the reaction of methanal with different phenols, e.g. benzene-1,3-diol, $1,3\text{-}HOC_6H_4OH$. If 4-substituted phenols, e.g. 4-methylphenol, $1,4\text{-}CH_3C_6H_4OH$, are employed, cross-linking between chains is inhibited and thermoplastics are obtained, unless of course the other substituent happens to be another hydroxyl group.

Carbamide-Methanal (Urea-Formaldehyde) Resins

These are obtained by condensing carbamide (urea) and methanal (formaldehyde) in the presence of an acid or a base catalyst. By carefully controlling the conditions, either linear or cyclic polymers can be obtained.

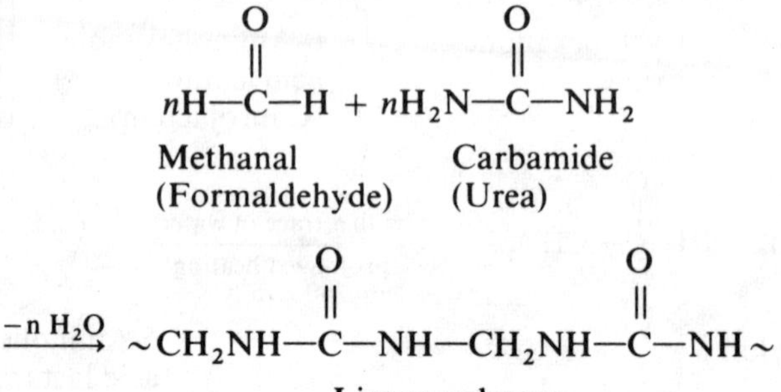

$$nH-\overset{\overset{\displaystyle O}{\parallel}}{C}-H + nH_2N-\overset{\overset{\displaystyle O}{\parallel}}{C}-NH_2$$

<table>
<tr><td>Methanal</td><td>Carbamide</td></tr>
<tr><td>(Formaldehyde)</td><td>(Urea)</td></tr>
</table>

$$\xrightarrow{-n\,H_2O} \sim CH_2NH-\overset{\overset{\displaystyle O}{\parallel}}{C}-NH-CH_2NH-\overset{\overset{\displaystyle O}{\parallel}}{C}-NH\sim$$

Linear polymer

$$
\begin{array}{c}
CONH_2 \\
N \\
\diagup \quad \diagdown \\
H_2C \qquad CH_2 \\
| \qquad\qquad | \\
H_2NOCN \qquad NCONH_2 \\
\diagdown \quad \diagup \\
C \\
H_2
\end{array}
$$

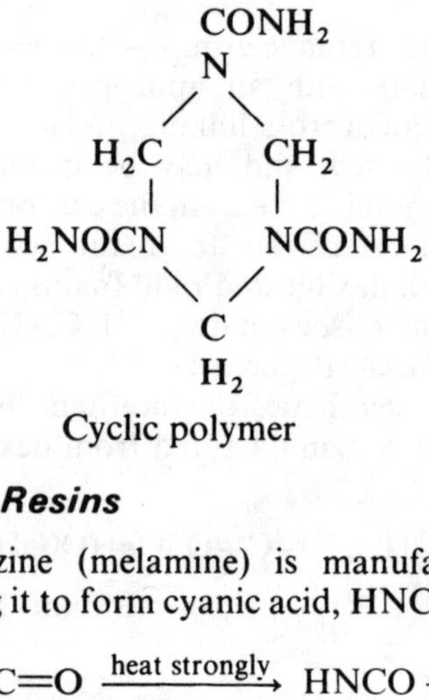

Cyclic polymer

Melamine–Methanal Resins

2,4,6-Triamino-1,3,5-triazine (melamine) is manufactured from carbamide (urea) by strongly heating it to form cyanic acid, HNCO, and ammonia,

$$(NH_2)_2C{=}O \xrightarrow{\text{heat strongly}} HNCO + NH_3$$

and then passing it over a heated catalyst.

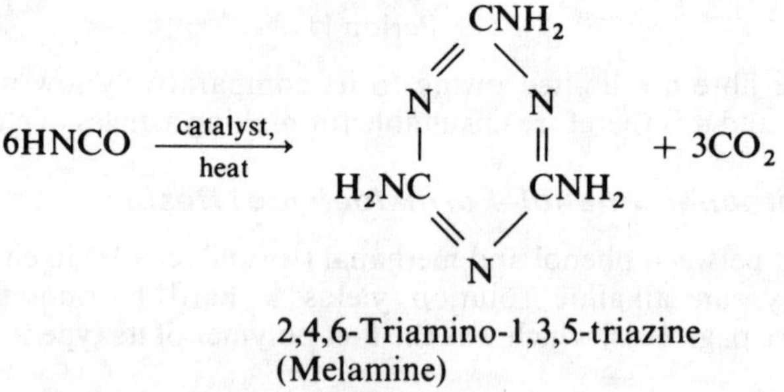

$$
6HNCO \xrightarrow[\text{heat}]{\text{catalyst,}}
\begin{array}{c}
CNH_2 \\
\diagup\!\!\diagup \quad \diagdown \\
N \qquad N \\
| \qquad\quad \parallel \\
H_2NC \qquad CNH_2 \\
\diagdown\!\!\diagdown \quad \diagup \\
N
\end{array}
+ 3CO_2
$$

2,4,6-Triamino-1,3,5-triazine
(Melamine)

The amino groups of melamine, like those of carbamide, condense with methanal to yield high relative molecular mass MELAMINE–METHANAL resins which in many ways resemble carbamide–methanal polymers but are distinguished by their extremely high resistance to heat.

Organosilicon Polymers: Silicones

Silicone polymers are manufactured by hydrolysing alkyl-substituted chlorosilanes, the nature of which determines the type of polymer produced, followed by dehydration. The polymers may possess either fairly simple or very complex structures.

The term silicone originates from the concept held at one time that, when dialkyldichlorosilanes underwent hydrolysis–dehydration, the organosilicon compound produced would have a structure analogous to that of ketones.

$$R_2SiCl_2 + 2H_2O \longrightarrow R_2Si(OH)_2 + 2HCl$$

$$R_2Si(OH)_2 \longrightarrow R_2Si{=}O + H_2O$$

In fact, no compound is known in which silicon forms a multiple bond. Alkylchlorosilanes are prepared by a Grignard reaction

$$SiCl_4 \ + \ RMgCl \xrightarrow{(C_2H_5)_2O} RSiCl_3 \ + \ MgCl_2$$

Silicon   Monoalkyl-
tetrachloride   trichlorosilane

$$RSiCl_3 + RMgCl \xrightarrow{(C_2H_5)_2O} R_2SiCl_2 \ + \ MgCl_2$$

Dialkyl-
dichlorosilane   etc.

or by the 'Direct Process',

$$Si + 2CH_3Cl \xrightarrow[300\,°C]{Cu\ cat} (CH_3)_2SiCl_2$$

the latter being used predominantly to prepare dimethylchlorosilane.

Both processes yield a mixture of products and careful fractional separation is necessary.

The R groups are generally methyl, but they may also be higher alkyl or even phenyl groups.

Trialkylmonochlorosilanes, R_3SiCl, undergo hydrolysis–dehydration to yield a simple, mobile and volatile compound, hexaalkylsiloxane.

$$2R_3SiCl + H_2O \longrightarrow R_3Si{-}O{-}SiR_3 \ + \ 2HCl$$

Hexaalkylsiloxane

Dialkyldichlorosilanes, R_2SiCl_2, polymerize to yield long straight-chain molecules,

$$nR_2SiCl_2 + nH_2O \longrightarrow \ \sim O{-}\underset{\underset{R}{|}}{\overset{\overset{R}{|}}{Si}}{-}O{-}\underset{\underset{R}{|}}{\overset{\overset{R}{|}}{Si}}{-}O{-}\underset{\underset{R}{|}}{\overset{\overset{R}{|}}{Si}}{-}O\sim \ + \ 2nHCl$$

Siloxane chain structure

and *monoalkyltrichlorosilanes*, $RSiCl_3$, form a complex, three-dimensional, cross-linked structure.

$$
n\text{RSiCl}_3 \xrightarrow{\text{H}_2\text{O}}
\begin{array}{c}
\quad\ \text{R}\quad\ \ \ \text{OH} \\
\quad\ | \qquad\ | \\
\sim\!\text{O}\!-\!\text{Si}\!-\!\text{O}\!-\!\text{Si}\!-\!\text{OH} \\
\quad\ | \qquad\ | \\
\quad\ \text{OH}\quad\ \text{R} \\[6pt]
\quad\ \text{OH}\quad\ \text{R} \\
\quad\ | \qquad\ | \\
\sim\!\text{O}\!-\!\text{Si}\!-\!\text{O}\!-\!\text{Si}\!-\!\text{OH} \\
\quad\ | \qquad\ | \\
\quad\ \text{R}\quad\ \ \ \text{OH}
\end{array}
\xrightarrow{\text{dehydration}}
\begin{array}{c}
\quad\ \text{R}\quad\ \ \ \text{O}\!\sim \\
\quad\ | \qquad\ | \\
\sim\!\text{O}\!-\!\text{Si}\!-\!\text{O}\!-\!\text{Si}\!-\!\text{O}\!\sim \\
\quad\ | \qquad\ | \\
\quad\ \text{O}\qquad\ \text{R} \\[6pt]
\quad\ | \qquad\ | \\
\quad\ \text{O}\qquad\ \text{R} \\
\quad\ | \qquad\ | \\
\sim\!\text{O}\!-\!\text{Si}\!-\!\text{O}\!-\!\text{Si}\!-\!\text{O}\!\sim \\
\quad\ | \qquad\ | \\
\quad\ \text{R}\quad\ \ \ \text{O}\!\sim
\end{array}
$$

Siloxane cross-linked structure

The degree of cross-linking and the extent of polymerization of mono-alkyltrichlorosilanes can be controlled by adding calculated quantities of R_3SiCl and R_2SiCl_2. Similarly, the length of the polymeric chain resulting from the hydrolysis–dehydration of dialkyl compounds can be limited by the addition of measured amounts of R_3SiCl, which serve to block the ends of the polymeric structures, to the reaction mixture.

Since in actual practice a rather complex mixture of products is yielded by the above hydrolysis processes, the reactions have been outlined very simply in order to illustrate the formation of the major products.

For straight-chain polymers, boiling points and viscosity increase with increasing relative molecular mass. One of the great assets of these compounds is their resistance to heat, most of them being stable to temperatures of at least 200 °C. This is most significant in phenyl and, to a lesser degree, methyl-substituted polymers. On heating in air to temperatures approaching 400 °C, the polymers become brittle and crack owing to cleavage of the polymeric molecules into smaller chains, some of which adopt cyclic structures.

Silicone polymers are used for manufacturing silicone rubbers, such as methylsilicone rubber, which is far more resistant to chemicals than natural and other synthetic rubbers and is capable of retaining its elasticity over a much wider range of temperature (-90 to $+250$ °C). Silicone resins are used in paints, varnishes and for water-repellent surface coatings. Linear polymers are employed as lubricants and have the advantage over hydrocarbon oils in that the viscosity changes only slowly with temperature. In addition, they find applications in waterproofing textiles, as electrical insulators, in polishes, in glassware and in the manufacture of numerous other materials. One unfortunate drawback is that they tend to be fairly expensive to produce.

QUESTIONS

1. Which one of the following compounds is a polyester?

   A dimethyl benzene-1,4-dicarboxylate
   B poly(ethenyl ethanoate)
   C Nylon 6.6
   D Terylene
   E poly(phenylethene) (polystyrene)

2. In what way does the extent of cross-linking in a polymer affect its physical properties? Give examples.

3. Explain the two basic modes of polymer formation, illustrate your answer with reference to poly(phenylethene) (polystyrene), poly(chloroethene), PVC, Nylon 6.6 and Terylene.

4. Compare and contrast the modes of formation and physical properties of high- and low-density poly(ethene)s. Give the probable mechanism for each process.

Chapter 1. Introduction
1. E

Chapter 2. The Nature of the Atom
1. C   2. D   3. B

Chapter 3. Bonding and Molecular Structure
2. C   3. E

Chapter 4. Naming Organic Compounds
1. A 2-methylbutane
   B 1-chloro-2-methylpentane
   C 2-chloro-2-methylbutan-1-ol
   D 3-chloro-4-methylhexan-2-ol

2. B

Chapter 5. Isomerism and Optical Activity
1. E   2. A   3. D   4. D   5. B

Chapter 6. Structure and Physical Properties
1. B   2. D   3. B

Chapter 7. Reactants and Reactions
1. C   2. A   3. B   4. C

Chapter 8. The Mechanism, Energetics and Kinetics of a Reaction
1. C   2. D

Chapter 9. Identification of Organic Compounds
1. D   2. $CH_3OCH_2CH_3$ 3. C

4. (a) O—H---O stretching (intermolecularly hydrogen bonded such as in I.R. liquid phase spectra of alcohols)
   (b) O—H stretching (free from intermolecular hydrogen bonding such as in I.R. vapour phase spectra of alcohols)

5. A 2 groups, relative areas 5:3
   B 1 group (both methyl groups are equivalent)

C 2 groups, relative areas 3:1
D 4 groups, relative areas 3:2:2:1

6. CH_3 absorption (relative area 3) splits into a doublet
   CH absorption (relative area 1) splits into a quadruplet

Chapter 10. Alkanes (Paraffins)
1. A 2-methylbutane
   B 2,4-dimethylhexane
   C 4-ethyl-2,4-dimethylheptane

2. A $CH_3CHCH_2CHCH_3$ B
       | |
      CH_3 CH_3

(structure for B: cyclopentane ring with $(CH_3)_2$ and CH_3 substituents)

C $CH_3CHCH_2CH_2CCH_2CH_3$
       | |
      CH_3 CH_3
   (with CH_2CH_3 on the central carbon)

D $CH_3CCH_2CHCH_3$
       | |
      CH_3 CH_3
   (with CH_3 above)

3. $CH_3CH_2CH_2CH_2CH_2CH_3$
   Hexane
   $(CH_3)_2CHCH_2CH_2CH_3$
   2-Methylpentane
   $CH_3CH_2CH(CH_3)CH_2CH_3$
   3-Methylpentane
   $(CH_3)_3CCH_2CH_3$
   2,2-Dimethylbutane
   $(CH_3)_2CHCH(CH_3)_2$
   2,3-Dimethylbutane

4. C   5. C   6. E   7. E

8. G,F,A,C,B,E,D

Chapter 11. Alkenes (Olefins)
1. A 2,5-dimethylhex-2-ene
   B cis-but-2-ene

C 3-chloro-3-methylbut-1-ene
D *trans*-1-chlorohex-3-ene

2. A $CH_3CHBrCH_2CH=CH_2$
B $(CH_3CH_2)_2CHCH=CH_2$
C $(CH_3)_3CCH=CHCH_2CH_3$
D $(CH_3)_2CH$ H

3. C   4. A   5. D

6. A CH_3CHICH_3; 2-iodopropane
B $(CH_3)_2CHCH_2Cl$; 1-chloro-2-methyl-propane
C $(CH_3)_3CBr$; 2-bromo-2-methylpropane
D

; 1-bromo-1-methylcyclohexane

7. A 1,2-dichloropropane
B 2-chloropropan-1-ol
C 1-bromopropan-2-ol

Chapter 12. *Alkynes (Acetylenes)*
1. A 4-chlorobut-1-yne
B 4-methylhex-2-yne
C 3-methylhept-1,5-diyne
D 3-ethylpent-1-yne

2. B   3. A

Chapter 13. *Aromaticity and Benzene*
1. D   2. E   3. B

6. D,B,A,E,C

10.A Cl; CHO B NO_2; Br
C NO_2; NH_2 D NR_2; $COOH$
E $COOH$; CH_3 F OH; Br

Chapter 14. *Methylbenzene (Toluene)*
1. A   2. C

Chapter 15. *Halohydrocarbons*
1. E   2. D   3. C

4. A 2- and 4-dibromobenzene; 2- and 4-$C_6H_4Br_2$
B phenylmagnesium bromide; C_6H_5MgBr

C 2- and 4-bromonitrobenzene;
2- and 4-$BrC_6H_4NO_2$
D no reaction
E no reaction
F 2- and 4-bromoethylbenzene;
2- and 4-$CH_3CH_2C_6H_4Br$
G 2- and 4-bromobenzenesulphonic acid;
2- and 4-$BrC_6H_4SO_3H$

7. A S_N2 B E1   C S_N1 D E2

Chapter 16. *Alcohols*
1. E   2. C   3. D

4. A $CH_3CH_2CH_2CH_2CH_2CH_2OH$;
hexan-1-ol
B $(CH_3)_2COHCH_2CH_3$;
2-methylbutan-2-ol
C $(CH_3)_2CHCHOHCH_3$,
3-methylbutan-2-ol
D

CH_2OH; cyclohexylmethanol

Chapter 17. *Phenols*
1. B   2. A   3. C

Chapter 18. *Ethers*
1. C

3. $CH_3CH_2CH_2CH_2OH$, butan-1-ol;
$CH_3CH_2CHOHCH_3$, butan-2-ol;
$(CH_3)_2CHCH_2OH$, 2-methylpropan-1-ol;
$(CH_3)_3CHOH$, 2-methylpropan-2-ol;
$CH_3OCH_2CH_2CH_3$, methoxypropane;
$CH_3CH_2OCH_2CH_3$, ethoxyethane;
$(CH_3)_2CHOCH_3$, 2-methoxypropane

Chapter 19. *Amines and their Derivatives*
1. D   2. C

Chapter 20. *Aldehydes and Ketones*
1. C   2. D   3. E

4. $CH_3CH_2CH_2CHO$, butanal;
$(CH_3)_2CHCHO$, 2-methylpropanal;
$CH_3CH_2COCH_3$, butan-2-one

Chapter 21. *Carboxylic Acids*
1. B

2. A methanoic, ethanoic, propanoic, butanoic

B 2-nitrobenzencarboxylic, benzenecarboxylic, ethanoic, 2-aminobenzenecarboxylic

C trifluoroethanoic, trichloroethanoic, monochloroethanoic, ethanoic

Chapter 22. Derivatives of Monocarboxylic Acids

1. C   2. D

3. $CH_3CH_2CH_2COOCH_3$;
$(CH_3)_2CHCOOCH_3$;
$CH_3CH_2COOCH_2CH_3$;
$CH_3COOCH_2CH_2CH_3$;
$CH_3COOCH(CH_3)_2$;
$HCOOCH_2CH_2CH_2CH_3$;
$HCOOCH_2CH(CH_3)_2$;
$HCOOC(CH_3)_3$;
$HCOOCH(CH_3)CH_2CH_3$

Chapter 23. Sulphonic Acids

1. D

Chapter 24. Amino Acids, Proteins and Polypeptides

1. C

Chapter 25. Carbohydrates

1. A

Chapter 26. Polymers

1. D

Index

Index

ABSORPTION BANDS, INFRA-RED, IDENTIFICATION, 70
Accelerators, vulcanizing, 136, 206, 301
Acetaldehyde (see Ethanal)
Acetaldoxime (Ethanal oxime), 235
Acetals (1,1-Dialkoxyalkanes), 227, 232
α-Acetamidoacetic (2-Ethanamidoethanoic) acid, 281
Acetamido (Ethanamido) group, 217
Acetanilide (N-Phenylethanamide), 217
Acetic acid (see Ethanoic acid)
Acetic (Ethanoic) anhydride, industrial source, 264
Acetone (see Propanone)
Acetophenone (Phenylethanone), 135, 228
Acetoxime (Propanone oxime), 235
Acetyl (Ethanoyl) chloride (see also Acyl chlorides), 178
Acetylene (Ethyne) (see Alkynes)
Acetylene dihalides (1,2-Dihaloethenes), 117
Acetylenes (see Alkynes)
Acetylene tetrahalides (1,1,2,2-Tetrahaloethanes), 117
Acetylsalicylic acid (Aspirin), 192
Acid anhydrides, 263–5
  industrial source, 264
  nomenclature, 263
  physical properties, 263
  reactions, 265
  symmetrical (simple), 263
  synthetic preparations, 264
  unsymmetrical, 263
Acidity constant, 41
Acids, 40
  Brønsted-Lowry, 40
  Lewis, 41
  strengths, 41
Acrilan, 310
Acrylonitrile (Propenonitrile, Vinyl cyanide), 118, 309
Activated complex, 49
Activating effects, benzene ring, 137
Activation energy, 49
Activity (Active mass), 41
Activity coefficient, 42
Acylation (see also Friedel-Crafts acylation), amino acids, 281
  amines, 211
  disaccharides, 294
  fructose, 292
  glucose, 288
  phenol, 191
  phenylamine (aniline), 211
Acyl chlorides, 259–63

nomenclature, 260
physical properties, 260
reactions, 261
synthetic preparations, 257, 260
Acyl group, 259
Acyl-hydroxy fission, carboxylic acids, 255
Addition-elimination (Condensation) reactions, 135, 229, **234**, **261**, 288, 292, 294
Addition reactions, 45
Adipic (Hexane-1,6-dioic) acid, 311
  manufacture, 312
Adiponitrile (Hexane-1,6-dinitrile), 310, 312
Adipyl chloride (Hexanedioyl dichloride), 312
Alanine (2-Aminopropanoic acid), optical isomers, 30
Albumins, 278
Alcohol, absolute, 169
  commercial, 109, 169
Alcohols, 166–80
  acid strength, 173
  aromatic, definition, 166
  basic strength, 172
  classification, 166
  dihydric, 166
  hydrogen bonding, 37, 167
  industrial source, 168
  monohydric, 166
  nomenclature, 167
  physical properties, 168
  pK_a values, 173
  polyhydric, 166
  reactions, 172
  synthetic preparations, 170
  trihydric, 166
Aldehyde ammonia, 234
Aldehyde cyanohydrins (2-Hydroxyalkanonitriles), 230
Aldehyde 2,4 dinitrophenylhydrazone, 236
Aldehyde group, 220
Aldehyde hydrazone, 235
Aldehyde hydrogensulphite (bisulphite), 231
Aldehyde phenylhydrazone, 236
Aldehydes, 106, 220–46
  distinguishing (from ketones), 243
  industrial source, 223
  nomenclature, 221
  physical properties, 222
  reactions, 228
  synthetic preparations, 163, 191, **225**, 262
Aldol condensation, 240
Aldoses, 284
Aliphatic compounds, 122
Alizarin, 1

Alkanes, 87–97
  cracking, 93
  cyclo-, 96
  isomerism, 87
  nomenclature, 24, 87
  physical properties, 88
  reactions, 93
  symmetrical, 92
  synthetic preparations, 91
Alkene bromohydrin (Bromoalcohol), 103
Alkene oxide (Epoxyalkane), 105
Alkenes, 98–113
  industrial source, 100
  isomerism, 99
  mixed products, 102
  nomenclature, 98
  orientation of addition, 107
  physical properties, 100
  reactions, 102
  rôle in industry, 109
  stability, 108
  synthetic preparations, 100
Alkoxide (Alkylate) ion, 172
1-Alkoxyalcohol (Hemiacetal), 232, 289
Alkoxy-hydrogen fission, alcohols, 172, 255
Alkylate (Alkoxide) ion, 172
Alkylation (*see also* Friedel-Crafts alkylation), phenols, 190
Alkylbenzenes, 135, 142
Alkylchlorosilanes, 315
Alkyldiazonium ion, 213
Alkyl group, 43
Alkyl halides (*see* Haloalkanes)
Alkyl hydrogensulphate, 104
Alkyl-hydroxy fission, alcohols, 172
Alkylmagnesium halide (*see* Grignard reagent)
Alkylphenols, 190
Alkynes, 114–21
  industrial source, 115
  nomenclature, 114
  physical properties, 115
  reactions, 116
  structure, 20, 114
  synthetic preparations, 116
Allyl halides, 149
Amide formation, 211, 257, 261, 265, 267, 269
Amides, 268–71
  classification, 268
  industrial source, 269
  nomenclature, 268
  physical properties, 268
  reactions, 269
  synthetic preparations, 211, 257, 261, 265, 267, **269**
Amine formation, 157, 206
Amine nitrite, 214
Amines, 201–19
  aromatic, 201, 203
  basic strength, 208
  classification, 201
  industrial source, 205
  nomenclature, 202
  physical properties, 204

pK_b values, 209
  reactions, 208
    with nitrous acid, 213
  structure, 201
  synthetic preparations, 157, 206
2-(α-)Amino acids, 278–83
  classification, 279
  nomenclature, 279
  physical properties, 280
  reactions, 280
  stereochemistry, 279
  synthetic preparations, 280
2-, 3- and 4-Aminobenzenesulphonic acids, 217
Aminoethanoic acid (Glycine), 279, 280
  acidic and basic strengths, 281
6-Aminohexanoic acid lactum (ε-Aminocaprolactam), 313
2-Aminopropanoic acid (Alanine), optical isomers, 30
Ammonia, addition to aldehydes, 234
Ammonium adipamide (Hexane-1,6-diamine), 311, 312
Ammonium adipate (Diammonium hexane-1,6-dioate), 312
Ammonium cyanate, 2, 271
Ammonium sodium 2,3-dihydroxybutanedioate (tartrate), 31
Aniline (*see* Phenylamine and Amines, aromatic)
Anilinium (Phenylammonium) ion, 205, 210
Anils (*see* Schiff bases)
Anionic polymerization, 306
Anisole (Methoxybenzene), 156, 195, 197
Anomeric carbon atom, 286
Anomerism, 286
Anthracene, 131
Anti-bonding orbital, 16
Anti-knock additives, 91, 110, 151
Anti-Markownikoff product, 109, 117
Anti-oxidants, 136, 206, 301
Arenes, 142
Armstrong, 123
Aromaticity, criteria, 122
Aryl groups, 127
Aryl halides, 148–65
  nomenclature, 149
  physical properties, 150
  reactions, 153
  structure, 154
  substitution in ring, 160
  synthetic preparations, 151
Asphalt (Bitumen), 90
Aspirin (2-Ethanoyloxybenzenecarboxylic acid or Acetylsalicylic acid), 192
Asymmetric (Chiral) carbon atom, **29**, 31, 159, 284, 286, 290
Atom, modern concepts, 7
  nature, 5
Aufbau principle, 12
Autoxidation, ether, 199
Axial bonds, 33
Azimuthal quantum number, 8

Azines, 235
Azo compounds, 136, 216
Azo-dyes, 136, 216
  soluble, formation, 276

BAGASSE, 292
Bakelite, **193**, 224, 313
Baking process, 217
Barley sugar, 293
Barrier to rotation, 21, 33
Bases, 40
  Brønsted-Lowry, 40
  Lewis, 41
  strengths, 41
BASF process (*see* Sachse process)
Basicity constant, 42
Beilstein's test, 62
Bending vibrations, 68
Benzal chloride ((Dichloromethyl)benzene),
  144, 225
Benzene, 119, 122–41
  addition vs. substitution, 129
  derivatives, nomenclature, 126
  enthalpy of hydrogenation, 128
  industrial source, 130
  physical properties, 130
  reactions, 132
  resonance energy, 128
  resonance theory, 124
  ring stability, 128
  structure, 122–5
  synthetic preparations, 131
  ultra-violet spectrum, 68
Benzencarbaldehyde (Benzaldehyde), industrial
  source, 225
Benzenecarbonyl (Benzoyl) chloride, structure,
  261
Benzenecarbonylation (Benzoylation), 211
Benzencarboxylate (Benzoate) anion, 253
Benzenecarboxylic (Benzoic) acid, 145
  industrial source, 250
Benzenediazonium compounds, 136, 215
  reactions, 215
Benzene-1,2-dicarboxylic (Phthalic) acid, 247
Benzene-1,4-dicarboxylic (Terephthalic) acid,
  311
Benzene-1,2-dicarboxylic (Phthalic) anhydride,
  250
Benzene-1,3-disulphonic acid, 274
Benzene hexabromide (1,2,3,4,5,6-
  Hexachlorocyclohexane), 134
Benzene hexachloride (1,2,3,4,5,6-
  Hexachlorocyclohexane), 134
Benzenesulphonic acid (*see also* Sulphonic
  acids), 134
  pK_a value, 275
Benzenesulphonyl chloride, 275
Benzene-1,3,5-trisulphonic acid, 274
Benzoate (Benzenecarboxylate) anion, 253
Benzoic (Benzenecarboxylic) acid, 145
  industrial source, 250
Benzole, 130
Benzonitrile (Benzenecarbonitrile), 216

formation, 276
Benzoylation (Benzenecarbonylation), 211
Benzoyl (Benzenecarbonyl) chloride, structure,
  261
Benzyl alcohol (*see* Phenylmethanol)
Benzyl chloride ((Chloromethyl)benzene), 144
Bimolecular reactions, 52
Bisulphite (Hydrogensulphite) compounds, 231
Bitumen (Asphalt), 90
Biuret test, 271, 282
Block polymers, 298
Boiling points, 37
Bond energies, carbon-carbon, 21
  length, carbon-carbon, 20
    benzene, 128
  order, 129
  strength, carbon-carbon, 21
Bonds, axial, 33
  equatorial, 33
Brady's reagent, 236
Branched-chain isomerism (*see* Chain
  isomerism)
Bromic(I) (Hypobromous) acid, 103
Bromination (*see* Halogenation)
Bromine water, 103
o- and *p*-Bromoacetophenone (2-and 4-
  Bromophenylethanone), 161
Bromoalcohol (Alkene bromohydrin), 103
o- and *p*-Bromoaniline (Bromophenylamine),
  218
Bromobenzene, 134, 216
2- and 4-Bromobenzenesulphonic acid, 161
3-Bromobenzenesulphonic acid, 277
Bromoethane (Ethyl bromide), hydrolysis, 159
Bromoethane (Methyl bromide), hydrolysis, 51
Bromoform (Tribromomethane), 238
  industrial source, 151
Bromo-2- and Bromo-4-methylbenzene
  (Bromotoluene), 138, 161
Bromo-3-nitrobenzene, 138
Bromo-2- and Bromo-4-nitrobenzene, 161
2- and 4-Bromophenol, 190
2- and 4-Bromophenylamine (Bromoaniline),
  218
2- and 4-Bromophenylethanone
  (Bromoacetophenone), 161
1-Bromopropane, 109
o- and *p*-Bromotoluene (Bromo-2-and Bromo-
  4-methylbenzene), 138, 161
Brønsted-Lowry, acids and bases, 40
Brown sugar, 292
Buiret test, 271, 282
Buna rubber, 302
Buna S rubber, 302
Buta-1,3-diene, 119, 302
  copolymers, 302
Butane-1,4-dioic (Succinic) acid, 246
Butane-1,4-diol, 119, 313
Butanes, structural isomers, 26
Butan-1-ol, mass spectrum, 83
Butan-2-ol, 175
  optical isomers, 29
Butanols (Butyl alcohols), structural isomers, 26
  chromatogram of mixture, 60

Butanone (Ethyl methyl ketone), industrial
source, 225
But-1-ene, 102, 175
But-2-ene, 102, 175
cis-Butenedioic (Maleic) acid, 28
physical properties, 28
reduction, 28
trans-Butenedioic (Fumaric) acid, 28
physical properties, 28
Butenes, positional isomers, 99
stability, 176
1-Buten-3-yne (Vinyl acetylene), 119, 301
Butylamines, structural isomers, 204
Butyne-1,4-diol, 119

CADMIUM DIALKYL COMPOUNDS (*see* Organo-
cadmium compounds)
Cannizzaro reaction, 171, 241
Canonical forms, 124
Caprolactam, 313
Caramel, 293
Carbamide (Urea), 2, 270
Carbamide-methanal (Urea-formaldehyde)
resins, 314
Carbanions, 229, 239, 306
Carbocation (Carbonium ion), 102, 107, 158,
172, 306
Carbohydrates, 283–96
classification, 283
configuration, 284
nomenclature, 283
Carbolic acid (*see* Phenol)
Carbon, unique nature, 2
valency, 14
Carbonation, 191, 251
Carbon atom, alpha, 48
chiral, 29, 31
classification, 88
electronic structure, 11
Carbon-carbon double bond, 19
Carbon-carbon single bond, 18
free rotation, 21
Carbon-carbon triple bond, 19
Carbonium ion (Carbocation), 102, 107, 158,
172, 306
Carbon tetrachloride (Tetrachloromethane), 95
Carbonyl compounds, 220–45
Carbonyl group, 220
polarity, 221
structure, 220
Carbonyl hydrogensulphites, 231
Carboxylate anion, 248, 253
stability, 248, 253
Carboxyl group, 246, 248
Carboxylic acids, 246–58
acidic strengths, 253
effect of media, 254
aromatic, 248
hydrogen bonding, 38, 248
2- or α-hydroxy, 230
industrial source, 249
nomenclature, 247
physical properties, 249

pK_a values, 253
reactions, 252
structure, 248
synthetic preparations, 250
Carius' method, halogens, 64
sulphur, 64
Casein, 278
Catalyst, halogen carrier, 134
'poisoned' (Lindlar), 117, 228, 262
Catenation, 3
Cationic polymerization, 306
Celite, 57
Cellophane, 299
Cellosolve, 111
Cellulose, 296
Centrifuging, 55
Chain initiation, 93, 94
Chain (Branched-chain) isomerism, 26
Chain length (kinetic term), 93
Chain propagation, 93, 94
Chain reaction, 93, 94
self propagating, 93, 94
Chain termination, 93, 94
Chemical shift, 79
Chiral centre, **29**, **31**, 159, 284, 286, 290
Chloral (Trichloroethanol), 175, 238
Chloral hydrate (2,2,2-Trichloroethanediol), 238
Chlorination (*see* Halogenation)
Chloroacetic (Chlorethanoic) acid, 253, 256, 280
Chlorobenzene, structure, 154
2-Chlorobuta-1,3-diene (Chloroprene), 119, 301
2-Chlorobutane, optical isomers, 29
Chlorodifluoromethane, 151, 304
Chloroethane, industrial source, 151
Chloroethanoic (Chloroacetic) acid, 253, 256,
280
2-Chloroethanol (Ethylene chlorohydrin), 111
Chloroethene (Vinyl chloride), 112, 307
Chloroform (Trichloromethane), 94, 238
infra-red spectrum, 73
Chloromethane (Methyl chloride), 94
dipole moment, 36
industrial source, 150
(Chloromethyl)benzene (Benzyl chloride), 144
Chloro-2- and Chloro-4-methylbenzene (*o-* and
p-Chlorotoluene), 145
Chloroprene (2-Chlorobuta-1,3-diene), 119, 301
Chromatogram, 56
Chromatography, 56
adsorption column, 56
adsorbents, 56
eluants, 56
gas, 58
gas/liquid, 58
gas/solid, 58
ion exchange, 56
paper, 57
partition, 57
thin layer, 57
cis Configuration, 23, 99
Citric (2-Hydroxypropanone-1,2,3-
tricarboxylic) acid, 1
Clemmensen reaction, 242

Coal gas, 130
Coal tar, **130**, 142, 184
  fractional distillation, 130
Cold Cure process, 301
Cold rubber, 302
Combustion, alkanes, 95
Competitive reactions, 137
Condensation (Addition-elimination) reactions, 135, 229, **234, 261**, 288, 292, 294
Configuration, absolute, 284
  2- or α-amino acids, 279
  cis, 23, 99
  2,3-dihydroxybutanedioic (tartaric) acid, 31
  disaccharides, 293
  fructose, 290
  glucose, 286
  inversion, 30
  trans, 23, 99
Conformations, 21
  boat, 33
  chair, 33
  eclipsed, 21
  staggered, 21
Conjugative effect (*see* Mesomeric effect)
Copymerization, 297
Copolymers, 120, 297
  buta-1,3-diene, 302
  linear, 297
  random, 298
Coper(I) dicarbide (acetylide), 120
Coupling reactions, 136, 215, 216
Covalent bond formation, 16
  pi, 17
  sigma, 17
Cracking (Pyrolysis), alkanes, 93
  petroleum, 93, 100, 115, 183
  propane, 93
Creosote, 131
Cross-linking, 297
  effect on physical properties, 298
Cumene ((1-Methylethyl)benzene), 183
Cumene hydroperoxide ((1-Methylethyl)benzene hydroperoxide), 184
Cuprammonium process, 299
Cyanic acid, 314
Cyanide (Nitrile) formation, 157
Cyanohydrin (2-Hydroxyalkanonitrile) formation, 230, 231
  synthesis of 2- or α-amino acids, 280
Cycloalkanes, 95
  orientation, 96
  physical properties, 96
  reactions, 96
Cyclobutane, 96
Cyclohexane, 96, 312
  conformations, 33
  infra-red spectrum, 72
Cyclohexanone, 220, 313
Cyclopentane, 96
Cyclopropane, 96

DACRON (Terylene, Fortrel), 310
Deactivating effect, benzene ring, 138

De Broglie, 6
Decane-1,10-dioic (Sebacic) acid, 312
Decarboxylation, calcium salts, 227
  carboxylic acids, 228
  sodium salts, 92, 258
Dehydration, alcohols, 101, 175
  partial, 176, 198
  disaccharides, 295
  fructose, 292
  glucose, 290
Dehydrogenation, ethanol, 224
  methanol, 223
  propan-2-ol, 224
Dehydrohalogenation, haloalkanes, 101, 160
Delocalization, 125
Delocalization energy (*see* Resonance energy)
Denaturation, 278
Detector, flame ionization, 60
Detergents, 267, 277
Dewar structures, benzene, 124
Dextrin, 295
Dialkoxyalkanes (Acetals), 227, 232
Dialkyl cadmium compounds (*see* Organo-cadmium compounds)
Dialkyldichlorosilanes, 315
Diamines, 201
Diammonium hexane-1,6-dioate (Ammonium adipate), 312
Diastase, 169, 286, 295
Diastereoisomerism, 31
Diazonium compounds (*see also* Benzenediazonium compounds), 136
Diborane, 257
1,2- and 1,4-Dibromobenzene, 161
Dicarboxylic acids, 247
Dichloroacetic (Dichloroethanoic) acid, 256
Dichlorodifluoromethane, 151
1,2-Dichloroethane (Ethylene dichloride), 307
  industrial source, 110
Dichloroethanoic (Dichloroacetic) acid, 256
1,1-Dichloroethene (Vinylidene chloride), 308
Dichloromethane, 94
(Dichloromethyl)benzene (Benzal chloride), 144
Diesel oil, 90
Diethyl ether (*see* Ethoxyethane)
gem—Dihalides, 149
vic—Dihalides, 149
1,1-Dihaloethanes (Ethylidene dihalides), 117
1,2-Dihaloethenes (Acetylene dihalides), 117
2,3-Dihydroxybutanedioic (Tartaric) acid, 1
  configuration, 31
  optical isomers, 31
Dihydroxyethyl benzene-1,4-dicarboxylate (Hydroxyethyl terephthalate), 311
Dimerization, ethyne, 119
N,N-Dimethylaniline (*N,N*-Dimethylphenylamine), 214
Dimethylbenzenes (Xylenes), 146
Dimethyl benzene-1,4-dicarboxylate (Dimethyl terephthalate), 311
Dimethylchlorosilane, 315
N,N-Dimethylphenylamine (*N,N*-Dimethylaniline), 214

1,3-Dinitrobenzene, 133, 137
2,4-Dinitrophenylhydrazine, 236
2,4-Dinitrophenylhydrazones, 236
Diols (Glycols), 105, 111, 166
Dioxan, 111
Dipolar ion (Zwitterion), 280
Dipole-dipole interactions, 36, 38
Dipole moment, 35
Directive effects (in monosubstituted benzenes), 137
Direct process, 315
Disaccharides, 283, 292
   constitution, 293
   natural sources, 292
   physical properties, 293
   reactions, 293
   structure, 293
Distillation, fractional, 55
   molecular, 55
   simple, 55
   steam, 55
Dumas' method, relative molecular mass, 65
   nitrogen, 63
Dyestuffs, 137, 216, 276
Dynel, 310

E1 REACTIONS, 160
E2 reactions, 160
Elastins, 278
Elastomers, 297
Electromeric effect, 47
Electron, dual nature, 6
Electronegativity, 2
   table, Pauling's values, 2
Electronic build-up (*see* Hund's rule)
Electronic effects, 46
   electromeric, 47
   inductive, 46
   mesomeric, 47
Electronic structure, excited state, 14
   ground state, 11
Electrons, energy levels, 6, 12
   opposed (paired), 7
Electron spin, 7
Electrophiles, 41
Electrophilic addition, alkenes, 102
   alkynes, 116
Electrophilic substitution, alcohols, aromatic. 173
   aldehydes, aromatic, 140, 245
   aryl halides, 160
   benzene, 132-40
   methylbenzene (toluene), 137, 138, 143, 145
   phenol, 139, 184, 186
   phenylamine (aniline), 139, 210, 217
   sulphonic acids, 275
Elements, tests for, 61
Elimination, Hofmann, 212
   Saytzeff, 176, 212
Elimination reactions, 45, 116
   alcohols, 100, 175, 176
   haloalkanes, 101, 159

Elimination vs. substitution, 160
Empirical formula, determination, 64
Enantiomers (Enantiomorphs), 29
   physical properties, 29
Endothermic reactions, 50
Energetics of reaction, 49
Energy, pairing, 11
   resonance, 128
Energy curves, 50
Enol structure, 27, 118, 229
Enthalpy of reaction, 50
Epimerism, 291
Epoxides, 111, 195
Epoxyalkane (Alkene oxide), 105
Epoxyethane (Ethene oxide), 195
   industrial source, 111
Epoxypropane (Propene oxide), 110
Equatorial bonds, 33
Ester exchange, 268
Esterification, **156**, 177, 186, **255**. 261, 266, 276, 282
   Fischer-Speier, 186, 255, 266
   steric factors influencing, 48
Esters, 265–8
   industrial source, 266
   nomenclature, 265
   physical properties, 266
   reactions, 266
   synthetic preparations, 156, 177, **255**, 261, **266**, 276, 282
Ethanal (Acetaldehyde), 118
   industrial source, 224
   synthetic preparations, 225
Ethanal oxime (Acetaldoxime), 235
Ethanal tetramer (Metaldehyde), 233
Ethanal trimer (Paraldehyde), 23
2-Ethanamidoethanoic (α-Acetamidoacetic) acid, 281
Ethanamido (Acetamido) group, 217
Ethane (*see also* Alkanes), conformational isomers, 21
   structure, 18
Ethanedioic (Oxalic) acid, 246
Ethanoic (Acetic) acid, 48, 246
   glacial, 249
   industrial source, 250
Ethanoic (Acetic) anhydride, industrial source, 264
Ethanol (Ethyl alcohol), 3, 48
   absolute, 169
   commercial, 109, 169
   industrial source, 109, 169
   infra-red spectrum, 75
   mass spectrum, 82
   NMR spectrum, 79
Ethanoyl (Acetyl) chloride, 178
2-Ethanoyloxybenzenecarboxylic acid (Aspirin), 192
Ethene (Ethylene) (*see also* Alkenes), 93, 101
   structure, 19, 98
Ethenone (Ketene), 264
Ethenyl ethanoate (Vinyl acetate), 307
Ethenyl (Vinyl) polymers, 120, 307

Ethenylsodium (Sodium acetylide), 120
Ether (*see* Ethoxyethane)
Ether formation, 155, 176, 186, 197
Etherification, continuous, 197
Ethers, 195–200
  autoxidation, 199
  cyclic, 195
  industrial source, 197
  nomenclature, 196
  physical properties, 196
  reactions, 198
  symmetrical (simple), 195
  synthetic preprations, 155, 176, 186, **197**
  unsymmetrical (mixed), 195
Ethoxybenzene (Phenetole), 156, 187
Ethoxyethane (Diethyl ether, 'Ether'), 3, 156, 176, 177
  absolute, 199
  complex formation, Grignard reagent, 162, 199
  industrial source, 197
  infra-red spectrum, 75
  pK_a value, 195
Ethyl ethanoate (acetate), 48, 156, 178
  infra-red spectrum, 77
  NMR spectrum, 80
Ethyl alcohol (*see* Ethanol)
Ethylamines, industrial source, 205
Ethylbenzene, 304
Ethyl cyanide (Propanonitrile), 157
Ethylene (*see* Ethene)
Ethylene chlorohydrin (2-Chloroethanol), 111
Ethylene dibromide (*see* 1,2-Dibromoethane)
Ethylene dichloride (*see* 1,2-Dichloroethane)
Ethylene glycol (*see* Ethane-1,2-diol)
Ethylene oxide (*see* Ethoxyethane)
Ethyl methyl ketone (Butanone), industrial source, 225
Ethyl esters of 1,1,1-Triethoxymethane (of orthocarboxylic acid), 163, 226
Ethylidene dihalides (*see* 1,1-Dihaloethanes)
Ethyl isocyanide (Isocyanoethane), 158
Ethyl isopropyl ether (2-Ethoxypropane), 156
Ethylmagnesium bromide (*see also* Grignard reagents), 163
Ethyl orthoformate (Triethoxymethane), 163
Ethyne (Acetylene) (*see also* Alkynes), structure, 20
Excited state, 14
Exclusion principle, Pauli, 9
Exhaustive methylation, 212
Exothermic reaction, 50
External compensation, 31

FEHLING'S TEST, 243
Fermentation, 169, 290, 292
Fibres, 297
Fibroin, 278
Filtration, 55
Fingerprint region, infra-red spectra, 69
Fire damp, 89
Fischer-Speier reaction, 177, 255, 266
Fittig's reaction, 143, 158

Flame ionization detector, 60
Fluon (*see* Poly(tetrafluoroethene))
Formaldehyde (*see* Methanal)
Formalin, 224, 232
Formic (Methanoic) acid, industrial source, 249
Fortrel, (*see* Terylene)
Fractional crystallization, 55
Fractional distillation, 55
Free radical mechanism, cracking, alkanes, 93
  halogenation, alkanes, 94
  methylbenzene (toluene), 143
  propane, 93
  polymerization, 305
Free radicals, 40
Free rotation, 21
  barrier to, 21
Freon-22, 304
Frequency of radiation, 6
Friedel-Crafts acylation, aryl halides, 161
  benzene, **135**, 228, 262, 265
  methylbenzene (toluene), 146
  phenol, 191
Friedel-Crafts alkylation, aryl halides, 161
  benzene, **135**, 143, 304
  methylbenzene (toluene), 146
  phenol, 190
Fries rearrangement, 191
β-Fructofuranose, 291
β-Fructopynanose, 291
Frustose (Laevulose), 290
  constitution, 290
  industrial source, 290
  physical properties, 291
  reactions, 291
  structure, 290
Fumaric (*trans*-Butenedioic) acid, 28
  physical properties, 28
Functional group isomerism, 27
Functional groups, 43
  tests for, 62
Fundamental particles, atom, 5
Furan, 291
Furanose, 291

(+)-GALACTOSE, 286
Gallic (3,4,5-Trihydroxybenzenecarboxylic) acid, 1
Gas oil, 90
Gasoline (Petrol), 90
Geometrical isomerism, 23, 27, 99
Glucose (Dextrose), 285
  configuration, 286
  constitution, 286
  industrial source, 169, 286
  physical properties, 287
  reactions, 287
  structure, 286
Glucose cyanohydrin (Hydroxynitrile derivative), 288
Glucose oxime, 288
Glucose phenylhydrazone, 289
Glucose phenylosazone, 289
Glucoside formation, 289

Glycaric (Saccharic) acid, 287
Glyceraldehyde, 284
   configuration, 284
Glycerol (Propane-1,2,3-triol), 166, 177
Glycine (Aminoethanoic acid), 279, 280
   acidic and basic strengths, 281
Glycogen, 278, 295
Glycols (Diols), 105, 111, 166
Glycosides, 289
Glycosidic carbon atom, 289
Goodyear, Charles, 301
Green oil, 131
Grignard reagent, 92, 162, 195
   complex formation, 162, 199
   synthetic applications, 92, **162–4**, 170, 226,
      227, 231, 251, 267
Grignard synthesis, alcohols, 163, 170, 231, 267
   aldehydes, 163
   alkanes, 92, 162
   alkynes, 162
   carboxylic acids, 164, 251
   ketones, 164, 227, 267
Ground state, 11
GRS rubber, 302
Gutta-percha, 300

HALIDE EXCHANGE REACTION, 152, 158
Haloalkanes (Alkyl halides), 148–65
   classification, 148
   industrial source, 150
   nomenclature, 149
   physical properties, 150
   reactions, 153
   synthetic preparations, 104, 151
Haloethenes (Vinyl halides), 117, 118, 148
   reactivity, 154
Haloform (Trihalomethane) reaction, 238
Halogenation, alcohols, 151, 174
   aldehydes, 237
   alkanes, 94
   alkenes, 102
   alkynes, 117
   aryl halides, 161
   benzene, 134, 153
   carboxylic acids, 256
   diazonium compounds, 216
   ethers, 199
   ketones, 237
   methane, 94, 150
   methylbenzene (toluene), 143
   phenol, 187, 190
   phenylamine (aniline), 218
Halogen carrier catalyst, 134
Halonium ion, 102
Heavy oil, 131
Heisenberg uncertainty principle, 7
Helium atom, 6
Hell-Volhard-Zelinsky reaction, 257
Hemiacetal (1-Alkoxyalcohol), 232, 289
Heptanoic acid, 288
Heterolytic fission, 40
Hexaalkylsiloxane, 315
1,2,3,4,5,6-Hexabromocyclohexane (Benzene

hexabromide), 134
1,2,3,4,5,6-Hexachlorocyclohexane (Benzene
   hexachloride), 134
Hexamethylenediamine (Hexane-1,6-diamine),
   310, 312
   manufacture, 312
Hexane, 130
   infra-red spectrum, 71
Hexane-1,6-diamide (Ammonium adipamide),
   312
Hexane-1,6-diamine (Hexamethylenediamine),
   312
   manufacture, 312
Hexane-1,6-diisocyanate, 313
Hexane-1,6-dinitrile (Adiponitrile), 310, 312
Hexane-1,6-dioic (Adipic) acid, 312
   manufacture, 312
Hexanedioyl dichloride (Adipyl chloride), 312
Hofmann degradation, amides, 206, 270
Hofmann elimination, 212
Homologous series, 43
Homologues, 43
Homolytic fission, 40
Huls process, 115
Hund's rule, 11
Hybridization, carbon, sp^3, 14
   sp^2, 15
   sp, 16
Hydrazine, 235, 289
Hydrazones, 235, 289
Hydrocarbons, saturated, 44
   unsaturated, 44
Hydrogen, atom, 6
   classification, 88
Hydrogenation, alkenes, 91, 106
   alkynes, 117
   benzene, 128
   cyclohexene, 128
   methylbenzene (toluene), 145
Hydrogen bonding, 37
   alcohols, 37, 168
   amines, 204, 208
   carboxylic acids, 38, 245
   intermolecular, **37**, 168, 181, 182, 204, 208,
      248
   intramolecular, 38, 182
   nitrophenols, 38, 182
   phenols, 181
   water, 37
Hydrogensulphite, addition compounds,
   231
Hydrolysis, acid anhydrides, 265
   acyl chlorides, 261
   amides, 270
   bromoethane, 160
   bromomethane, 49
   chlorobenzene, 183
   (chloromethyl)benzene (benzyl chloride), 172
   diazonium salts, 184, 216
   esters, 251, 266
   haloalkanes, 154, 171
   maltose, 294
   nitriles, 251

sucrose, 294
sulphonic acids, 275
2-Hydroxyalkanonitriles (Aldehyde
    cyanohydrins), 230, 231
2-Hydroxy-2-alkylalkanonitrile (Ketone
    cyanohydrins), 230, 231
2-Hydroxybenzenecarbaldehyde
    (Salicylaldehyde), 192
4-Hydroxybenzenecarbaldehyde, 192
2-Hydroxybenzenecarboxylic (Salicylic) acid,
    191
2-Hydroxybutanedioic (Malic) acid, 1
2- or α-Hydroxycarboxylic acids, 230
2- and 4-Hydroxybenzenesulphonic (*o*- and *p*-
    Phenolsulphonic) acids, 188
Hydroxyethylterephthalate (Dihydroxyethyl
    benzene-1,4-dicarboxylate), 311
Hydroxylamine, 235, 288
(4-Hydroxyphenyl)azobenzene, 136, 216
2-Hydroxypropanoic (Lactic) acid, 1
    optical isomers, 30
2-Hydroxypropanone-1,2,3-tricarboxylic
    (Citric) acid, 1
Hydroxylation, alkenes, 105
Hydroxynitrile derivative of glucose, 288
2- and 4-Hydroxyphenylethanone (*o*- and *p*-
    Hydroxyphenyl ethyl ketone), 191
Hypobromous (Bromic(I) acid, 103

ICI HIGH PRESSURE PROCESS, POLY(ETHENE), 302
Identification, organic compounds, 54–84
Imine group, 234
Indigo, 1
Inductive effect, 46
    carbon-chlorine bond, 46
Infra-red spectra, characteristic absorptions,
    70–1
Infra-red spectrometer, 67
Infra-red spectroscopy, 68
    modes of vibration, 68
Infra-red spectrum, cyclohexane, 72
    ethanol, 75
    ethoxyethane (diethyl ether), 75
    ethyl ethanoate (acetate), 76
    hexane, 71
    methanol, 74
    methylbenzene (toluene), 73
    nujol, 72
    poly(phenylethene) (polystyrene), 72
    propanone (acetone), 76
    trichloromethane (chloroform), 73
Insulin, 278
Intermolecular hydrogen bonding, **37**, 168, 181,
    182, 204, 208, 248
Internal compensation, 31
Intramolecular hydrogen bonding, 38, 182
Inulin, 295
Inversion, 294
Invertase, 286
Invert sugar, 294
Iodobenzene, 216
Iodoform (Triiodomethane) reaction, 238
Ionic polymerization, 306

Ionic product, water, 42
Isocyanates, 270
Isocyanide (Carbylamine) test, 211
Isocyanides, 158, 211
Isocyanoethane (Ethyl isocyanide), 158
Isoelectric point, 281
Isolation, 53–60
Isomerism, 26
    stereo-, 27
    structural, 26
Isopropyl cyanide (2-Methylpropanonitrile, 157
Isotopic labelling, 51, 177, 255

KEKULÉ STRUCTURE, BENZENE, 122–4
Keratins, 278
Kerosene (Paraffin), 90
Ketene (Ethenone), 264
Keto-enol tautomerism, 27, 118, 229
Ketone cyanohydrin (2-Hydroxy-2-
    alkylalkanonitrile), 230, 231
Ketone hydrogensulphite (bisulphite),
    231
Ketone 2,4-dinitrophenylhydrazone, 236
Ketone hydrazone, 235
Ketone phenylhydrazone, 236
Ketones, 220–45
    aromatic, 135, 262, 265
    distinguishing (from aldehydes), 243
    industrial source, 225
    nomenclature, 222
    reactions, 228
    synthetic preparations, 164, 178, **225**, 262,
        265, 267
Knocking, 90
    scale, 91
Kolbé-Schmitt reaction, 191
Kolbé synthesis, 92, 258

LACTALBUMIN, 278
Lactic (2-Hydroxypropanoic) acid, 1
    optical isomers, 30
Lactose, 293
Ladenberg, 123
Lassaigne sodium fusion test, 61
Latex, 300
Lavoisier, 1
Lewis, G. N., acids and bases, 41
Light, ordinary, 32
    plane polarized, 29, 32
Light oil, 130
Light petroleum (Petroleum ether), 90
Ligroin (Light naptha), 90
Liming out, 274
Lindlar ('poisoned') catalyst, 117, 228, 262
Lithium tetrahydridoaluminate III) (Lithium
    aluminium hydride), 171   42, 257
Lithium tetrahydidoborate(II) (Lithium
    borohydride), 171
Lubricating oil, 90

MAGNETIC QUANTUM NUMBER, 8
Maleic (*cis*-Butenedioic) acid, 28
    physical properties, 28

reduction, 28
Malic (2-Hydroxybutanedioic) acid, 1
Maltase, 169, 286, 294
Maltose, 169, 293, 294
(+)-Mannose, 286
Markownikoff's rule, 107, 116
Marsh gas, 89
Mass spectrometer, 81
Mass spectrometry, 54, 65, **80**
Mass spectrum, ethanol (schematic form), 82
   methane, 82
Mechanism, reaction, 49
Melamine (2,4,6-Triamino-1,3,5-triazide), 314
Melting point, 36
   determination, 54
   'mixed', 54
Mesitylene (1,3,5-Trimethylbenzene), 233
Mesomeric (Conjugative) effect, 47
Metaldehyde (Ethanal tetramer), 233
Metamerism, 26
Metanilic (3-Aminobenzenesulphonic) acid,
   217
Methanal (Formaldehyde), 118
   industrial source, 223
Methanal trimer (Trioxan), 232
Methane, dipole moment, 36
   halogenation, 93
   mass spectrum, 82
   natural sources, 89
   structure, 18
   synthetic preparations (specific), 92
Methanoic (Formic) acid, industrial source, 249
Methanol, 1
   industrial source, 168
   infra-red spectrum, 74
   NMR spectrum, 79
Methoxybenzene (Anisole), 156, 195, 197
2- and 4-Methylacetophenone
   (Methylphenylethanone), 146
Methylacetylene (Propyne), 120
Methylamines, industrial source, 205
Methylbenzene (Toluene), 135, 142–7
   industrial source, 142
   infra-red spectrum, 73
   physical properties, 142
   reactions, 143
   synthetic preparations 135, **143**, 243
2,4-Methylbenzene (2,4-Toluene) diisocyanate,
   313
2,6-Methylbenzene (2,6-Toluene) diisocyanate,
   313
Methyl benzenecarboxylate (benzoate), 255
4-Methylbenzenecarboxylic (p-Toluic) acid, 247
Methylbenzenesulphonate, 276
2-Methylbenzenesulphonic (o-
   Toluenesulphonic) acid, 146, 275
4-Methylbenzenesulphonic (p-
   Toluenesulphonic) acid, 146
Methyl bromide (*see* Bromomethane)
Methyl Cellosolve, 111
Methyl chloride (*see* Chloromethane)
Methylcyclohexane, 142, 145
(1-Methylethyl)benzene (Cumene), 183

(1-Methylethyl)benzene hydroperoxide
   (Cumene hydroperoxide), 184
1-Methylethyl ethanoate (Isopropyl acetate),
   183
Methyl ethyl ketone (Butanone), industrial
   scource, 225
Methyl α-glucose, 289
Methyl β-glucose, 289
Methyl 2-methylpropenoate
   (Methylmethacrylate), 310
Methyl-2- and Methyl-4-nitrobenzene (o- and
   p-Nitrotoluene), 137, 146
N-Methylphenylamine (N-Methylaniline),
   214
2- and 4-Methylphenylethanone
   (Methylacetophenone), 146
2-Methylpropanonitrile (Isopropyl cyanide),
   157
Methyl-2,4,6-trinitrobenzene (2,4,6-
   Trinitrotoluene, TNT), 136, 142, 146
Middle oil, 131
Middleton's test, 62
Mixed products, 102
Molasses, 292
Molecular (evaporative) distillation, 55
Molecular formula, determination, 65
Molecularity of reaction, 52
Molecular vibration, 68
Molecular weight (Relative molecular mass),
   determination, 65
Molecules, formation, 14
Monoalkyltrichlorosilanes, 315
Monocarboxylic acids (*see also* Carboxylic
   acids), derivatives, 259–72
   physical properties, 259
   reactivity, general, 259
   saturated aliphatic, 246
Monosaccharides, 283, 285
Mutarotation, 286

NAPHTHALEN-2-OL (2- or β-NAPHTHOL), 136
Natta, Giulio, 303
Natural gas, 89
   industries, 109
Neoprene (Poly(2-chlorobuta-1,3-diene))
   rubber, 301
Nernst glower, 69
Nicol lens, 32
Nitrating mixture, 132
Nitration, alkanes, 95
   aryl halides, 161
   benzene, 132
   benzenesulphonic acid, 277
   methylbenzene (toluene), 137, 146
   nitrobenzene, 137
   phenol, 188
   phenylamine (aniline), 217
Nitrile (Cyanide) formation, 157
o- and p-Nitroaniline (2- and 4-
   Nitrophenylamine), 217
m-Nitrobenzaldehyde (3-
   Nitrobenzenecarbaldehyde), 245

Nitrobenzene, 133
3-Nitrobenzenecarbaldehyde (*m*-Nitrobenzaldehyde), 245
Nitro compounds, synethetic applications, 136
Nitroglycerine (Propane-1,2,3-triyl trinitrate), 177
Nitronium (Nitryl) cation, 133
2-Nitrophenol, 140, 182, 188
   intramolecular hydrogen bonding, 37, 182
3-Nitrophenol, 182
4-Nitrophenol, 140, 182, 188
   intermolecular hydrogen bonding, 182
2- and 4-Nitrophenylamine (*o*- and *p*-Nitroaniline), 217
N-Nitrosoamines, 214
N-Nitroso-*N,N*-dialkylamines, 214
4-Nitroso-*N,N*-dimethylphenylamine (*p*-Nitroso-*N,N*-dimethylaniline), 214
4-Nitrosophenol, 189
o- and *p*-Nitrotoluene (Methyl-2- and Methyl-4-nitrophenol), 137, 146
Nitrosonium (Nitrosyl) cation, 189
Nitryl (Nitronium) cation, 133
Nodal plane, 10
Nodal surface, 10
Nomenclature, introduction, 24–5
   common, 24
   IUPAC, 25
Non-bonded interaction 21, 36
North Sea gas, 89
Nuclear magnetic resonance (NMR) spectrometer, 77
Nuclear magnetic resonance (NMR) spectroscopy, 77
Nuclear magnetic resonance (NMR) spectrum, ethanol, 79
   ethyl ethanoate (acetate), 80
   methanol, 79
Nucleophiles, 41
Nucleophilic addition, alkynes, 116, 118
   carbonyl compounds, 228
Nucleophilic substitution, aromatic, 132, 140
   aryl halides, 155
   diazonium compounds, 215
   haloalkanes, 154
   mechanism, 158
Nujol, 70
   infra-red spectrum, 72
Nylon 6 (Perlon L), 312
Nylon 6.6, 311
Nylon 6.10, 312

OCTANE RATING, 91
Olefins (*see* Alkenes),
Oppenauer oxidation, 226
Optical activity, 29
Optical isomerism, 29
Optical isomers, resolution, 31
Orbitals, anti-bonding, 16
   atomic, 7
   bonding, 16

molecular, 16
   orientation, 8
   shapes of, *s, p, d* and *f*, 8
Order of reaction, 51
Organic chemistry, 1
Organic compounds, characteristic **properties**, 3
   identification, 54–84
   isolation, 54
Organo-cadmium compounds, **164, 227**
Organo-lithium compounds, 164
Organo-metallic compounds (*see also* **Grignard** reagents), 164
Organosilicon polymers (*see* Silicones),
Orlon, 309
Orthanilic (2-Aminobenzenesulphonic) **acid**, 217
Osazone formation, 289
Oxalic (Ethanedioic) acid, 246
Oxidation, 41
   alcohols, 178, 224
   aldehydes, 241
   disaccharides, 294
   ethanol, 178, 224
   fructose, 291
   glucose, 287
   ketones, 242
   methanol, 223
   methylbenzene (toluene), 144
   propane/butane, 224
   propan-2-ol, 178, 224
Oximes, 235, 288
Ozonides, 105
Ozonolysis, alkenes, 105

PARAFFIN (KEROSENE), 90
Paraffins (*see* Alkanes),
Paraffin wax, 90
Paraformaldehyde (Poly(methanal)), 232
Paraldehyde (Ethanal trimer), 233
Pasteur, Louis, 31
Pauli exclusion principle, 99
Pentaethanoyl (Pentaacetyl) glucose, 288
Peptide linkage, 278
   synthesis, 281
Perlon L (Nylon 6), 312
Perlon U, 313
Perspex, 224, 310
Petrochemical industries, 109
Petrol (Gasoline), 90
Petroleum, **89**, 93, 100, 115, 130, 142, 183
   chromatogram, 59
   fractional distillation, 89
   fractions, 90
   jelly, 90
   uses, 90
Phenetole (Ethoxybenzene), 156, 187
Phenol, 136, 139, 155, 183, 276
Phenol formation, 136, 155, 183, 276
Phenol-methanal (Phenol-formaldehyde) resins, 193, 313
Phenols, 181–94
   industrial source, 183
   physical properties, 181

pK_a values, 186
 reactions, 184
 synthetic preparations, 136, 155, **183**, 276
o- and *p*-Phenolsulphonic (2- and 4-
  Hydroxybenzenesulphonic) acid, 191
Phenones, 222
Phenoxide (Phenate) ion, stability, 185
 structure, 185
Phenylamine (Aniline) (*see also* Amines,
  aromatic), 208
Phenylammonium (Anilinium) ion, 205, 210
1-(Phenylazo)naphthalen-2-ol (Phenylazo-2-
  naphthol), 136
N-Phenylethanamide (Acetanilide), 217
Phenyl ethanoate (acetate), 186
Phenylethanone (Acetophenone), 135, 228
Phenylethene (Styrene), 176, 304
1-Phenylethanol, 176
Phenyl group, 127
Phenylhydrazine, 235, 289, 292, 294
Phenylhydrazones, 236, 289, 292, 294
Phenyllithium, 164
Phenylmethanol (Benzyl alcohol), 172
Phillips process, poly(ethene), 303
Phthalic (Benzene-1,2-dicarboxylic) acid, 247
Phthalic (Benzene-1,2-dicarboxylic) anhydride,
  250
Picric acid (2,4,6-Trinitrophenol), 184, 188
Pitch, 133
pK_a values, 42
 alcohols, 173
 aminoethanoic acid (glycine), 281
 benzenesulphonic acid, 275
 carboxylic acids, 254
 ethers, 198
 phenols, 186
pK_b values, 42
 amines, 209
 aminoethanoic acid (glycine), 281
Planck's constant, 7
Plastics, 297
Platforming (Reforming), 130
'Poisoned' (Lindlar) catalyst, 117, 228, 262
Polarimeter, 30, 32
Polarization, covalent bond, 35
Polarizer, 32
Polaroid lens, 32
Polyacrylonitrile (Poly(propenonitrile)), 309
Polyamides, 312
Poly(2-chlorobuta-1,3-diene) (Neoprene)
  rubber, 301
Polyesters, 310
Poly(chloroethene) (Polyvinyl chloride), 112,
  307
Poly(ethene), 106, 302
 high density, 303
 low density, 303
Poly(ethanol) (Polyvinyl alcohol), 308
Poly(ethenyl ethanoate) (Polyvinyl acetate), 307
Polymerization, 106, 120
 addition, 297, 300–10
 condensation, 297, 310–16
 conditions, 299

ethyne (acetylene), 119, 132
 free radical, 304
 ionic, 306
  anionic, 306
  cationic, 306
 stabilizers, 305
Polymers, 297–317
 addition, 106, 300–10
 classification, 297–8
 condensation, 310–6
 ethenyl (vinyl), 307
 linear, 297
 massively cross-linked, 298
 minor cross-linked, 298
natural and synthetic, 299
Poly(methanal) (Paraformaldehyde), 232
trans-Poly(2-methylbuta-1,3-diene) (Gutta-
  percha), 300
Poly(methyl 2-methylpropenoate) (Perspex),
  310
Polypeptide chain, 278
Polypeptides, 278
Poly(phenylethene) (Polystyrene), 304
 infra-red spectrum, 72
Poly(propene), 106, 303
 atactic, 303
 isotactic, 303
Poly(propenonitrile) (Polyacrylonitrile), 309
Polysaccharides, 284, 295
Polystyrene (Poly(phenylethene)), 304
 infra-red spectrum, 72
Polyterpene, 300
Poly(tetrafluoroethene) (PTFE, Teflon, Fluon),
  106, 304
Polyurethanes, 313
Polyvinyl acetate (Poly(ethenyl ethanoate)), 307
Polyvinyl alcohol (Poly(ethenol)), 308
Polyvinyl chloride (Poly(chloroethene)), 112, 307
Positional isomerism, 27
Principal quantum number, 6
Propane, chlorinolysis, 95
 cracking, 93
Propane-1,3-dioic (Malonic) acid, 246
Propanenitrile (Ethyl cyanide), 157
Propane-1,2,3-triol (Glycerol), 166,177
Propane-1,2,3,-triyl trinitrate (Nitroglycerine),
  177
Propan-2-ol, 48
 industrial source, 104, 110
Propanone (Acetone), industrial source, 224
 infra-red spectrum, 76
 synthetic preparations, 225
Propanone oxime (Acetoxime), 235
Propene (Propylene), 93, 107, 109, 110, 309
Propene oxide (Epoxypropane), 110
Propenonitrile (Acrylonitrile, Vinyl cyanide),
  118, 309
Propyne (Methylacetylene), 120
Proteins, 278
 conjugated, 278
 fibrous, 278
 globular, 278
 simple, 278

structure, 278–9
Prototropy (Prototropic isomerism), 118, 229
PTFE (Poly(tetrafluoroethene), 106, 304
Pyran, 291
Pyranose, 291
Pyroligneous acid, 1
Pyrolysis (*see* Cracking),

QUALITATIVE ANALYSIS, ORGANIC COMPOUNDS, 61
Quantitative analysis, organic compounds, 63
Quantum, 6
Quantum number, 6
Quantum theory, 6

RACEMATES (RACEMIC MIXTURES), 30
Raschig process, 183
Rate constant, 52
Rate-determining step, 52
Rate of reaction, 51
Rayon, 299
Reaction, energetics, 49
 molecularity, 52
 profiles, 50
 rate, 51
Reactions, addition, 45
 addition-elimination (condensation), 135
 competitive, 137
 elimination, 45
 factors influencing, 46
 rearrangement, 45
 substitution (displacement), 44
Reagent, 40
Recrystallization, 55
Reduction, 41
 aldehydes, 242
 benzenecarboxylates (benzoates), 172
 cis—butenedioic (maleic) acid, 257
 carbonyl compounds, 170
 carboxylic acids, 257
 esters, 268
 fructose, 292
 glucose, 287
 haloalkanes, 91
 ketones, 242
 nitriles (cyanides), 206
Reforming (Platforming), 130
Regnault, 65
Reimer-Tiemann reaction, 191
Relative molecular mass (Molecular weight),
 determination, 65
Reppe, 132
Resins, 297
Resonance energy, 124
 benzene, 128
Resonance hybrid, 124
Resonance theory, 124
Retention times, 60
R_F values, 58
Ribose, 284
Ring substitution reactions, aldehydes,
 aromatic, 245
 aryl halides, 160

benzene, 132–41
 ketones, aromatic, 245
 methylbenzene (toluene), 145
 phenol, 187
 phenylamine (aniline), 217
 sulphonic acids, 276
Rosenmund reaction, 228, 262
Rotation, barrier to, 21, 33
 free, 21
Rubber, natural, 300
 synthetic, 301
 vulcanized, 300
Rutherford-Bohr theory, 5

SACCHARIC (GLYCARIC) ACID, 287
Sachse (BASF) process, 115
Salicylaldehyde (2-Hydroxybenzenecarb-
 aldehyde, 192
Salicylic (2-Hydroxybenzenecarboxylic) acid,
 191
Salting out, 274
Sandmeyer reaction, 153, 216
Saponification, 251, 267
Saran, 308
Saturated hydrocarbons, 44
Saytzeff elimination, 176, 212
SBA-Kellogg process, 115
SBR rubber, 302
Scheele, 1
Schiff bases (Anils), 237
Schiff's test, 243
Schrödinger wave equation, 7
Schweitzer's reagent, 299
Semicarbazide, 236
Semicarbazones, 236
Silicones, 315
Silicon tetrachloride, 315
Siloxane structures, 315
Silver(I) dicarbide (acetylide), 120
'Silver mirror' test, 243
Simple distillation, 55
S_N1 reaction, 158, 216
S_N2 reaction, 159
Soap, 1, 267, 277
Sodium acetylide (Ethenyl-sodium), 120
Sodium benzenesulphonate, 183, 275
Sodium fusion test, Lassaigne, 61
Sodium hydrogensulphite (bisulphite),
 addition to aldehydes, 231
 addition to ketones, 231
Sodium 2-hydroxybenzenecarboxylate
 (salicylate), 191
Sodium tetrahydridoborate(III) (borohydride),
 171, 242
Solubility, 38
Sommerfield, 7
Sorbitol, 287, 292
Specific rotation, 32
Spectral studies, 8
Spectrometer, basic infra-red and ultra-violet,
 67
 mass, 80
 NMR, 77,

Spectrometry, 80
Spectroscopy, infra-red, 68
  NMR, 77
  ultra-violet, 67
Spin quantum number, 8
Stabilizers, polymerization, 305
Starch, 169, 284, 295
  reactions, 296
Steam distillation, 55
Steam reforming, 168
Stereoisomerism, 26, 27
Steric effects, 48
Strecker synthesis, 280
Stretching vibrations, 68
Structural isomerism, 26
Structure, determination, 66
  use of molecular spectra, 66
Styrene (Phenylethene), 176, 304
Sublimation, 55
Substitution vs. elimination, 160
Substrate, 40
Succinic (Butane-1,4-dioic) acid, 246
Sucrose, 286, 293
Sulphanilic (4-Aminobenzenesulphonic) acid, 217
Sulphonation, aryl halides, 161
  benzene, 273
  methylbenzene (toluene), 146, 275
  phenol, 189
  phenylamine (aniline), 217
Sulphonic acid group, 134
Sulphonic acids, 273–7
  industrial source, 274
  nomenclature, 273
  physical properties, 273
  reactions, 275
  synthetic preparations, 133, 146, 161, 189,
    217, **274**
  uses, 276
Sulphonyl chloride formation, 275
Synthesis gas, 169

TARTARIC ACID (*see* 1,3-dihydroxybutanedioic acid)
Tautomerism, 27, 118, 229
Tau units, 79
Teflon (*see* Poly(tetrafluoroethene)
Terephthalic (Benzene-1,4-dicarboxylic) acid,
  311
Terylene (Dacron, Fortrel), 310
1,1,2,2-Tetrabromoethane, 22
Tetrachloromethane (Carbon tetrachloride), 95
  dipole moment, 36
  manufacture, 95
Tetraethyllead(IV), 91, 151, 308
Tetrafluoroethene, 106, 151, 304
1,1,2,2-Tetrahaloethanes (Acetylene
  tetrahalides), 117
Tetrahydrofuran, 162, 195
  pK_a value, 198
Tetramethyllead(IV), 151
Tetramethylsilane, 78
Thermoplastics (Thermosoftening), 298
Thermosetting plastics, 298
Thiel, 123

Third body, 94
Threose, 284
Tollen's reagent, 244
Toluene (*see* Methylbenzene)
2,4-Toluene (2,4-Methylbenzene) diisocyanate,
  313
o-Toluenesulphonic (2-
  Methylbenzenesulphonic) acid, 146, 275
p-Toluenesulphonic (4-
  Methylbenzenesulphonic) acid, 146, 275
p-Toluic (4-Methylbenzenecarboxylic) acid, 247
trans configuration, 23, 99
Transesterification, 268, 311
Transition state, 49
2,4,6-Triamino-1,3,5-triazide (Melamine), 314
Trialkylmonochlorosilanes, 315
Tribromoethane (Bromoform), 238
2,4,6-Tribromophenol, 190
2,4,6-Tribromophenylamine,
  (Tribromoaniline), 218
Tricel, 299
Trichloroethanal (Chloral), 175, 238
2,2,2-Trichloroethanediol (Chloral hydrate),
  238
Trichloroethanoic (Trichloroacetic) acid, 253,
  256
Trichloromethane (Chloroform), 94, 238
  infra-red spectrum, 73
(Trichlormethyl)benzene (Benzotrichloride),
  144
2,4,6-Trichlorophenol, 190
2,4,6-Trichlorophenylamine (Trichloroaniline),
  218
Triethoxymethane (Ethyl orthoformate), 163
Trihalomethane (Haloform) reaction, 238
3,4,5-Trihydroxybenzenecarboxylic (Gallic)
  acid, 1
Triiodoketone, 239
Triiodomethane (Iodoform) reaction, 238
1,3,5-Trimethylbenzene (Mesitylene), 233
2,2,4-Trimethylpentane, 91
1,3,5-Trinitrobenzene (TNB), 133, 146
2,4,6-Trinitrophenol (Picric acid), 184, 188
2,4,6-Trinitrotoluene, TNT (Methyl-2,4,6-
  trinitrobenzene), 136, 142, 146
Triols, 166
Trioxan (Methanal trimer), 232

ULTRA-VIOLET SPECTROMETER, 67
Ultra-violet spectroscopy, 67
Ultra-violet spectrum, benzene, 68
Uncertainty principle, Heisenberg, 7
Unimolecular reaction, 52
Unsaturated hydrocarbons, 44
Unsaturation, tests for, 103, 107, 120
Unstable intermediates, 51
Urea (Carbamide), 2, 270
Urea-formaldehyde (Carbamide-methanal)
  resins, 314
Urethane group, 313
Uric acid, 1

VALENCE SHELLS, 12

Van der Waals' forces, 21, 36, 38
Vibrational energy, in molecules, 68
Vicinal dihalides, 149
Victor Meyer, 65, 125
Vinyl acetate, (Ethenyl ethanoate), 307
Vinyl acetylene (1-Buten-3-yne), 119, 301
Vinyl chloride (Chloroethane), 112, 307
Vinyl cyanide (Acrylonitrile or Propenonitrile), 118, 309
Vinyl ethanoate (acetate), 307
Vinyl halides (Haloethenes), 117, 118, 148
    reactivity, 154
Vinylidene chloride (*see* 1,1-Dichloroethene)
Vinyl (Ethenyl) polymers, 120, 307
Vinyon, 308
Vinyon N, 310
Viscose process, 299
Viscosity, 38
Visible region, 67
Vorlander's rule, 139
Vulcanization, 300

accelerators, 136, 206, 301

WACKER PROCESS, 224
Walden inversion reaction, 30
Water, hydrogen bonding, 37
    ionic product, 42
Wave equation, Schrödinger, 7
Williamson's synthesis, 155, 186, 197
Wine, 1, 247
Wintergreen, oil of, 192
Wohler, 1, 270
Wulff process, 115
Wurtz synthesis, 92

XYLENES (Dimethylbenzenes), 146

ZEISEL METHOD, 199
Ziegler process, poly(ethene), 303
Zwitterion, 280
Zymase, 169, 290